A STEP-BY-STEP GUIDE TO EXPLORATORY FACTOR ANALYSIS WITH R AND RSTUDIO

This is a concise, easy to use, step-by-step guide for applied researchers conducting exploratory factor analysis (EFA) using the open source software **R**.

In this book, Dr. Watkins systematically reviews each decision step in EFA with screen shots of **R** and RStudio code, and recommends evidence-based best practice procedures. This is an eminently applied, practical approach with few or no formulas and is aimed at readers with little to no mathematical background. Dr. Watkins maintains an accessible tone throughout and uses minimal jargon and formula to help facilitate grasp of the key issues users will face while applying EFA, along with how to implement, interpret, and report results. Copious scholarly references and quotations are included to support the reader in responding to editorial reviews.

This is a valuable resource for upper-level undergraduate and postgraduate students, as well as for more experienced researchers undertaking multivariate or structure equation modeling courses across the behavioral, medical, and social sciences.

Marley W. Watkins earned a Ph.D. in Educational Psychology and Measurements with a specialty in School Psychology from the University of Nebraska-Lincoln, USA. He is currently Research Professor in the Department of Educational Psychology at Baylor University, USA, and has authored more than 200 articles, books, and chapters and presented more than 150 papers at professional conferences.

"This book is an important contribution to the field. I have been publishing articles using EFA for over 30 years, yet it provided me with new insights and information on EFA. More importantly, the material is easy to follow and accessible to researchers and graduate students new to EFA. I highly recommend it to anyone seeking to become competent in EFA."

—Joseph J. Glutting, Ph.D., University of Delaware, USA

"*A Step-by-Step Guide to Exploratory Factor Analysis with R and RStudio* is an important contribution to the applied exploratory factor analytic literature. It is extremely well-written and portends to be a useful resource to researchers and students alike. It does a commendable job of describing how to implement exploratory factor analysis using R. I highly recommend this book."

—Stefan C. Dombrowski, Ph.D., Rider University, USA

"This book is an amazing resource for those new to factor analysis as well as those who have used it for some time. It is a terrific guide to best practices in exploratory factor analysis with rich explanations and descriptions for why various procedures are used and equally terrific in providing resources and guidance for using R for conducting factor analysis. I highly recommend this book."

—Gary L. Canivez, Ph.D., Eastern Illinois University, USA

A STEP-BY-STEP GUIDE TO EXPLORATORY FACTOR ANALYSIS WITH R AND RSTUDIO

Marley W. Watkins

Routledge
Taylor & Francis Group

NEW YORK AND LONDON

First published 2021
by Routledge
52 Vanderbilt Avenue, New York, NY 10017

and by Routledge
2 Park Square, Milton Park, Abingdon, Oxon, OX14 4RN

Routledge is an imprint of the Taylor & Francis Group, an informa business

Library of Congress Cataloging-in-Publication Data
Names: Watkins, Marley W., 1949- author.
Title: A step-by-step guide to exploratory factor analysis with R and
Rstudio / Marley W. Watkins.
Description: New York, NY : Routledge, 2021. | Includes bibliographical
references and index. |
Identifiers: LCCN 2020038116 (print) | LCCN 2020038117 (ebook) | ISBN
9780367636258 (hardback) | ISBN 9780367634681 (paperback) | ISBN
9781003120001 (ebook)
Subjects: LCSH: Factor analysis–Computer programs. | R (Computer program
language)
Classification: LCC QA278.5 .W38 2021 (print) | LCC QA278.5 (ebook) |
DDC 519.5/354–dc23
LC record available at https://lccn.loc.gov/2020038116
LC ebook record available at https://lccn.loc.gov/2020038117

ISBN: 978-0-367-63625-8 (hbk)
ISBN: 978-0-367-63468-1 (pbk)
ISBN: 978-1-003-12000-1 (ebk)

Typeset in Bembo
by MPS Limited, Dehradun

Access the Support Material: https://www.routledge.com/9780367634681

CONTENTS

LIST OF FIGURES

PREFACE

Exploratory factor analysis (EFA) was developed more than 100 years ago (Spearman, 1904) and has been extensively applied in many scientific disciplines across the ensuing decades (Finch, 2020a). A *PsychInfo* database search of "exploratory factor analysis" found more than 12,000 citations for the years 2000–2019. However, EFA is a complex statistical tool that is all too easy to misapply, resulting in flawed results and potentially serious negative consequences (Preacher & MacCallum, 2003). Surveys of published research have consistently found that questionable or inappropriate EFA methods were applied (Conway & Huffcutt, 2003; Fabrigar et al., 1999: Ford et al., 1986; Gaskin & Happell, 2014; Henson & Roberts, 2006; Howard, 2016; Izquierdo et al., 2014; Lloret et al., 2017; McCroskey & Young, 1979; Norris & Lecavalier, 2010; Park et al., 2002; Plonsky & Gonulal, 2015; Roberson et al., 2014; Russell, 2002; Sakaluk & Short, 2017; Thurstone, 1937). The uniformity of these results across scientific disciplines (e.g., business, psychology, nursing, disability studies, etc.) and 80 years is striking.

Many graduate courses in multivariate statistics in business, education, and the social sciences provide relatively little coverage of EFA (Mvududu & Sink, 2013). A non-random online search for syllabi found, for example, that a graduate course in multivariate statistics at Oklahoma State University devoted three weeks to a combination of principal components analysis, EFA, and confirmatory factor analysis (CFA), whereas a multivariate course at the Graduate School of Business at Columbia University allocated two weeks to cover all forms of factor analysis. In recent decades, courses in structural equation modeling (SEM) have become popular and might include EFA as an introduction to CFA. For instance, an SEM course at the University of Nebraska devoted less than one week to coverage of EFA, whereas a similar course at the University of Oregon failed to include any mention of EFA. Of course, there is no assurance that all, or most, students are exposed to even the minimal content found in these courses. A survey of colleges of education found that doctoral programs typically required only four methods courses of which the majority were basic (Leech & Goodwin, 2008). Likewise, surveys of curriculum requirements in psychology have revealed that a full course in factor analysis was offered in only 18% of doctoral psychology programs, whereas around 25% offered no training at all (Aiken et al., 2008). As summarized by Henson et al. (2010), "the general level of training is inadequate for many, even basic, research purposes" (p. 238).

Researchers must make several thoughtful and evidence-based methodological decisions while conducting an EFA (Henson & Roberts, 2006). There are a number of options available for each decision, some better than others (Lloret et al., 2017). Poor decisions can produce "distorted and potentially meaningless solutions" (Ford et al., 1986, p. 307) that can negatively affect the development and refinement of theories and measurement instruments (Bandalos & Gerstner, 2016; Fabrigar & Wegener, 2012; Henson & Roberts, 2006; Izquierdo et al., 2014; Lloret et al., 2017) and thereby "create an illusion of scientific certainty and a false sense of objectivity" (Wang et al., 2013, p. 719). From a broader perspective, "understanding factor analysis is key to understanding much published research" (Finch, 2020a, p. 1) and "proficiency in quantitative methods is important in providing a necessary foundation for what many have conceptualized as scientifically based research" (Henson et al., 2010, p. 229).

In short, researchers tend to receive little formal training in EFA and as a result habitually rely on suboptimal EFA methods. Researchers are unlikely to make better methodological choices as they gain experience because the professional literature is littered with poor-quality EFA reports that model questionable EFA methods (Plonsky & Gonulal, 2015). Additionally, researchers tend to utilize software with unsound default options for EFA (Carroll, 1978, 1983; Izquierdo et al., 2014; Lloret et al., 2017; Osborne, 2014; Widaman, 2012).

Conway and Huffcutt (2003) suggested several potential solutions to improve EFA practice. One suggestion was for "well-written books of the type that researchers are likely to turn to when conducting EFA (e.g., books on using specific software packages). These articles and books need to clearly spell out the appropriate use of EFA as well as different EFA choices and their implications and urge readers to think carefully about their decisions rather than accepting default options" (p. 166). Following that suggestion, this book systematically reviews each decision step in EFA and recommends evidence-based methodological procedures that are "markedly better than others" (Fabrigar et al., 1999, p. 294) along with the **R** software (**R** Core Team, 2020) commands needed to implement each recommended procedure. As such, this is an eminently applied, practical approach with few or no formulas. Rather, this book is intended to provide readers with a conceptual grasp of the main issues along with precise implementation instructions to supplement the more mathematical approach found in many multivariate and SEM books and courses. Copious scholarly references and quotations are included to provide the reader with additional resources that might be needed to respond to editorial reviews. This approach should be valuable for students as well as for more experienced researchers who wish to implement EFA in an evidence-based, best practice, scientifically defensible manner.

1

INTRODUCTION

Historical Foundations

The idea that unobservable phenomena underlie observed measurements is very old and pervasive. In fact, it may be a basic scientific principle (Hägglund, 2001). Philosophers and scientists such as Plato, Descartes, Bacon, Locke, Hume, Quetelet, Galton, Pearson, and Mill articulated these philosophical and mathematical foundations. However, it was Spearman (1904) who explicated a mathematical model of the relations between observed measures and latent or unmeasured variables (Mulaik, 1987).

Spearman (1904) described his mathematical model as a "'correlational psychology' for the purpose of positively determining all psychical tendencies, and in particular those which connect together the so-called 'mental tests' with psychical activities of greater generality and interest" (p. 205). That is, to analyze the correlations between mental tests in support of his theory of intelligence. Spearman posited a general intelligence (labeled g) that was responsible for the positive relationships (i.e., correlations) he found among mental tests. Given that this general intelligence could not account for the totality of the test inter-correlations, he assumed that a second factor specific to each test was also in-volved. "Thus was born Spearman's 'two-factor' theory which supposed that the observed value of each variable could be accounted for by something common to all variables (the general, or common, factor) and the residual (the specific factor)" (Bartholomew, 1995, p. 212). Spearman also assumed that mental test scores were measured with some degree of error that could be approximated by the correlation of two repeated measurements (i.e., test–retest reliability).

Exploratory factor analysis (EFA) methods were further debated and refined over the ensuing decades with seminal books appearing in the middle of the

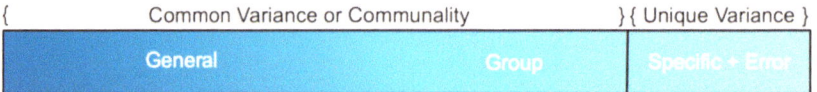

FIGURE 1.1 Variance Components

century (Burt, 1940; Cattell, 1952; Holzinger & Harman, 1941; Thomson, 1950; Thurstone, 1935, 1947; Vernon, 1961). These scholars found Spearman's two-factor theory over simple and proposed group factors in addition to general and specific factors. Thus, the observed value of each variable could be accounted for by something common to all measured variables (general factor), plus something common to some but not all measured variables (group factors), plus something unique to each variable (specific factor), plus error. Common variance, or the sum of variance due to both general and group factors, is called communality. The combination of specific variance and error variance is called uniqueness (Watkins, 2017). As portrayed in Figure 1.1, this is the common factor model: total variance = common variance + unique variance (Reise et al., 2018).

The contributions of Thurstone (1931, 1935, 1940, 1947) were particularly important in the development of EFA. He studied intelligence or ability and applied factor analysis to many datasets and continued the basic assumption that "a variety of phenomena within the domain are related and that they are determined, at least in part, by a relatively small number of functional unities, or factors" (1940, p. 189). Thurstone believed that "a test score can be expressed, in first approximation, as a linear function of a number of factors" (1935, p. vii) rather than by general and specific factors. Thus, he analyzed the correlation matrix to find multiple common factors and separate them from specific factors and error. To do so, Thurstone developed factorial methods and formalized his ideas in terms of matrix algebra. Using this methodology, Thurstone identified seven intercorrelated factors that he named primary mental abilities. Eventually, he recognized that the correlations between these primary mental ability factors could also be factor analyzed and would produce a second-order general factor. Currently, a model with general, group, and specific factors that identifies a hierarchy of abilities ranging in breadth from general to broad to narrow is ascendant (Carroll, 1993).

A variety of books on factor analysis have been published. Some presented new methods or improved older methods (Cattell, 1978; Harman, 1976; Lawley & Maxwell, 1963). Others compiled the existing evidence on factor analysis and presented the results for researchers and methodologists (Child, 2006; Comrey & Lee, 1992; Fabrigar & Wegener, 2012; Finch, 2020a; Garson, 2013; Gorsuch, 1983; Kline, 1994; Mulaik, 2010; Osborne, 2014; Osborne & Banjanovic, 2016; Pett et al., 2003; Rummel, 1970; Thompson, 2004; Walkey & Welch, 2010). In addition, there has been a veritable explosion of book chapters and journal articles explicitly designed to present best practices in EFA (e.g., Bandalos, 2018; Beaujean, 2013; Benson & Nasser, 1998; Briggs & Cheek, 1986; Budaev, 2010; Carroll, 1985, 1995a; Comrey, 1988; Cudeck, 2000; DeVellis, 2017; Fabrigar et al., 1999; Ferrando & Lorenzo-Seva, 2018; Floyd & Widaman, 1995; Goldberg & Velicer, 2006; Hair et al., 2019; Hoelzle & Meyer, 2013; Lester & Bishop, 2000; Nunnally & Bernstein, 1994; Osborne et al., 2007; Preacher & MacCallum, 2003; Schmitt, 2011; Tabachnick & Fidell, 2019; Watkins, 2018; Widaman, 2012; Williams et al., 2010).

Conceptual Foundations

As previously noted, EFA is based on the concept that unobserved or latent variables underlie the variation of scores on observed or measured variables (Bollen, 2002). Alternative conceptualizations have been described by Epskamp et al. (2018). A correlation coefficient between two variables might exist due to: (a) a random relationship between those two variables, (b) one variable causing the other, or (c) some third variable being the common cause of both. Relying on the third possibility, EFA assumes that the correlations (covariance) between observed variables can be explained by a smaller number of latent variables or factors (Mulaik, 2018). "A factor is an unobservable variable that influences more than one observed measure and which accounts for the correlations among these observed measures" (Brown, 2013, p. 257).

Theoretically, variable intercorrelations should be zero after the influence of the factors has been removed. This does not happen in reality because no model is perfect and a multitude of minor influences is present in practice. Nevertheless, it is the ideal. As described by Tinsley and Tinsley (1987), EFA "is an analytic technique that permits the reduction of a large number of interrelated variables to a smaller number of latent or hidden dimensions. The goal of factor analysis is to achieve

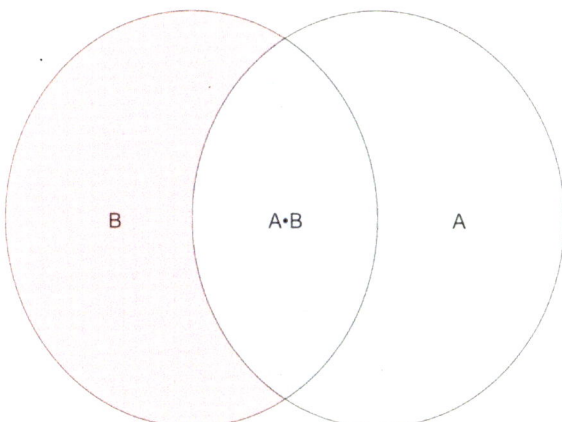

FIGURE 1.2 Correlation of Two Variables

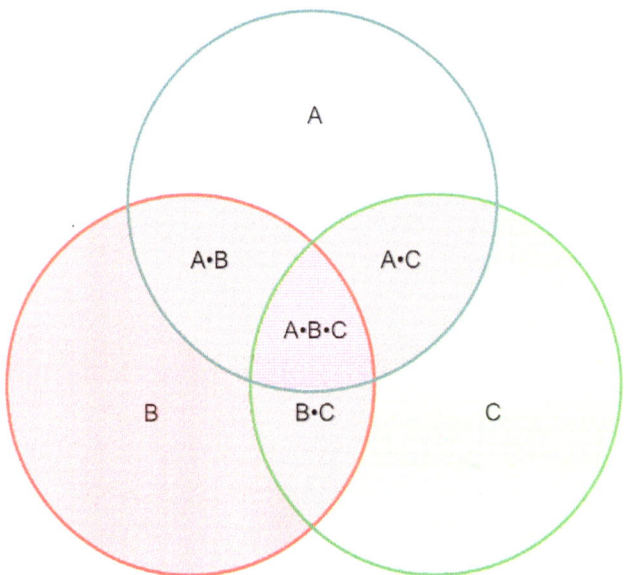

FIGURE 1.3   Correlation of Three Variables

parsimony by using the smallest number of explanatory concepts to explain the maximum amount of common variance in a correlation matrix" (p. 414).

The simplest illustration of common variance is the bivariate correlation (r) between two continuous variables represented by the circles labeled A and B in Figure 1.2. The correlation between variables A and B represents the percentage of variance they share, which is area A•B. The amount of overlap between two variables can be computed by squaring their correlation coefficient. Thus, if r = .50, then the two variables share 25% of their variance.

With three variables, the shared variance of all three is represented by area A•B•C in Figure 1.3. This represents the general factor. The proportion of error variance is not portrayed in these illustrations but it could be estimated by 1 minus the reliability coefficient of the total ABC score.

EFA is one of a number of multivariate statistical methods. Other members of the multivariate "family" include multiple regression analysis, principal components analysis, confirmatory factor analysis, and structural equation modeling. In fact, EFA can be conceptualized as a multivariate multiple regression method where the factor serves as a predictor and the measured variables serve as criteria. EFA can be used for theory and instrument development as well as assessment of the construct validity of existing instruments (e.g., Benson, 1998; Briggs & Cheek, 1986; Carroll, 1993; Comrey, 1988; DeVellis, 2017; Haig, 2018; Messick, 1995; Peterson, 2017; Rummel, 1967; Thompson, 2004). For example, EFA was instrumental in the development of modern models of intelligence (Carroll, 1993) and personality (Cattell, 1946; Digman, 1990), and has been extensive applied for the assessment of evidence for the construct validity of numerous tests (Benson, 1998; Briggs & Cheek, 1986; Canivez et al., 2016; Watkins et al., 2002).

Readers should review the following statistical concepts to ensure that they possess the requisite knowledge for understanding EFA methods: reliability (internal consistency, alpha, test-rest, and alternate forms), true score (classical) test theory, validity (types of validity evidence), descriptive statistics (mean, mode, skew, kurtosis, standard deviation, and variance), Pearsonian correlations (product moment, phi, and point-biserial), polychoric correlation, tetrachoric correlation, partial correlation, multiple correlation, multiple regression, sample, population, multicollinearity, level of measurement (nominal, ordinal, interval, and ratio), confidence interval, and standard error of measurement. Readers can consult the textbooks written by Bandalos (2018) and Tabachnick and Fidell (2019) for exhaustive reviews of measurement and statistical concepts.

Graphical Displays and Vocabulary

Given the complexity of EFA, it is useful to display EFA models in path diagram form (Mueller & Hancock, 2019). This facilitates a quick grasp of the entire model and allows standardization of presentations. These graphs will visually illustrate the distinctions between latent variables (factors) and observed (measured) variables.

To this point, latent variables and factors have been used synonymously. Many other synonyms may be found in the professional literature, including unmeasured variables, unobserved variables, synthetic variables, constructs, true scores, hypothetical variables, and hypothetical constructs. Likewise, observed and measured variables have been used interchangeably, but terms such as manifest variables and indicator variables are also found in the professional literature. For this book, the terms factors and measured variables will be used to ensure consistency.

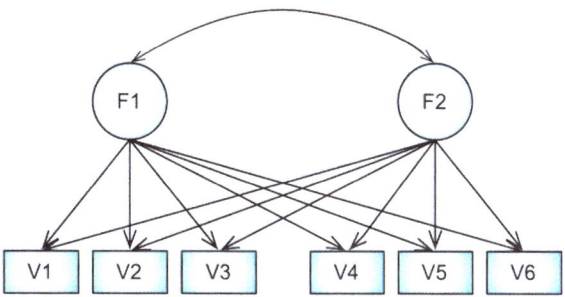

FIGURE 1.4 Simple EFA Model with Six Measured Variables and Two Factors

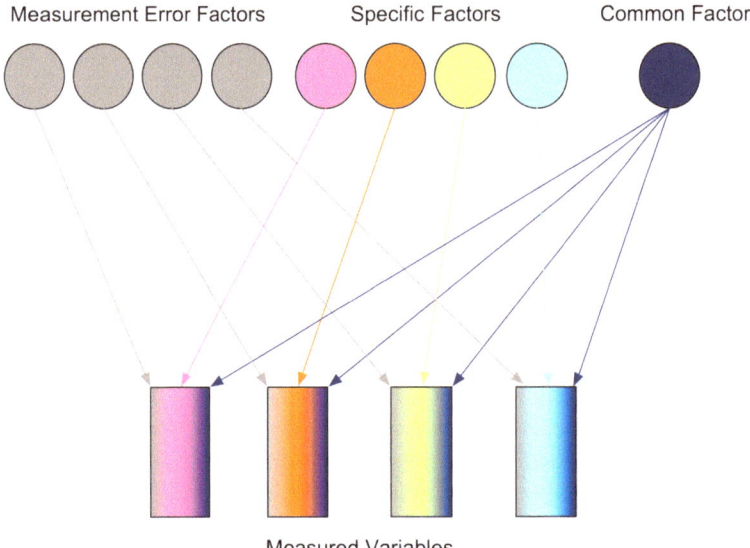

Measurement Error Factors   Specific Factors   Common Factor

Measured Variables

FIGURE 1.5   Conceptual Illustration of the Components of Variance of an EFA Model

A simple EFA model with two factors and six measured variables is presented in Figure 1.4. In path diagrams, ellipses represent factors and rectangles represent measured variables. Directional relationships between variables are indicated by single-headed arrows and non-directional (correlational) relationships by double-headed arrows. Although not included in this model, the strength of each relationship can be displayed on each directional and non-directional line. In this model, each factor directly influences all six measured variables and the two factors are correlated. Given correlated factors at a single level, this is an oblique, first-order, or correlated factors model. It represents an unrestricted solution because every factor is allowed to influence every measured variable. Path diagrams may also display error terms for measured variables, variances, etc. Although errors and variances should not be forgotten, they tend to visually clutter path diagrams and will not be displayed. Addition information about path diagrams has been provided by DeVellis (2017).

Path diagrams can also be used to conceptually illustrate the components of variance of an EFA model (Figure 1.5) with one general factor and four measured variables.

2

DATA

Four datasets are used in this book to illustrate the steps in EFA. They can be downloaded from https://www.routledge.com/9780367634681.

Dataset 1

The first dataset, labeled "iq", contains scores from eight tests developed to measure cognitive ability that was administered to 152 participants. This dataset is in spreadsheet format and the file is labeled "iq.xls". These scores are from continuous variables with a mean of 100 and standard deviation of 15 in the general population. It was anticipated that four tests would measure verbal ability and four tests would measure nonverbal ability. Table 2.1 briefly describes the eight measured variables in the data set.

The correlation matrix from that data file is provided in Table 2.2.

TABLE 2.1 Variables in iq dataset

Variable name	Description
vocab1	Provide correct definition of words
designs1	Recreate square designs with colored blocks
similar1	Describe how two words are similar
matrix1	Complete matrix designs
veranal2	Explain verbal analogies
vocab2	Recognize correct definition of words
matrix2	Recognize correct completion of matrix designs
designs2	Recreate geometric designs with puzzle pieces

TABLE 2.2 Correlation matrix of iq variables

	vocab1	designs1	similar1	matrix1	veranal2	vocab2	matrix2	designs2
vocab1	1.00	.58	.79	.62	.69	.82	.56	.51
designs1	.58	1.00	.57	.65	.51	.54	.59	.66
similar1	.79	.57	1.00	.60	.70	.74	.58	.55
matrix1	.62	.65	.60	1.00	.53	.57	.71	.62
veranal2	.69	.51	.70	.53	1.00	.71	.65	.51
vocab2	.82	.54	.74	.57	.71	1.00	.58	.53
matrix2	.56	.59	.58	.71	.65	.58	1.00	.62
designs2	.51	.66	.55	.62	.51	.53	.62	1.00

Dataset 2

The second dataset is used to illustrate EFA with categorical variables. Each variable is one item from a self-concept scale. This dataset (sdq.xls) is in spreadsheet format and contains 30 variables that were administered to 425 high school students (Table 2.3). Responses to each item ranged from 1 (*False*) to 3 (*More True Than False*) to 6 (*True*). Thus, the data are ordinal, not continuous. All negatively valanced items were reverse scored before entry and are identified by an "*r*" appended to the item number in the data file.

These 30 items are hypothesized to measure three aspects of self-concept: mathematical with 10 items, verbal with 10 items, and general with 10 items (Marsh, 1990). Reliability estimates in the .80 to .90 range have been reported for these dimensions of self-concept (Gilman et al., 1999; Marsh, 1990).

TABLE 2.3 Variables in sdq dataset

No.	Description	No.	Description
1.	Math is my best subject	16.	Do badly on math tests
2.	Overall, I'm proud	17.	Not much to be proud of
3.	Hopeless in English classes	18.	English is one of best subjects
4.	Need help in math	19.	Good grades in math
5.	Overall, I'm no good	20.	Do things as well as most people
6.	Look forward to English classes	21.	I hate reading
7.	Look forward to math classes	22.	Never want another math course
8.	Most things I do well	23.	My life is not very useful
9.	Do badly on reading tests	24.	Good grades in English
10.	Trouble understanding math	25.	Always done well in math
11.	Nothing ever turns out right	26.	Can do almost anything if try
12.	English class is easy	27.	Trouble with written expression
13.	I enjoy studying math	28.	Hate math
14.	Most things turn out well	29.	Overall I'm a failure
15.	Not good at reading	30.	Learn quickly in English classes

TABLE 2.4 Variables in Rmotivate dataset

No.	Description	No.	Description
1.	My friends think I am	11.	I have trouble with reading
2.	Read a book	12.	Reading well is
3.	Reading skill	13.	I can answer teacher questions
4.	My friends think reading is	14.	I think reading is boring-interesting
5.	Can figure out unknown words	15.	For me, reading is easy-hard
6.	Tell friends about books	16.	Will spend time reading when adult
7.	Understand what I read	17.	I understand reading assignments
8.	People who read are	18.	Would like more reading time
9.	As a reader, I am	19.	When reading aloud
10.	I think libraries are	20.	Books as presents

Dataset 3

The third dataset is the first Practice Exercise. This dataset (Rmotivate.xls) is also in spreadsheet format and contains 20 variables (Table 2.4). Each variable is one item from a reading motivation scale that was administered to 500 students in grades 2 through 6 (100 at each grade level). Responses to each item ranged from 1 to 4 to represent increasingly positive opinions. For example, "My friends think I am: (1) a poor reader, (2) an OK reader, (3) a good reader, (4) a very good reader". Thus, the data are ordinal with four categories, not continuous. All negatively valanced items were reverse scored before entry.

These 20 items are hypothesized to reflect two aspects of reading motivation: reading self-concept (odd items) and value of reading (even items). Reliability estimates of .87 have been reported for each these dimensions of reading motivation (Watkins & Browning, 2015).

Dataset 4

The fourth dataset is used for the second Practice Exercise. This dataset (adhd.xls) is also in spreadsheet format and contains ten variables. Each variable is one item from a scale designed to tap the symptoms of attention-deficit hyperactivity disorder (ADHD) that was completed by 500 young adults. Respondents reported the frequency of each behavior on a four-point scale: 0 (*Never or Rarely*), 1 (*Sometimes*), 2 (*Often*), and 3 (*Very Often*). Thus, the data are ordered categories and not continuous (Table 2.5).

These 10 items are hypothesized to reflect two behavioral aspects of ADHD: attention problems and over-activity/impulsivity problems. It was assumed that the first five items would tap the attention problems dimension,

TABLE 2.5 Variables in adhd dataset

Item	*Description*
instruct	Follow instructions
effort	Sustain mental effort
organize	Organization problems
forget	Forgetful
attention	Sustain attention
go	Constantly on the go
talks	Talk excessively
fidgets	Fidget
turns	Difficulty waiting turn
runs	Runs about

whereas the final five items would tap the over-activity/impulsivity dimension. Similar scales with 15 to 20 items have typically found internal consistency reliability coefficients of around .85 to .90 for these factors (Nichols et al., 2017).

3

R AND RSTUDIO SOFTWARE

R and RStudio

There are many commercial software packages that can be used to conduct EFA. SPSS, SAS, and Stata are probably the most popular. Although these packages might be inexpensive for students and faculty, they are costly for other users. Additionally, these commercial software packages tend to be complex and often implement default options that are ill advised or inappropriate for EFA (Carroll, 1978; Izquierdo et al., 2014; Lloret et al., 2017; Osborne & Banjanovic, 2016).

A review of statistical software used in academic articles found that SPSS was cited most frequently, followed by **R**, SAS, and Stata. However, the use of SPSS and SAS peaked several years ago and their use is in decline, whereas **R** is growing in popularity (see http://r4stats.com/articles/popularity). Consequently, the **R** software environment and its helper application, RStudio, will be employed in this book.

The **R** software environment is free, publicly available, open source, and runs on Windows, Macintosh, and Linux operating systems. **R** consists of a base program and more than 16,000 add-on packages for statistical and graphical techniques that were developed by independent researchers and programmers. **R** relies on commands rather than a graphical interface. Consequently, it can have a steep learning curve. This is ameliorated by RStudio, another free software package, that interfaces with **R** and increases its flexibility and ease of use via a graphical interface.

R software and packages can be downloaded from the Comprehensive **R** Archive Network (CRAN), which is a central repository for all R-related software. Helpfully, copies of CRAN have been moved to locations all around

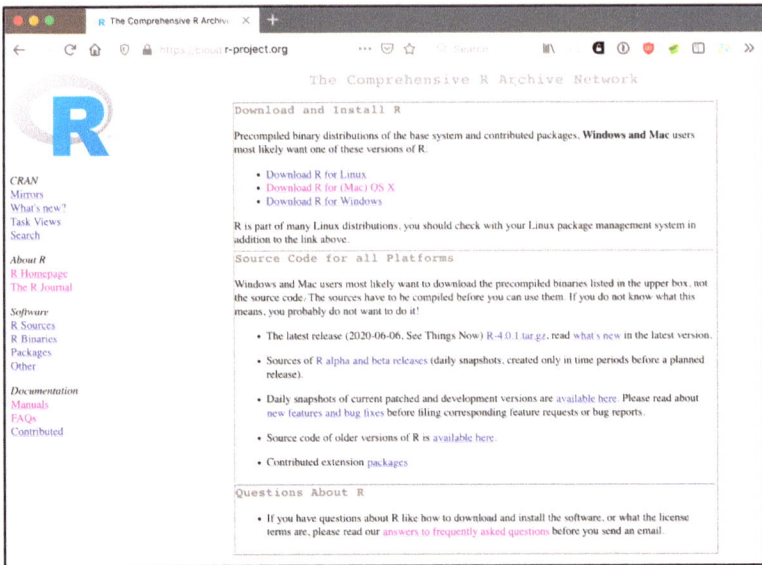

FIGURE 3.1 Download **R** from the Comprehensive R Archive Network

the world so users can select any CRAN "mirror" site they wish. There are many sources for information on **R** and RStudio, including books (e.g., Crawley, 2012; Field et al., 2012; Horton & Kleinman, 2015) as well as numerous online tutorials (e.g., many can be found on CRAN).

To download **R**, go to http://www.r-project.org and click on the CRAN mirror link (Figure 3.1). Next, select the most convenient mirror site and click its link. That page will offer the opportunity to download and install **R** for Linux, Mac, and Windows operating systems. The examples provided in this book will be for the Macintosh operating system but other operating systems should be very similar. Click on the operating system of your computer and select the latest release of the base **R** package. Follow the installation instructions of that release consistent with your computer system.

Once downloaded and saved in the Applications folder of the Macintosh, **R** can be launched by double clicking its icon. That will produce the **R** opening page. As displayed in Figure 3.2, there is a set of menus (e.g., File, Edit, Format, etc.), a set of icons, and a text area where commands can be entered following the > character. Detailed installation instructions for both Windows and Macintosh computers can be found at https://little-book-of-r-for-multivariate-analysis. readthedocs.io/en/latest/.

While offering a basic graphics-oriented interface, **R** remains enigmatic. This can be remedied by downloading the appropriate version of RStudio from http://www.rstudio.com and installing it on your computer. RStudio assumes

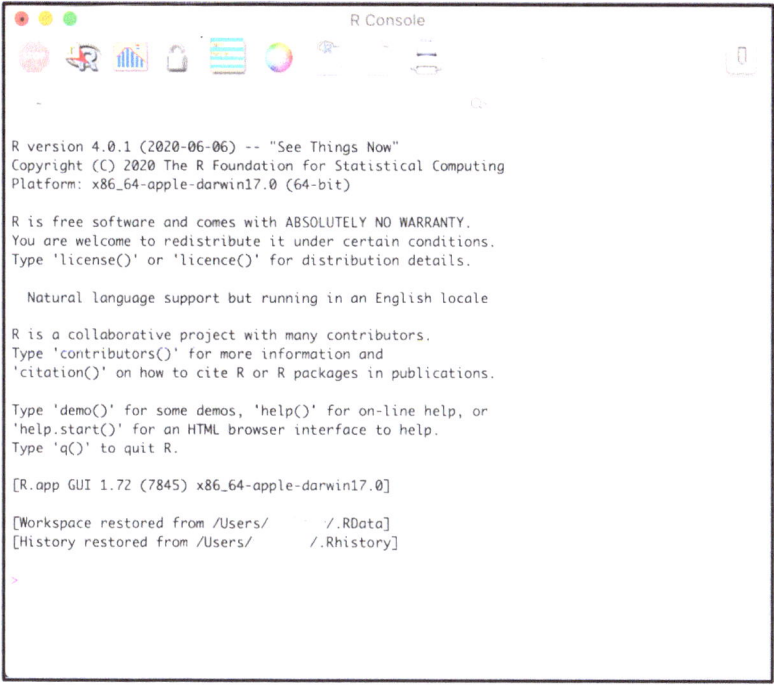

R version 4.0.1 (2020-06-06) -- "See Things Now"
Copyright (C) 2020 The R Foundation for Statistical Computing
Platform: x86_64-apple-darwin17.0 (64-bit)

R is free software and comes with ABSOLUTELY NO WARRANTY.
You are welcome to redistribute it under certain conditions.
Type 'license()' or 'licence()' for distribution details.

  Natural language support but running in an English locale

R is a collaborative project with many contributors.
Type 'contributors()' for more information and
'citation()' on how to cite R or R packages in publications.

Type 'demo()' for some demos, 'help()' for on-line help, or
'help.start()' for an HTML browser interface to help.
Type 'q()' to quit R.

[R.app GUI 1.72 (7845) x86_64-apple-darwin17.0]

[Workspace restored from /Users/   /.RData]
[History restored from /Users/   /.Rhistory]

>

FIGURE 3.2 **R** Screen

that **R** has been installed on the same computer as RStudio. When launched, RStudio appears as illustrated in Figure 3.3. Tutorials on **R** and RStudio are available online at https://swirlstats.com.

RStudio automatically launches the **R** base system and integrates it into the lower left quadrant of the screen. The upper left quadrant can contain a data spreadsheet (i.e., variables in columns, participants in rows). Alternatively, that quadrant can contain the **R** source code editor. We are unlikely to create new packages in **R** so this pane will be reserved for data in this book. The upper right quadrant also contains multiple options that can be switched by clicking the four folder tabs: *Environment*, *History*, *Connections*, or *Tutorial*. The *History* tab displays a history of all **R** commands that have been executed. The *Connections* tab is specialized for connecting with external database programs like SQLS and Oracle. The *Tutorial* tab provides tutorials on the use of **R**. Leave the *Environment* tab selected to allow future datasets and workplaces to be displayed. The lower right quadrant has five tabs for alternative displays: *Files*, *Plots*, *Packages*, *Help*, and *Viewer*. For now, select the *Packages* tab.

The size of the total screen as well as the dimensions of each quadrant can be adjusted by hovering the mouse over the horizontal and vertical gray lines as illustrated.

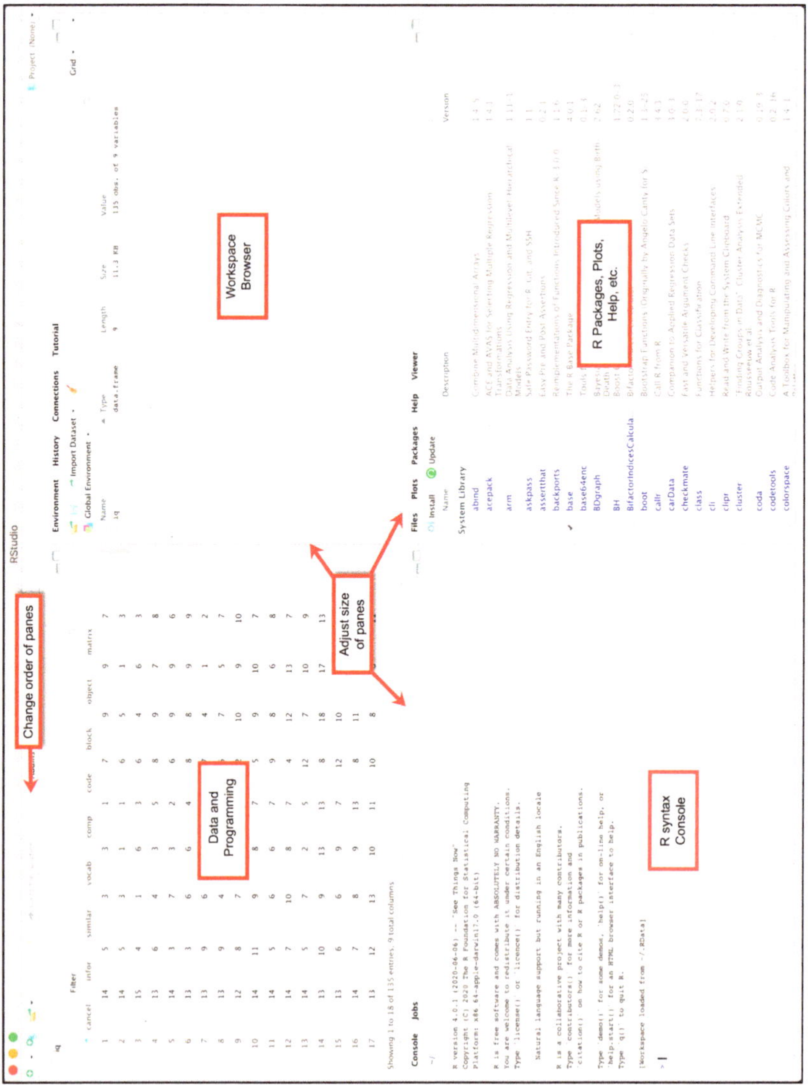

FIGURE 3.3 RStudio Screen

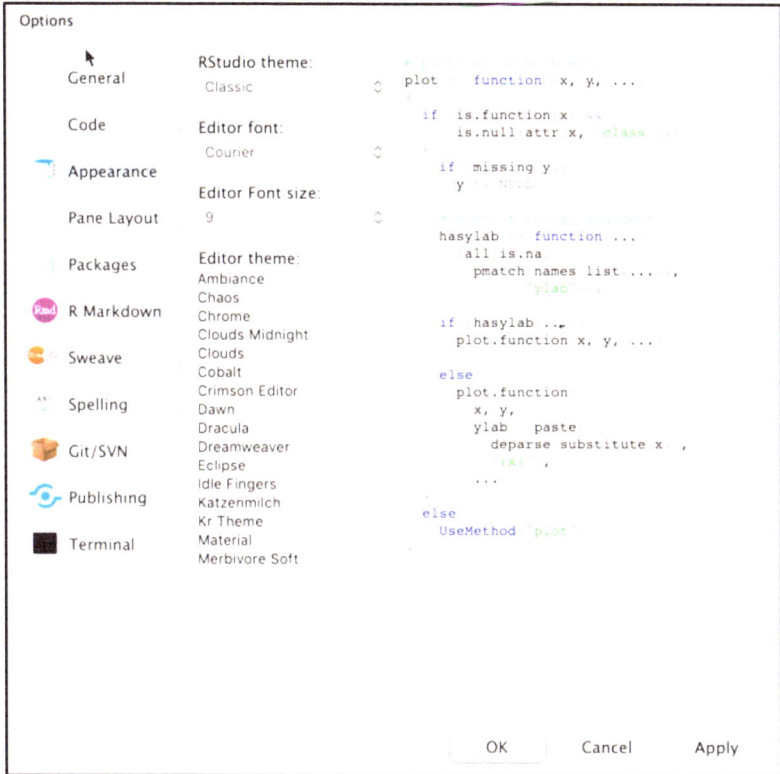

FIGURE 3.4   RStudio Preferences

The order of these four panes can be changed by selecting the Pane Layout option in the *Preferences* menu.

RStudio offers a full set of menus similar to other software. Those menus will be used for a variety of purposes as we proceed through analyses. When encountered, menus and their options will be denoted by bold italic type as per: *View > Panes > Show All Panes*. Most menu functions are also available as a tab or button on the RStudio screen.

Many aspects of the RStudio display can be modified by "Preferences" that are located in the usual Windows or Macintosh preferences window (*RStudio > Preferences*) location (also *Tools > Global Options*). These options include the font type and size as well as the appearance and arrangement of the RStudio window (Figure 3.4). It may also prove efficient in the long run to identify a working directory via *Session > Set Working Directory > Choose Directory*. This will be the directory used by RStudio to open and save files, save data, etc.

For effective use of **R**, it is important to understand some of its organizational principles. Basically, **R** is a computer language with pre-compiled functions and routines that are collected into *packages* that perform a variety of graphical and statistical functions. As previously noted, **R** is a command line system. The **R** Console panel of RStudio (lower left quadrant) is where **R** commands are entered and where the output from those commands is displayed. Objects are anything created in **R**, such as a variable, group of variables, correlation matrix, dataset, results from a statistical analysis, etc. There is a specific vocabulary used to identify object types, for example, matrices, data frames, lists, and vectors. Matrices are similar to the familiar correlation matrix with rows and columns containing homogeneous elements, lists are similar to any list of letters and/or numbers, and data frames are similar to a spreadsheet with variables in the columns and participants in the rows.

R signifies its readiness for a command to be input with the > symbol in the Console. **R** assumes that commands will apply a function from an initialized package to an object. The object is entered first, followed by the function. For example, the object might be a single measured variable and the function might be to compute its mean value. A second option would be to compute its mean value rounded to a whole integer. Alternatively, the object might be an entire data frame of multiple variables and the function might be to perform an exploratory factor analysis.

BOX 3.1 ORGANIZATION OF COMMANDS AND OUTPUT IN R

```
## Descriptive comments.
## R for computation of descriptive statistics for a single variable
> M = mean(iq$vocab1)
> print(M)
[1] 97.5
## Round to a whole integer
> print(round(M,0))
[1] 98
## Probability functions
> pnorm(1.96,mean=0,sd=1)
[1] 0.9750021
> qnorm(.975,mean=0,sd=1)
[1] 1.959964
## Display decimal rather than scientific notation.
## Negative for reverse. Default = 0.
> options(scipen=999)
```

Each function can contain multiple default specifications as defined by instructions that can be found in the package that contains it. The mean examples and their output are illustrated previously. Note that RStudio presents commands in colored text that can be modified in its Preferences menu. In this book, **R** console input and output will be presented in shaded boxes in the Courier font with comments, commands, and output in brown, blue, and black type, respectively.

R purists prefer to use <– instead of the = used in this example. I prefer the equal sign as it is commonly used in other programming languages and only requires one key press. The console pane will retain all commands and output and can be become quite messy after many exploratory analyses. The entire pane can be erased via *Edit > Clear Console*.

R Packages

The **R** base program comes with several add-on packages installed automatically. To conduct EFA, several additional packages must be downloaded from the CRAN site. Select the *Help* tab in the lower right quadrant and then click the *Home* button to display a listing of resources. From that list of resources, select the *Packages* option. This generates an exhaustive list of all available **R** packages. Alternatively, the **R** Console can be used to search for all packages that deal with a specific topic. For example, a search for factor analysis packages is demonstrated in Figure 3.5.

Note that the lower right quadrant of the RStudio window has automatically selected the *Help* tab and displayed an extensive list of packages (and the specific procedures in each package) that deal with factor analysis. Each entry is a link. Click a link and detailed information about that particular procedure is displayed. Use the directional arrow buttons atop that quadrant to move between help windows.

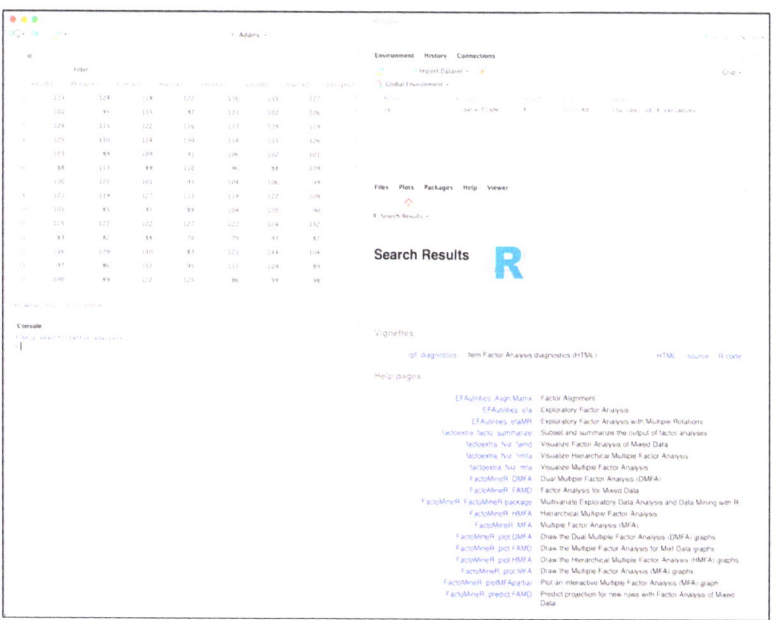

FIGURE 3.5 **R** Help Search

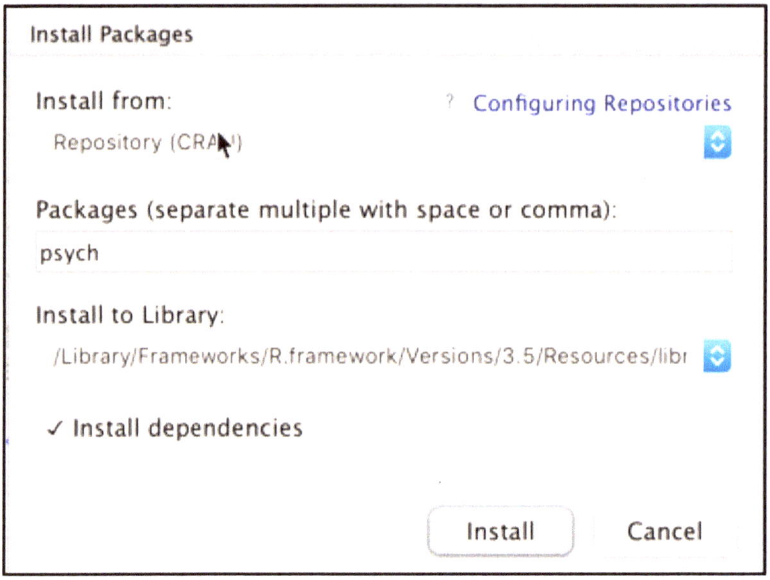

Install Packages

Install from: ?   Configuring Repositories

   Repository (CRAN)   ⬍

Packages (separate multiple with space or comma):

psych

Install to Library:

/Library/Frameworks/R.framework/Versions/3.5/Resources/libr ⬍

✓ Install dependencies

                                    Install   Cancel

FIGURE 3.6   Install Packages Screen

Packages can be downloaded via the **R** Console or RStudio menus. The later method is easier. Select **Tools** > **Install Packages**. This triggers the Install Packages window (Figure 3.6). Alternatively, select the **Packages** tab in the lower right quadrant of the RStudio window and then click the **Install** button.

One **R** package listed in the Help output that performs a number of EFA functions is the *psych* package by Revelle (2019). For efficiency, each package can call on other packages to perform statistical subroutines. It is a good idea to automatically download those packages as well, which is enabled by checking the **Install dependencies** box. The library should probably be left at its default location on your computer. Typing "psych" into the Packages field and clicking the **Install** button allows RStudio to install the *psych* package and all other packages that it depends on for its computations. For detailed information about this package and its use, visit http://personality-project.org/r/.

The **Packages** tab in the lower right panel will immediately display installation of the *psych* package, its general description, and its version number (Figure 3.7).

Files	Plots	Packages	Help	Viewer		
O) Install	⊙ Update					
Name		Description			Version	
psych		Procedures for Psychological, Psychometric, and Personality Research			1.9.12.31	

FIGURE 3.7   The *Psych* Package in the Packages Display

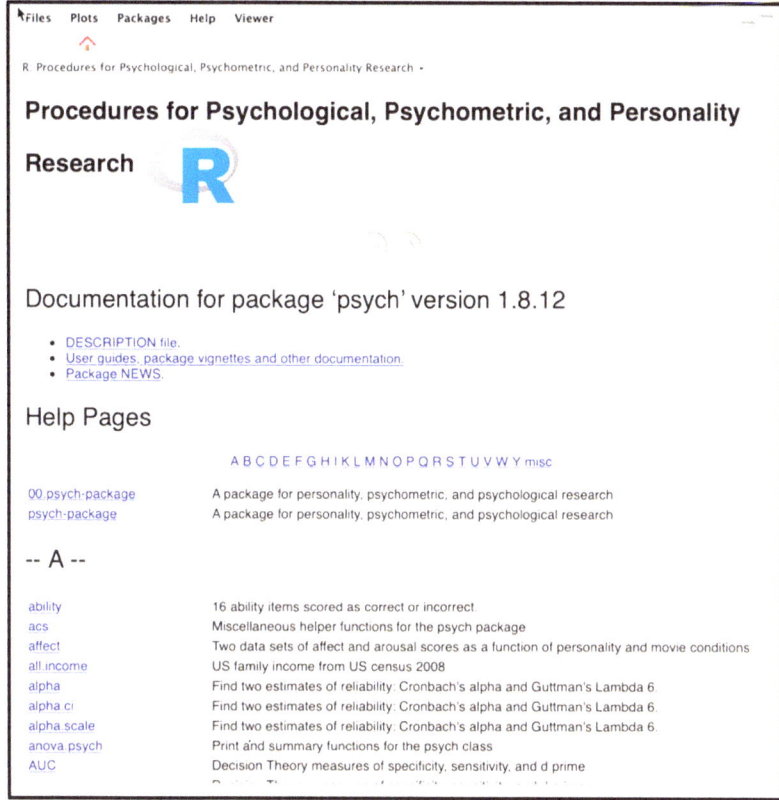

FIGURE 3.8   Documentation for the *Psych* Package

A package can be removed by clicking the small ⊗ to the right of the version number and web-based information about the package can be accessed by clicking the small globe to the right of the version number. The *psych* package could also have been installed within the **R** console by typing `library(psych)` at the > prompt.

Information about the various procedures available within the *psych* package can be obtained by clicking the *psych* link. The ***Help*** tab automatically opens to display that information (Figure 3.8). Each procedure in the list is also a link that will display more detailed information about that procedure.

Packages may also be found on the web. The following sites might be helpful for locating packages:

https://www.statmethods.net/index.html

http://finzi.psych.upenn.edu/

https://www.rdocumentation.org/

https://rseek.org/

http://dirk.eddelbuettel.com/cranberries/

https://www.r-bloggers.com/

http://www.cookbook-r.com/

https://www.burns-stat.com/documents/tutorials/impatient-r/

http://personality-project.org/r/r.guide.html

http://www.metaresearch.de/exlib/namespaces.html

Other graphical and statistical packages might also be useful for EFA. Using the **Tools** > **Install Packages** menu, install the following packages at this time: *EFAutilities, factoextra, FactoMineR, faoutlier, GPArotation, lavaan, MASS, MBESS, nFactors, readxl, sem,* and *userfriendlyscience*. Be aware that function names are case sensitive so use upper and lower case letters as indicated. These packages will be installed in RStudio and become automatically available for application when that program is launched in the future. If other packages are needed for specific purposes, they will be identified as they are encountered.

To obtain a list of all the packages installed on this computer and where those packages are stored:

BOX 3.2 PACKAGE COMMANDS

```
## Display all packages installed on computer
> library()
## Display location of installed packages
> .libPaths()
## Installing packages from R Console
> install.packages("psych")
## Display the default packages installed by R
> getOption("defaultPackages")
[1] "datasets" "utils" "grDevices" "graphics" "stats" "methods"
```

Packages that have been installed will be listed in the **Packages** pane of the RStudio window as illustrated earlier. However, they are not available for use until they have been activated by clicking the box to the left of the package name (Figure 3.9). Downloaded packages always remain installed but each package must be activated before being used in an RStudio session.

Alternatively, an **R** command (install.packages) can accomplish the same task. Plus, information about packages, procedures within packages, and **R** commands can be obtained with **R** commands. It will be beneficial to occasionally check for

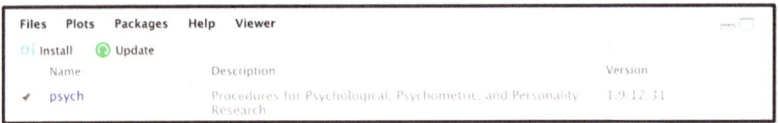

FIGURE 3.9 Activate *Psych* Package

package updates because authors sometimes revise them to correct errors or add new procedures. Clicking the *Update* button on the *Packages* tab of the RStudio window will identify those needed by your system.

BOX 3.3   HELP, PACKAGE, AND VARIABLE COMMANDS

```
## Reference a package in R
> library(psych)
## To obtain information about packages, procedures, and commands
> ?psych
> help("pch")
> help("fa")
> ?fa
> help("attach")
> help("mean")
> help("round")
> help("names")
## To update packages
> update.packages()
## Display graphs (and commands that generated them) that R can produce
> demo("graphics")
## Display examples and commands for statistics or graphs
> example("mean")
> example("boxplot")
## Display the addressable variables within an object.
## Here, a ploychoric matrix
> names(polyout)
[1] "rho"    "tau"   "n.obs" "Call"
## Each variable can be directly addressed by using the $ function
> polyout$n.obs
[1] 425
## Display addressable variables within an object with a different
## command. Here a factor object.
> attributes(f2)
$names
 [1] "residual"      "dof"         "chi"         "nh"            "rms"
 [6] "EPVAL"         "crms"        "EBIC"        "ESABIC"        "fit"
[11] "fit.off"       "sd"          "factors"     "complexity"    "n.obs"
[16] "objective"     "criteria"    "STATISTIC"   "PVAL"          "Call"
[21] "null.model"    "null.dof"    "null.chisq"  "TLI"           "RMSEA"
[26] "BIC"           "SABIC"       "r.scores"    "R2"            "valid"
[31] "score.cor"     "weights"     "rotation"    "communality"   "communalities"
[36] "uniquenesses"  "values"      "e.values"    "loadings"      "model"
[41] "fm"            "rot.mat"     "Phi"         "Structure"     "method"
[46] "scores"        "R2.scores"   "r"           "np.obs"        "fn"
[51] "Vaccounted"
## Display demonstrations available in each package
> demo()
```

As noted, packages may call on other packages to perform statistical subroutines (dependencies). For example, referencing the *faoutlier* package causes it to automatically reference (and download if not in the library) the *sem*, *mvtnorm*, and *parallel* packages. If many packages are referenced, there may be some conflict because of duplicated names of statistical routines internal to each package. The simplest way to deal with these conflicts is to quit and then restart RStudio and only activate the packages needed for a specific task.

4

IMPORTING AND SAVING DATA AND RESULTS

Commands are required to import data into **R**. These commands are relatively unwieldy and prone to error. RStudio provides an improved set of data input commands that vastly simplify data entry. For the iq data in spreadsheet format, select **File** > **Import Dataset** > **From Excel** that will produce an input window allowing the file to be located. Similar input windows are available for text, SPSS, SAS, and Stata files. Once the file has been located, RStudio displays a preview of the data and allows the user to name the dataset, identify whether or not the first row contains variable names, limit the number of rows and/or variables, etc. It is important that any missing data indicator be identified in the **NA:** field and that the correct type of data (i.e., character, numeric, or date) be specified in each variable's drop-down menu. When satisfied, click the **Import** button on the bottom, right corner of the import screen (Figure 4.1).

RStudio immediately reads the data into its memory and reflects that new situation with changes in its panes: the upper left panel displays the data in a spreadsheet format, whereas the upper right **Environment** panel displays the name of the object that was imported as well as its dimensions (152 rows and 8 columns). To ensure that the correct data have been imported, scroll through the data spreadsheet and verify that the object's dimensions correspond to the known dimensions of the iq data file.

Neither **R** nor RStudio are very intuitive in terms of data manipulation, so that is best reserved for the source program (e.g., SPSS, SAS, Stata, Excel, etc.). Nevertheless, a basic data editor package can be installed into RStudio by downloading the *editData* package and then accessing it through the menus: **Tools** > **Addins** > **Browse Addins** > **editData**. More comprehensive data management options are available in the *tidyverse* package (Lee et al., 2020).

At this point, RStudio has loaded the data into memory. However, it is important to ensure that **R** "sees" the iq object as rows and columns of data

FIGURE 4.1   Import Excel Data in RStudio

(i.e., as a data frame object). This allows R to address each variable by name and consider the dataset as a whole for exploratory factor analysis (EFA).

BOX 4.1   DATA COMMANDS

```
## Identify iq object as a data frame
> iq = as.data.frame(iq)
## Allow variables in the iq object to be addressed by name
> attach(iq)
## Mean of a variable addressed by name after attach command
> mean(vocab1)
[1] 97.5
## How to address a variable by name if attach command not employed
> mean(iq$vocab1)
[1] 97.5
## Another way to address a variable if attach command not employed
> with(iq,mean(vocab1))
[1] 97.5
## Display structure of a data frame in brief format
> str(iq)
'data.frame':            152 obs. of  8 variables:
 $ vocab1  : num  113 100 124 125 103 88 100 121 101 125 ...
 $ designs1: num  124 95 115 110 89 113 101 119 85 122 ...
 $ similar1: num  118 115 122 124 109 89 101 127 95 122 ...
 $ matrix1 : num  122 97 116 130 91 110 95 113 89 127 ...
 $ veranal2: num  116 121 117 114 106 96 104 119 104 122 ...
 $ vocab2  : num  115 102 109 115 102 88 106 122 100 124 ...
 $ matrix2 : num  127 106 119 126 101 109 99 109 90 132 ...
 $ designs2: num  105 112 118 127 97 111 99 115 83 111 ...
## Display structure of an R created object in brief format
> str(f2)
```

R will now consider the iq object to be a data frame with rows representing participants and columns representing variables. The attach command allows the contents of each variable to be viewed simply by entering the variable name. This can sometimes cause a problem if variable names are shared by multiple data frames. Thus, it is a good practice to use the detach command once a data frame is no longer needed or after any change to the data file.

BOX 4.2 VARIABLE AND DATA COMMANDS

```
## List all values in a variable in a data frame after attach has been
commanded
> vocab1
  [1] "113" "100" "124" "125" "103" "88"  "100" "121" "101" "125" "83"  "116" "97"  "100"
 [15] "95"  "101" "107" "119" "91"  "107" "98"  "124" "104" "98"  "98"  "115" "95"  "137"
 [29] "77"  "118" "97"  "112" "86"  "74"  "113" "74"  "119" "98"  "92"  "106" "112" "121"
 [43] "94"  "134" "98"  "124" "88"  "124" "97"  "97"  "103" "110" "116" "97"  "107" "95"
 [57] "106" "101" "98"  "121" "121" "119" "106" "89"  "88"  "91"  "101" "113" "124" "119"
 [71] "95"  "131" "89"  "92"  "101" "88"  "106" "109" "101" "86"  "98"  "94"  "107" "119"
 [85] "104" "92"  "91"  "109" "97"  "62"  "91"  "80"  "91"  "55"  "62"  "85"  "88"  "106"
 [99] "88"  "103" "79"  "74"  "64"  "91"  "83"  "76"  "128" "103" "97"  "91"  "89"  "97"
[113] "55"  "94"  "109" "91"  "94"  "86"  "110" "91"  "55"  "112" "95"  "80"  "113" "109"
[127] "85"  "109" "125" "61"  "61"  "68"  "104" "62"  "98"  "55"  "82"  "76"  "71"  "86"
[141] "91"  "100" "76"  "98"  "101" "113" "116" "89"  "79"  "95"  "91"  "77"
## List all variables in a data frame after attach has been commanded
> names(iq)
[1] "vocab1"   "designs1" "similar1" "matrix1"  "veranal2" "vocab2"
"matrix2"
[8] "designs2"
## Compute mean (or median, etc.) for each participant in a data frame
> apply(iq,1,mean)
  [1] 117.500 106.000 117.500 121.375  99.750 100.500 100.625 118.125
93.375 123.125
:::::::::::::::::::::::::::::::::::::::::::::::::::::::::::::::::::::::::::
[144] 105.250 103.125 111.375 107.375  97.500 100.875  91.000 101.625
82.000
## Compute mean (or median, etc.) for each variable in a data frame
> apply(iq,2,mean)
  vocab1  designs1  similar1   matrix1  veranal2    vocab2   matrix2
designs2
97.50000  97.65132 103.59211  99.53289 101.50658 100.63158 101.44737
100.64474
## Remove data frame variable names from work space
> detach(iq)
## Remove object from R environment
> remove(iq)
```

A dataset can be imported each time RStudio is run or it can be saved in a native **R** format called a work space via *Session > Save Workspace As*. Workspace files have the .RData suffix and can be loaded via *Session > Load Workspace*. A workspace is simply the data and variable names currently in the computer's memory.

Although not applicable to this data, there will be occasions when one or more of the variables in the data file should not be included in the EFA, which can be accomplished with **R** commands. See Crawley (2012) for details of data manipulation. It may be easier to accomplish these data manipulations in Excel, SPSS, SAS, or Stata and then import the data into RStudio.

BOX 4.3   DELETE AND SELECT VARIABLE COMMANDS

```
## Delete the nth variable from the current data frame
## (8th - matrix2 in this example)
> newiq=iq[,-8]
## Delete the nth participant from the current data frame
## (1st in this example)
> newiq2=iq[-1,]
## Select the first 4 variables from the current data frame
> iq2=subset(iq,select=vocab1:matrix1)
## Select the first and 5th variables from the current data frame
> iq25=iq[,c(1,5)]
```

Importing a Correlation Matrix

Raw data are not always available. For example, journal articles may provide the correlation matrix but not the raw data. Correlation matrices can also be input for later use in EFA. There are several methods for doing so. One of the easiest is to use the clipboard function offered by the computer's operating system and the read.clipboard function in the *psych* package.

To import the full correlation matrix of the iq data: First, ensure that the *psych* and *psychTools* packages have been downloaded and activated. Second, ensure that the correlation matrix is in a table with tabs separating the columns. Third, copy the correlation matrix, including the first row that contains the variable names (but not the first column of names) to the clipboard as highlighted in Box 4.4.

BOX 4.4   COPY CORRELATION MATRIX ONTO CLIPBOARD

	vocab 1	designs 1	similar 1	matrix 1	veranal 2	vocab 2	matrix 2	designs 2
vocab1	1.00	0.58	0.79	0.62	0.69	0.82	0.56	0.51
designs1	0.58	1.00	0.57	0.65	0.51	0.54	0.59	0.66
similar1	0.79	0.57	1.00	0.60	0.70	0.74	0.58	0.55
matrix1	0.62	0.65	0.60	1.00	0.53	0.57	0.71	0.62
veranal2	0.69	0.51	0.70	0.53	1.00	0.71	0.65	0.51
vocab2	0.82	0.54	0.74	0.57	0.71	1.00	0.58	0.53
matrix2	0.56	0.59	0.58	0.71	0.65	0.58	1.00	0.62
designs2	0.51	0.66	0.55	0.62	0.51	0.53	0.62	1.00

Finally, execute the following **R** commands.

BOX 4.5 IMPORT FULL CORRELATION MATRIX VIA THE CLIPBOARD

```
## Import full correlation matrix from clipboard
> library(psych)
> library(psychTools)
> iqCor = as.matrix(read.clipboard(header=TRUE))
## Print corr matrix to ensure correct
> print(iqCor)
     vocab1 designs1 similar1 matrix1 veranal2 vocab2 matrix2 designs2
[1,]  1.00    0.58     0.79    0.62     0.69    0.82    0.56     0.51
[2,]  0.58    1.00     0.57    0.65     0.51    0.54    0.59     0.66
[3,]  0.79    0.57     1.00    0.60     0.70    0.74    0.58     0.55
[4,]  0.62    0.65     0.60    1.00     0.53    0.57    0.71     0.62
[5,]  0.69    0.51     0.70    0.53     1.00    0.71    0.65     0.51
[6,]  0.82    0.54     0.74    0.57     0.71    1.00    0.58     0.53
[7,]  0.56    0.59     0.58    0.71     0.65    0.58    1.00     0.62
[8,]  0.51    0.66     0.55    0.62     0.51    0.53    0.62     1.00
```

Note that the correlation matrix has been imported into the matrix object named iqCor. Alternatively, only a lower triangular matrix with variable labels in the first column may be available.

BOX 4.6 LOWER TRIANGULAR CORRELATION MATRIX

	vocab1	designs1	similar1	matrix1	veranal2	vocab2	matrix2	designs2
vocab1	1.00							
designs1	0.58	1.00						
similar1	0.79	0.57	1.00					
matrix1	0.62	0.65	0.60	1.00				
veranal2	0.69	0.51	0.70	0.53	1.00			
vocab2	0.82	0.54	0.74	0.57	0.71	1.00		
matrix2	0.56	0.59	0.58	0.71	0.65	0.58	1.00	
designs2	0.51	0.66	0.55	0.62	0.51	0.53	0.62	1.00

R commands and the clipboard can also be used to import that type of matrix. Copy the first column of the matrix that includes the variable names (but not the first row that contains the same variable names) and the remainder of the correlation matrix.

BOX 4.7 IMPORT LOWER TRIANGULAR CORRELATION MATRIX VIA THE CLIPBOARD

```
## Import lower correlation matrix from clipboard
> iqCorLow = as.matrix(read.clipboard.lower(diag=TRUE,names=TRUE))
## Print corr matrix to ensure correct
> print(iqCorLow)
         vocab1 designs1 similar1 matrix1 veranal2 vocab2 matrix2 designs2
vocab1    1.00    0.58     0.79    0.62     0.69    0.82    0.56     0.51
designs1  0.58    1.00     0.57    0.65     0.51    0.54    0.59     0.66
similar1  0.79    0.57     1.00    0.60     0.70    0.74    0.58     0.55
matrix1   0.62    0.65     0.60    1.00     0.53    0.57    0.71     0.62
veranal2  0.69    0.51     0.70    0.53     1.00    0.71    0.65     0.51
vocab2    0.82    0.54     0.74    0.57     0.71    1.00    0.58     0.53
matrix2   0.56    0.59     0.58    0.71     0.65    0.58    1.00     0.62
designs2  0.51    0.66     0.55    0.62     0.51    0.53    0.62     1.00
```

Sometimes, only the upper triangular correlation matrix may be available. In this case, copy the first row that includes the variable names (but not the first column that contains the same variable names) to the clipboard. The **R** commands to input an upper triangular matrix are presented in Box 4.8.

BOX 4.8 IMPORT UPPER TRIANGULAR CORRELATION MATRIX VIA THE CLIPBOARD

```
## Import upper correlation matrix from clipboard
> iqCorUp = as.matrix(read.clipboard.upper(diag=TRUE,names=TRUE))
## Print corr matrix to ensure correct
> print(iqCorUp)
          vocab1 designs1 similar1 matrix1 veranal2 vocab2 matrix2 designs2
vocab1     1.00    0.58     0.79    0.62     0.69    0.82    0.56     0.51
designs1   0.58    1.00     0.57    0.65     0.51    0.54    0.59     0.66
similar1   0.79    0.57     1.00    0.60     0.70    0.74    0.58     0.55
matrix1    0.62    0.65     0.60    1.00     0.53    0.57    0.71     0.62
veranal2   0.69    0.51     0.70    0.53     1.00    0.71    0.65     0.51
vocab2     0.82    0.54     0.74    0.57     0.71    1.00    0.58     0.53
matrix2    0.56    0.59     0.58    0.71     0.65    0.58    1.00     0.62
designs2   0.51    0.66     0.55    0.62     0.51    0.53    0.62     1.00
```

In both instances, if there is no diagonal filled with 1s, then thediag command should be changed to diag=FALSE. Likewise, if there are no variable names, then thenames command should be changed to names=FALSE.

An object can be removed from the Environment pane if it is no longer needed or was loaded in error, for example, the iqCorUp object. Other potentially useful **R** commands get the number of variables in a list or data frame, number of cases in a variable within a list or data frame, and dimensions of a list or data frame.

BOX 4.9 USEFUL COMMANDS

```
## Remove an object from the Environment pane
> remove(iqCorUp)
## Display number of variables in a data frame
> length(iq)
[1] 8
## Display number of cases in a variable
> length(vocab1)
[1] 152
## Display the dimensions (cases by variables) of a data frame
> dim(iq)
[1] 152    8
```

As may be apparent, the use of **R** commands in the Console pane of RStudio can result in an extremely long list of commands and resultant output in the Console. Previous commands are "memorized" by RStudio and can be sequentially recalled with the up and down arrow keys. All contents in the Console can be erased with the menu sequence of ***Edit > Clear Console***. Regardless of erasures of the Console, the entire history of commands are retained in memory

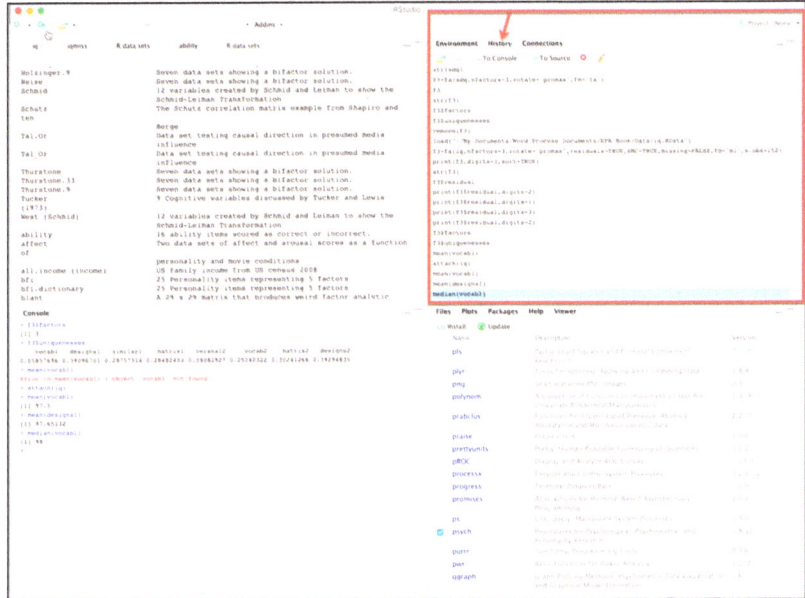

FIGURE 4.2 RStudio History Tab

and listed under the ***History*** tab in the upper, right pane of RStudio (Figure 4.2). Clicking on a command in the history list automatically prints it into the Console pane, ready for entry. The history list can be saved to a file by clicking the disc icon and specifying its title and location.

Data Packages

Many **R** packages come with sample data that can be directly addressed from the **R** Console. For example, the *psych* package contains several dozen data files.

BOX 4.10   DATA FILE COMMANDS

```
## Display datasets available to R
> data()
## Display data files available in psych package
> data(package="psych")
## Display documentation of a data file
> help("bfi")
## Load a data file from the default utils package into
## a data frame for use
> bfi=data.frame(bfi)
## New object named bfi in Environment pane--2800 participants
## and 28 variables
```

Saving Data

As previously noted, data in memory can be saved in a native **R** format called a work space via *Session > Save Workspace As.* This procedure allows the user to navigate the file structure on the computer and save the data in a preferred location. Data can also be saved to the working directory through **R** Console commands.

BOX 4.11   SAVE DATA FILE COMMANDS

```
## Save a data file in memory as a comma-separated (.csv) readable
## by spreadsheet programs. Automatically saves to working directory
## Find working directory
> getwd()
[1] "/Users/mwxxx"
> write.csv(iq, file = "iq.csv", row.names = TRUE)
## Save a data file in memory as an R format file
> saveRDS(iq, file = "iq.rds")
```

Saving Results

As illustrated previously, the results of analyses are displayed in the **R** Console pane of the RStudio window. Results can be selected and copied from that pane and then pasted into Word or other programs. The resulting document will have proper alignment if a monospaced font (e.g., Courier or Monaco) is used.

Alternatively, the **R** output can be diverted to a text file. This example sends descriptive statistics to an external text file.

BOX 4.12   COMMANDS TO SAVE OUTPUT TO AN EXTERNAL FILE

```
## Divert results to an external text file. Automatically saves to
## the working directory. First sink command names the text file to
## be used and initiates output to file.
> sink("DescribeOutput.txt")
> describe(iq)
## Final sink command returns output to the R Console
> sink()
## Location of working directory where text file was saved
> getwd()
## Results in R Console
> describe(iq)
          vars   n   mean    sd median trimmed   mad min max range  skew kurtosis   se
vocab1       1 152  97.50 17.34     98   98.19 14.83  55 137    82 -0.31    -0.05 1.41
designs1     2 152  97.65 14.47     97   98.03 13.34  58 130    72 -0.21    -0.06 1.17
similar1     3 152 103.59 17.26    104  104.39 16.31  55 145    90 -0.45     0.26 1.40
matrix1      4 152  99.53 16.61    102  100.42 14.83  55 134    79 -0.52     0.07 1.35
veranal2     5 152 101.51 14.77    104  102.39 11.86  57 134    77 -0.62     0.34 1.20
vocab2       6 152 100.63 16.42    102  101.78 13.34  37 144   107 -0.80     1.72 1.33
matrix2      7 152 101.45 16.17    103  102.21 14.83  49 137    88 -0.57     0.78 1.31
designs2     8 152 100.64 13.92    102  101.03 11.86  45 137    92 -0.45     1.30 1.13
```

Contents of the "DescribeOutput" text file are identical to those found in the **R** Console. Note that only results, and not **R** commands, are diverted to the text file.

BOX 4.13 RESULT OF COMMANDS TO SAVE OUTPUT TO AN EXTERNAL FILE

```
          vars   n   mean     sd median trimmed   mad min max range  skew kurtosis   se
vocab1       1 152  97.50 17.34     98   98.19 14.83  55 137    82 -0.31    -0.05 1.41
designs1     2 152  97.65 14.47     97   98.03 13.34  58 130    72 -0.21    -0.06 1.17
similar1     3 152 103.59 17.26    104  104.39 16.31  55 145    90 -0.45     0.26 1.40
matrix1      4 152  99.53 16.61    102  100.42 14.83  55 134    79 -0.52     0.07 1.35
verana12     5 152 101.51 14.77    104  102.39 11.86  57 134    77 -0.62     0.34 1.20
vocab2       6 152 100.63 16.42    102  101.78 13.34  37 144   107 -0.80     1.72 1.33
matrix2      7 152 101.45 16.17    103  102.21 14.83  49 137    88 -0.57     0.78 1.31
designs2     8 152 100.64 13.92    102  101.03 11.86  45 137    92 -0.45     1.30 1.13
```

5

DECISION STEPS IN EXPLORATORY FACTOR ANALYSIS

Researchers must make several thoughtful and evidence-based methodological decisions while conducting an EFA (Henson & Roberts, 2006). There are a number of options available for each decision, some better than others (Lloret et al., 2017). Those decisions (steps in the EFA process) are charted in Figure 5.1.

Flowchart of Decision Steps (Figure 5.1)

Note that each decision might be sufficient for movement to the next step or it might necessitate a return to a previous step. The visual presentation of the flow chart emphasizes the exploratory nature of EFA and the knowledge that the evidence for some decisions is uncertain or dependent upon prior results (Figure 5.1).

Checklist of Decision Steps (Figure 5.2)

There are numerous decision steps and each step contains several complex components. Accordingly, users are encouraged to print Figure 5.2 and use it as a checklist as they conduct an EFA. That practice will ensure consistent implication of evidence-based, best practice decisions (Watkins, 2009).

Decision Steps in Exploratory Factor Analysis

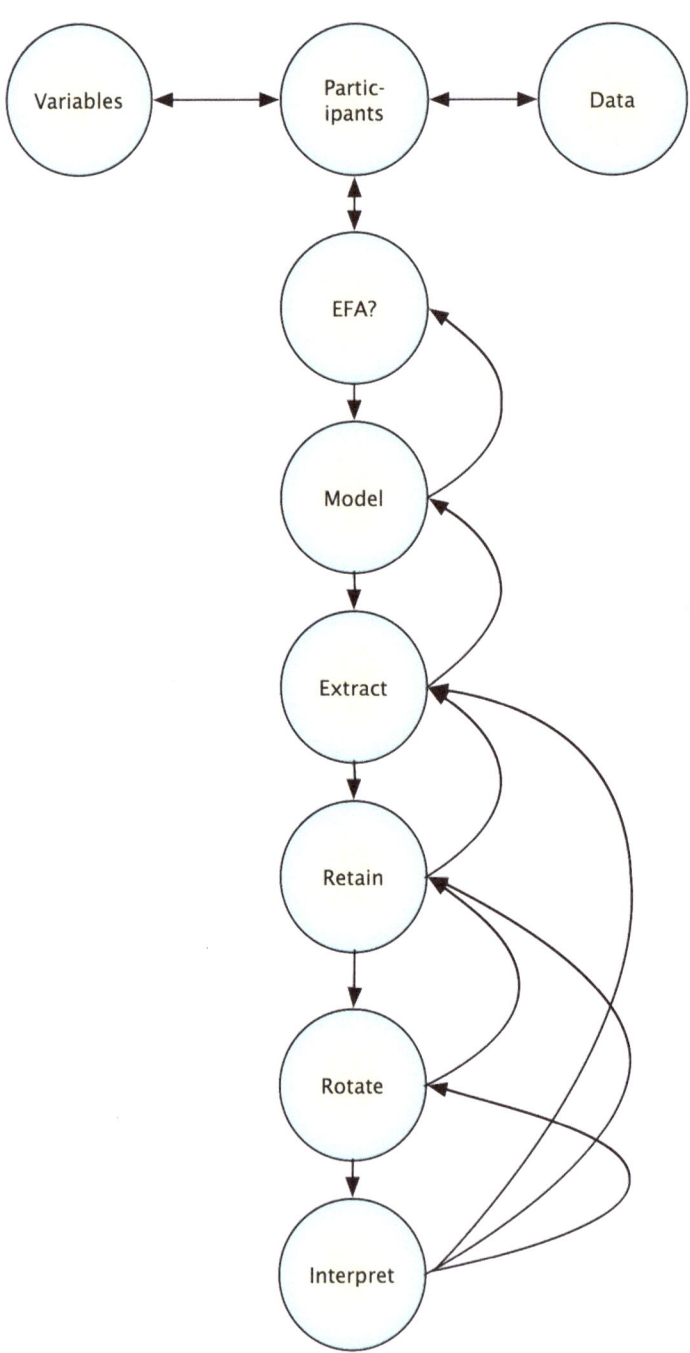

FIGURE 5.1   Flowchart of Decision Steps in Exploratory Factor Analysis

Decision Steps in Exploratory Factor Analysis

What variables to include
- ☐ Number of variables per factor
- ☐ Adequate representation of the domain
- ☐ Avoid low communality
- ☐ Avoid low reliability
- ☐ Variables cannot be dependent upon each other

What participants to include
- ☐ Number of participants
- ☐ Adequate representation of the population

Is data appropriate
- ☐ Accuracy (out of range values, plausible summary values)
- ☐ Missing data (amount and distribution)
- ☐ Univariate and multivariate outliers
- ☐ Linearity
- ☐ Univariate and multivariate normality

Is EFA appropriate
- ☐ Bartlett's test of sphericity
- ☐ Kaiser-Meyer-Olkin test of sampling adequacy
- ☐ Correlation matrix

Model of factor analysis
- ☐ Principal components analysis
- ☐ Common factor analysis

Factor extraction method
- ☐ Weak factors/Nonnormal: Least-squares, Principal Axis
- ☐ Multivariate normal: Maximum Likelihood

How many factors to retain
- ☐ Parallel analysis
- ☐ Minimum average partials (MAP)
- ☐ Visual scree
- ☐ Theoretical convergence and parsimony
- ☐ Others

Rotate factors
- ☐ Orthogonal: Varimax
- ☐ Oblique: Oblimin, Promax

Interpret results
- ☐ Simple structure
- ☐ Theoretical convergence and parsimony

Report results
- ☐ All decision steps

FIGURE 5.2 Checklist of Decision Steps in Exploratory Factor Analysis

6

STEP 1

Variables to Include

The choice of variables to include in the exploratory factor analysis (EFA) is important because "if the indicators are not selected well, the recovered structure will be misleading and biased" (Little et al., 1999, p. 209). Consequently, the measured variables must be selected after careful consideration of the domain of interest (Cattell, 1978; Widaman, 2012). Some domains will be relatively narrow (e.g., depression) whereas others will be broad (e.g., psychopathology). Nevertheless, variables that assess all important aspects of the domain of interest should be sampled (Carroll, 1985; Wegener & Fabrigar, 2000).

The psychometric properties of the measured variables must also be carefully considered. When EFA is conducted on measured variables with low communalities (those that do not share much common variance), substantial distortion can result. One obvious reason is low reliability. Scores can vary due to true responses of the examinees or due to error. The reliability coefficient estimates the proportion of true score variance. For example, a reliability coefficient of .40 indicates 40% true score variance and 60% error. Error variance, by definition, cannot be explained by factors. Because of this, variables with low reliability will have little in common with other variables and should be avoided in EFA (Fabrigar et al., 1999). Therefore, the reliability of measured variables should be considered when selecting them for inclusion in an EFA (Feldt & Brennan, 1993; Watkins, 2017). "If $r_{xx} < .50$, then most of the total variance is due to measurement error. Indicators with such low score reliabilities should be excluded from the analysis" (Kline, 2013, p. 173). Nevertheless, decisions about variables to include in EFA must also consider the possibility that systematic error might have artificially inflated reliability estimates at the expense of validity (see Clifton, 2020 for a discussion of this phenomenon).

A second psychometric reason that a variable might have a low communality is that it is reliable, but unrelated to the domain of interest and thus shares little common variance with the variables that tap that domain. Thus, the validity of measured variables must also be respected (Messick, 1995). This is related to reliability in that reliability is necessary but not sufficient for validity. Validity suggests that the relationship between the measured variables and factors should be congruent. Given that EFA assumes that the factors influence the measured variables, what measured variables make sense given the domain of interest? For instance, if the domain of interest is assumed to be depression, it makes no sense to include variables that measure body mass, family income, and height because they are not reasonably influenced by depression. This is an example of construct irrelevance. Likewise, it makes little sense to include only addition and subtraction problems as variables if the domain of interest is arithmetic. That domain includes multiplication and division as well as addition and subtraction. This is an example of construct underrepresentation (Spurgeon, 2017). Readers should consult texts on measurement and scale development to gain a better understanding of these psychometric issues (Bandalos, 2018; Clifton, 2020; Cooper, 2019; DeVellis, 2017; Kline, 2000).

It might be useful to include variables with known properties that have previously been studied (marker variables) in an EFA if the remainder of the measured variables are relatively unknown (Carroll, 1985; Comrey & Lee, 1994; Gorsuch, 1988; Nunnally & Bernstein, 1994; Tabachnick & Fidell, 2019; Zhang & Preacher, 2015). For example, vocabulary tests have long been used as measures of verbal ability so a vocabulary test might be included in an EFA if several new tests that purport to measure verbal ability are analyzed.

In theory, there are situations where the measured variables are more properly treated as determinants rather than effects of latent variables (Edwards & Bagozzi, 2000). These are called *formative* indicators. That is, the causal direction goes from measured variables to the latent variable. For example, loss of job and divorce are measures of exposure to stress that might best be thought of as causal indicators. Each event creates stress rather than the reverse. Education, income, and occupational prestige may be causal indicators of socioeconomic status (SES). Clearly, more education and income and a high prestige job cause higher SES; SES does not cause these indicators. Thus, losing one's job would lead to lower SES, but this lowered status would leave one's years of education unchanged. Eliminating one causal indicator (say, education) from the model changes the meaning of the SES scale because part of the SES construct is not represented. For most purposes, we will assume *effect* indicators and proceed accordingly but the type of indicators should be carefully considered because application of EFA with formative indicators may produce severely biased results (Rhemtulla et al., 2020).

Finally, how many variables should be included in an EFA? Too few variables per factor "becomes not only an issue of model identification and replication, but also a matter of construct underrepresentation" (Schmitt et al., 2018, p. 350). The number of measured variables will also impact the sample size decision. The requisite number of variables is also influenced by the reliability and validity of the measured variables. Fewer variables might be needed if they exhibit high reliability and validity. For example, subscales from individually administered tests of cognitive ability typically meet this definition and only three to four variables per factor might be needed. It is generally recommended that at least three to six reliable variables representing each common factor be included in an analysis (Carroll, 1985; Comrey & Lee, 1992; Fabrigar & Wegener, 2012; Fabrigar et al., 1999; Goldberg & Velicer, 2006; Gorsuch, 1988; Hair et al., 2019; Hancock & Schoonen, 2015; Kline, 2013; McCoach et al., 2013; McDonald, 1985; Mulaik, 2010; Streiner, 1994; Tabachnick & Fidell, 2019). In contrast, individual items on both ability and personality tests are generally of low reliability so many more might be needed to adequately represent the domain of interest. Kline (1994) recommended that at least 10 individual items should be included for finalizing a test and many more if the test is in the development stage.

Report

The eight measured variables in this study were developed to measure cognitive ability. Based on typical ability tests, these variables are expected to exhibit good psychometric properties. As suggested by Fabrigar et al. (1999), four variables were hypothesized to represent each factor.

7

STEP 2

Participants

Characteristics of Participants

First, which participants? This is primarily a matter of logic and common sense. To which population are the results to generalize? Sample from that population. Does the sample make sense given the factors you are attempting to measure?

Child (2006) warned against using samples collected from different populations to compute correlations because factors that are specific to a population might be obscured when pooled. Tabachnick and Fidell (2019) and Comrey and Lee (1992) also warned about pooling the results of several samples, or the same sample measured across time. Sampling procedures are acceptable, but there must be a clear understanding of sample-population differences (Widaman, 2012).

Additionally, negligent responses from unmotivated participants may introduce bias. Woods (2006) found that factor analysis results were affected when more than 10% of the participants responded carelessly. Thus, the validity of participants' responses must be considered.

Number of Participants

Beyond which participants to include in an exploratory factor analysis (EFA), it is also important to know how many participants to include. Correlation coefficients tend to be less reliable when estimated from small samples. For example, with a true population correlation of zero, about 95% of the correlations will fall between −.20 and +.20 when the sample size is 100. In contrast, about 95% of the correlations will fall between −.09 and +.09 when the sample size is 500. One simulation study found that 1,000 participants were needed to estimate correlation coefficients within ±.05 and 250 participants were needed for "reasonable trade-offs between accuracy and confidence" (Schönbrodt & Perugini, 2013, p. 611).

Guidelines for estimating the number of participants required for an EFA have focused on the: (a) absolute number of participants, (b) ratio of participants to measured variables, (c) quality of the measured variables, and (d) ratio of measured variables to factors. In the first case, Comrey and Lee (1992) suggested that 100 participants is poor, 200 is fair, 300 is good, 500 is very good, and 1,000 or more is excellent. Regarding the participant to variable ratio, both Child (2006) and Gorsuch (1983) recommended five participants per measured variable with a minimum of 100 participants. Other measurement experts have suggested a 10:1 or 20:1 ratio of participants to measured variables (Benson & Nasser, 1998; Hair et al., 2019; Osborne & Banjanovic, 2016). Unfortunately, "these guidelines all share three characteristics: (1) no agreement among different authorities, (2) no rigorous theoretical basis provided, and (3) no empirical basis for the rules" (Velicer & Fava, 1998, p. 232).

In contrast, sample size guidelines based on the quality of measured variables and the variable to factor ratio have often been based on statistical simulation studies where the number of variables, number of participants, number of variables per factor (factor overdetermination), and the percent of variance accounted for by the factors (communality) were systematically modified and evaluated (Guadagnoli & Velicer, 1988; Hogarty et al., 2005; MacCallum et al., 2001; MacCallum et al., 1999; Mundfrom et al., 2005; Velicer & Fava, 1998; Wolf et al., 2013). These simulation studies have used dissimilar numbers of factors, variables, variance estimates, EFA methods, etc. so their results are not always compatible. However, factor overdetermination (i.e., number of measured variables per factor) and communality were consistently found to be important determinants of sample size. Higher factor overdetermination and communality tended to require smaller sample sizes than the reverse. Further, sample size, factor overdetermination, and communality seemed to interact so that "strength on one of these variables could compensate for a weakness on another" (Velicer & Fava, 1998, p. 243).

Although "it is impossible to derive a minimum sample size that is appropriate in all situations" (Reise et al., 2000, p. 290), the guidelines for good factor recovery presented in Table 7.1 are consistent with the tables provided by Mundfrom et al. (2005) and the results reported in other studies (Guadagnoli & Velicer, 1988; Hogarty et al., 2005; MacCallum, 1999, 2001; Velicer & Fava, 1998).

Two additional considerations in determining the appropriate sample size are type of data and amount of missing data. The above recommendations are based on data from continuous, normally distributed data. Dichotomous variables (two response options) are neither continuous nor normally distributed and will require three to ten times more participants (Pearson & Mundfrom, 2010; Rouquette & Falissard, 2011).

Additionally, models with 10% missing data may require a 25% increase in sample size and models with 20% missing data may need a 50% increase in sample

TABLE 7.1 Sample size based on communality and variable : factor ratio

Communality	Variables per factor	Number of factors	Number of participants
	3	2	100
≥.60	3	3	170
	3	4	260
	3	5	300
	4	2	100
	4	3	120
	4	4	170
	4	5	220
	5	3	100
	5	4	100
	5	5	130
	10	6	100
	3	2	160
.20–.80	3	3	450
	3	4	500
	3	5	700
	4	3	130
	4	4	240
	4	5	320
	5	3	100
	5	4	110
	5	5	140
	10	6	100
≤.20	3	3	1,200
	3	4	1,200
	3	5	1,300
	4	3	230
	4	4	250
	4	5	400
	5	3	150
	5	4	170
	5	5	180
	10	6	150

size (Wolf et al., 2013). Regardless of type of data and missing values, more data is always better "because the probability of error is less, population estimates are more accurate, and the findings are more generalizable" (Reio & Shuck, 2015, p. 15).

For ordinal data, a simulation study by Rouquette and Falissard (2011) suggested that stable and accurate factor solutions can be obtained with: (a) 350 to 400 participants when there are 10 variables per factor; (b) 400 to 450 participants when there are seven or eight variables per factor; and (c) 500 to 600 participants when there are five or six variables per factor.

Report

The participants in this study were children in grades two through six who were referred for assessment for consideration of special educational accommodations. The average communality of variables similar to those in this study is ≥.60 (Dombrowski et al., 2018). Additionally, these cognitive variables were relatively reliable ($\alpha \geq .80$) and normally distributed. Given the communality, number of factors, and number of variables, 75 participants would be needed for good factor recovery and 150 participants for excellent factor recovery (Mundfrom et al., 2005). Thus, the current sample of 152 participants appears to be adequate for EFA.

8

STEP 3

Data Screening

Effective data screening involves inspection of both statistics and graphics (Hoelzle & Meyer, 2013; Malone & Lubansky, 2012). Either alone is insufficient. This was famously demonstrated by Anscombe (1973) who created four x-y data sets with relatively equivalent summary statistics. A quick scan seems to indicate relatively normal distributions with no obvious problem.

BOX 8.1 DESCRIPTIVE STATISTICS AND CORRELATION MATRIX FOR ANSCOMBE QUARTET DATA

```
> describe(Anscombe)
   vars  n mean   sd median trimmed  mad  min   max range  skew kurtosis   se
x1    1 11  9.0 3.32   9.00    9.00 4.45 4.00 14.00 10.00  0.00    -1.53 1.00
y1    2 11  7.5 2.03   7.58    7.49 1.82 4.26 10.84  6.58 -0.05    -1.20 0.61
x2    3 11  9.0 3.32   9.00    9.00 4.45 4.00 14.00 10.00  0.00    -1.53 1.00
y2    4 11  7.5 2.03   8.14    7.79 1.47 3.10  9.26  6.16 -0.98    -0.51 0.61
x3    5 11  9.0 3.32   9.00    9.00 4.45 4.00 14.00 10.00  0.00    -1.53 1.00
y3    6 11  7.5 2.03   7.11    7.15 1.53 5.39 12.74  7.35  1.38     1.24 0.61
x4    7 11  9.0 3.32   8.00    8.00 0.00 8.00 19.00 11.00  2.47     4.52 1.00
y4    8 11  7.5 2.03   7.04    7.20 1.90 5.25 12.50  7.25  1.12     0.63 0.61
> cor(x1,y1);cor(x2,y2);cor(x3,y3);cor(x4,y4)
[1] 0.8164205
[1] 0.8162365
[1] 0.8162867
[1] 0.8165214
```

However, there is danger in relying on summary statistics alone. When this "Anscombe quartet" is graphed, the real relationships in the data emerge (Figure 8.1). Specifically, the x1–y1 data appear to follow a rough linear relationship with some variability, the x2–y2 data display a curvilinear rather than a linear relationship, the x3–y3 data depict a linear relationship except for one large

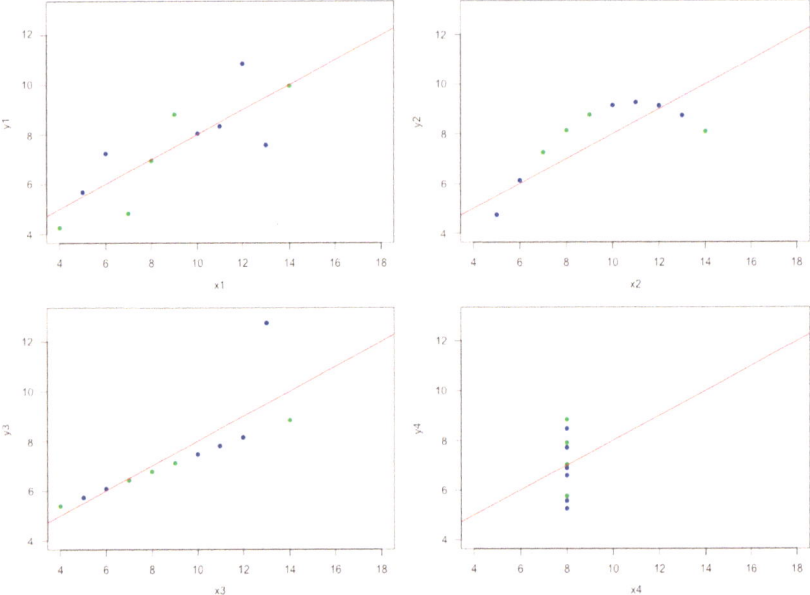

FIGURE 8.1 Ansco Scatterplots for Anscombe Quartet Data

outlier, and the x4–y4 data show x remaining constant except for one (off the chart) outlier.

Assumptions

All multivariate statistics are based on assumptions that will bias results if they are violated. The assumptions of exploratory factor analysis (EFA) are mostly conceptual: It is assumed that some underlying structure exists, that the relationship between measured variables and the underlying common factors are linear, and that the linear coefficients are invariant across participants (Fabrigar & Wegener, 2012; Hair et al., 2019).

However, EFA is based on Pearson product-moment correlations that also rely on statistical assumptions. Specifically, it is assumed that a linear relationship exists between the variables and that there is an underlying normal distribution. To meet these assumptions, variables must be measured on a continuous scale (Bandalos, 2018; Puth et al., 2015; Walsh, 1996). Violation of the assumptions that underlie the Pearson product-moment correlation may bias EFA results. As suggested by Carroll (1961), "there is no particular point in making a factor analysis of a matrix of raw correlation coefficients when these coefficients represent manifest relationships which mask and distort latent relationships" (p. 356).

More broadly, anything that influences the correlation matrix can potentially affect EFA results (Carroll, 1985; Onwuegbuzie & Daniel, 2002). As noted by Warner (2007), "because the input to factor analysis is a matrix of correlations, any problems that make Pearson *r* misleading as a description of the strength of the relationship between pairs of variables will also lead to problems in factor analysis" (p. 765). Accordingly, the data must be carefully screened before conducting an EFA to ensure that some untoward influence has not biased the results (Flora et al., 2012; Goodwin & Leech, 2006; Hair et al., 2019; Walsh, 1996). Potential influences include restricted score range, linearity, data distributions, outliers, and missing data. "Consideration and resolution of these issues before the main analysis are fundamental to an honest analysis of the data" (Tabachnick & Fidell, 2019, p. 52).

Restricted Score Range

The range of scores on the measured variables must be considered. If the sample is more homogeneous than the population, restriction of range in the measured variables can result and thereby attenuate correlations among the variables. This attenuation can result in biased EFA estimates. For example, using quantitative and verbal test scores from the 1949 applicant pool of the U.S. Coast Guard Academy, the quantitative and verbal test score correlations dropped from .50 for all 2,253 applicants to only .12 for the 128 students who entered the Academy (French et al., 1952). In such cases, a "factor cannot emerge with any clarity" (Kline, 1991, p. 16).

Linearity

Pearson coefficients are measures of the linear relationship between two variables. That is, their relationship is best approximated by a straight line. Curvilinear or nonlinear relationships will not be accurately estimated by Pearson coefficients. Although subjective, visual inspection of scatterplots can be used to assess linearity. The built-in *graphics* package offers a simple scatterplot for multiple variables. After loading the iq data, a scatterplot for two measured variables can be created.

BOX 8.2 SCATTERPLOT WITH REGRESSION LINE FROM *GRAPHICS* PACKAGE

```
## Ensure that iq object is a data frame and has been attached
> iq = as.data.frame(iq)
> attach(iq)
## Scatterplot from graphics package with color, plot symbols,
## regression line. Color dictionary at
## https://www.rapidtables.com/web/color/RGB_Color.html
## Plot symbols listed by command: help("pch")
> plot(vocab1,similar1,main="Scatterplot,pch=16,col=(c("blue","green")))
## Include regression line
> abline(lm(vocab1~similar1), col="red")
```

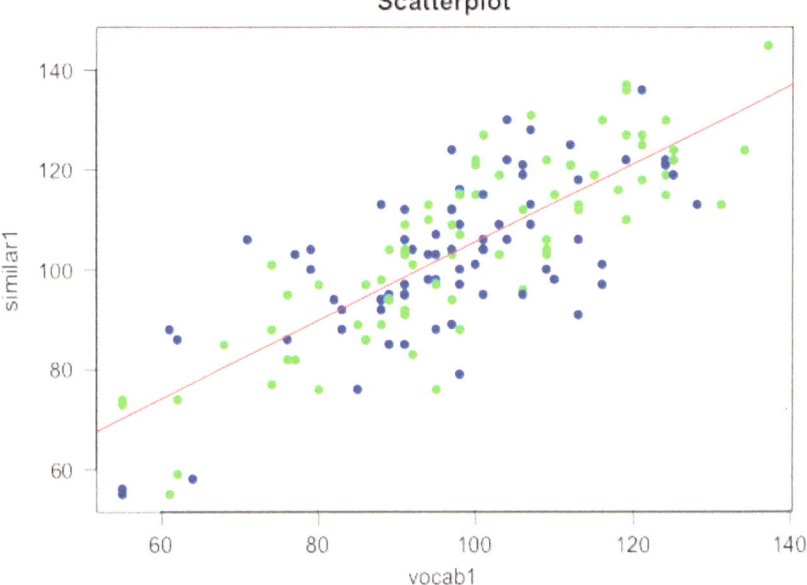

FIGURE 8.2 Scatterplot for Two Variables

RStudio implements this command and automatically displays that scatterplot in the **Plots** tab as demonstrated in Figure 8.2. The scatterplot can be exported as an image by selecting the **Export > Save as Image** from the **Plots** menu. That selection brings up a new window that allows the type of image file (TIFF, PNG, JPEG, etc.) to be specified as well as the image's dimensions and file location.

It may be more efficient to review a scatterplot matrix rather than individual scatterplots (Figure 8.3). This is easily accomplished in **R** using the pairs.panels function from the *psych* package. A scatterplot matrix can also be exported as a graphics file.

After reviewing the scatterplots, it appears that the iq variables are linearly related.

BOX 8.3 SCATTERPLOT MATRIX FROM *GRAPHICS* PACKAGE

```
## Simple scatterplot from graphics package with 3 variables included
> pairs(~vocab1+similar1+veranal2,data=iq,pch="*",main="Scatterplot")
## Simple scatterplot from graphics package with all variables included
> pairs(iq)
## Scatterplot matrix for all 8 variables from psych package
> library(psych)
> pairs.panels(iq,pch='.',lm=T,ellipses=F,scale=F,method="pearson",
  main="Scatterplot Matrix")
## Scatterplot matrix of first 3 variables without options for better
## readability
> pairs.panels(iq[,1:3])
```

Scatterplot   Matrix

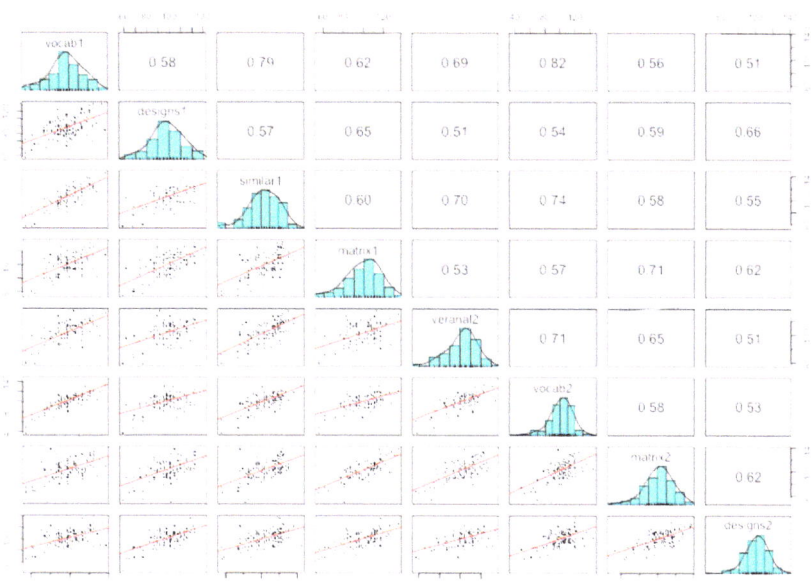

FIGURE 8.3   Scatterplot Matrix

Data Distributions

Pearson correlation coefficients theoretically range from -1.00 to $+1.00$. However, that is only possible when the two variables have exactly the same distribution. If, for example, one variable is normally distributed and the other distribution is skewed, the maximum value of the Pearson correlation is less than 1.00. The more the distribution shapes differ, the greater the restriction of r. Consequently, it is important to understand the distributional characteristics of the measured variables to be included in an EFA. For example, it has long been known that dichotomous items that are skewed in opposite directions may produce what are known as difficulty factors when submitted to EFA (Bernstein & Teng, 1989; Greer et al., 2006). That is, a factor may appear that is an artifact of variable distributions rather than the effect of their content. Using procedures from the *psych* package, statistics can be computed to describe variable distributions.

BOX 8.4 SUMMARY STATISTICS FROM *PSYCH* PACKAGE

```
## Summary statistics for the iq data from psych package
## Add na.rm=TRUE if missing data not deleted
> describe(iq)
          vars   n    mean    sd median trimmed    mad min max range  skew kurtosis   se
vocab1       1 152   97.50 17.34     98   98.19 14.83  55 137    82 -0.31    -0.05 1.41
designs1     2 152   97.65 14.47     97   98.03 13.34  58 130    72 -0.21    -0.06 1.17
similar1     3 152  103.59 17.26    104  104.39 16.31  55 145    90 -0.45     0.26 1.40
matrix1      4 152   99.53 16.61    102  100.42 14.83  55 134    79 -0.52     0.07 1.35
veranal2     5 152  101.51 14.77    104  102.39 11.86  57 134    77 -0.62     0.34 1.20
vocab2       6 152  100.63 16.42    102  101.78 13.34  37 144   107 -0.80     1.72 1.33
matrix2      7 152  101.45 16.17    103  102.21 14.83  49 137    88 -0.57     0.78 1.31
designs2     8 152  100.64 13.92    102  101.03 11.86  45 137    92 -0.45     1.30 1.13
```

Skew > 2.0 or kurtosis > 7.0 would indicate severe univariate nonnormality (Curran et al., 1996). These univariate statistics seem to indicate that all eight measured variables are relatively normally distributed (skew < 1.0 and kurtosis < 2.0) so there should not be much concern about correlations being restricted due to variable distributions. Skew (departures from symmetry) and kurtosis (distributions with heavier or lighter tails and higher or flatter peaks) of all variables seem to be close to normal (normal distributions have expected values of zero). The histograms displayed in the scatterplot matrix support that assumption.

BOX 8.5 BOXPLOT FROM *GRAPHICS* PACKAGE

```
## Boxplot with colors, plot symbols from graphics package
> boxplot(iq,notch=TRUE,boxfill="royalblue",whiskcol="blue",pch=16
  outcol="firebrick")
```

Graphs can be useful for visual verification of this conclusion. A multi-colored boxplot that displays the distributional statistics of the measured variables can be generated with the **R** code presented in Box 8.5. Boxplots, as depicted in Figure 8.4, have the following characteristics: the thick line in the box is the median, the bottom of the box is the first quartile, the top of the box is the third quartile, the "whiskers" show the range of the data (excluding outliers), and the circles identify outliers (defined as any value 1.5 times the interquartile range).

A group of measured variables might exhibit univariate normality and yet be multivariate nonnormal. That is, the joint distribution of all the variables might be nonnormal. The *psych* package offers an implementation of Mardia's multivariate tests (1970) and an accompanying Q–Q plot. The mardia output is somewhat confusing because its descriptions are based on the notation found in the 1970 paper by Mardia. For this case, we would report multivariate skew = 6.15 ($p = .015$) and multivariate kurtosis = 83.02 ($p = .14$).

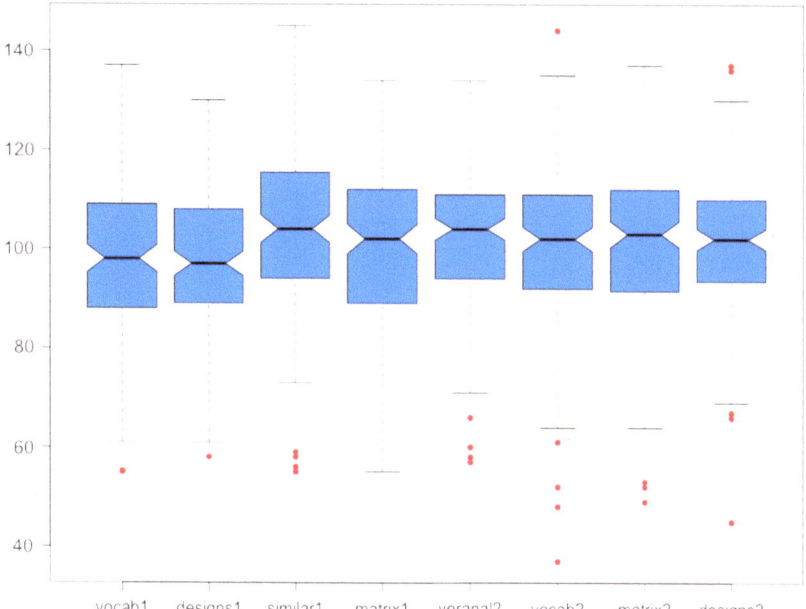

FIGURE 8.4   Boxplot

BOX 8.6   MARDIA'S MULTIVARIATE SKEW AND KURTOSIS FROM *PSYCH* PACKAGE

```
## Mardia multivariate normality from psych package.
> mardia(iq,na.rm=TRUE, plot=TRUE)
n.obs = 152   num.vars =  8
b1p =   6.15 · skew =  155.87  with probability =  0.015
 small sample skew =  159.64  with probability =  0.0091
b2p =  83.02 kurtosis =  1.47  with probability =  0.14
```

The diagonal line in the Q–Q plot, displayed in Figure 8.5, represents a theoretical normal distribution whereas the circles represent scores on the measured variables in the iq data set. A linear trend in the measured variables visually illustrates that it is plausible that the iq data came from a normal distribution.

As with many other procedures in **R**, the same results might be obtained from a different package. For example, multivariate normality tests are also available in the *QuantPsyc* package.

BOX 8.7   MARDIA'S MULTIVARIATE SKEW AND KURTOSIS FROM *QUANTPSYC* PACKAGE

```
> library(QuantPsyc)
> mult.norm(iq)
$mult.test
           Beta-hat      kappa      p-val
Skewness   6.152569 155.865075 0.01539035
Kurtosis 83.020239   1.471882 0.14105268
```

Normal Q-Q Plot

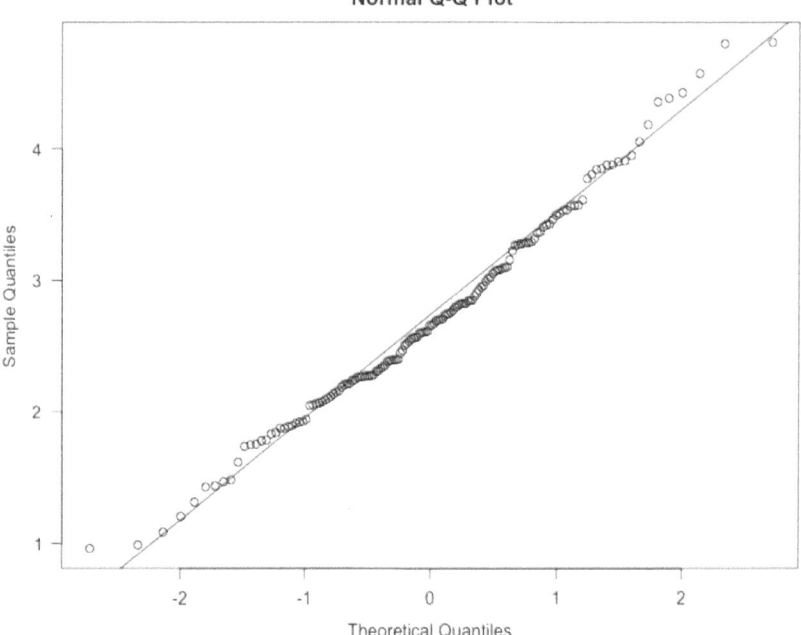

FIGURE 8.5 Normal Q–Q Plot

Nonnormality, especially kurtosis, can bias Pearson correlation estimates and thereby bias EFA results (Cain et al., 2017; DeCarlo, 1997; Greer et al., 2006). The extent to which variables can be nonnormal and not substantially affect EFA results has been addressed by several researchers. Curran et al. (1996) opined that univariate skew should not exceed 2.0 and univariate kurtosis should not exceed 7.0. Other measurement specialists have agreed with those guidelines (Bandalos, 2018; Fabrigar et al., 1999; Wegener & Fabrigar, 2000). In terms of multinormality, statistically significant multivariate kurtosis values > 3.0 to 5.0 might bias factor analysis results (Bentler, 2005; Finney & DiStefano, 2013; Mueller & Hancock, 2019). Spearman or other types of correlation coefficients might be more accurate in those instances (Bishara & Hittner, 2015; Onwuegbuzie & Daniel, 2002; Puth et al., 2015).

Outliers

As describe by Tabachnick and Fidell (2019), "an outlier is a case with such an extreme value on one variable (a univariate outlier) or such a strange combination of scores on two or more variables (multivariate outlier) that it distorts statistics" (p. 62). Outliers are, therefore, questionable members of the data set. Outliers may have been caused by data collection errors, data entry errors, a participant not understanding the instructions, a participant deliberately entering invalid responses, or a valid but extreme value. Not all outliers will influence the size of correlation coefficients and subsequent factor analysis results but some may have a major effect (Liu et al., 2012). For example, the correlation between the vocab1 and designs1 variables in the iq data set is .58. That correlation drops to -.04 when the final value in the matrix variable was entered as -999 rather than the correct value of 113. A data entry error like this might be the result of a typo or considering a missing data indicator as real data.

Obviously, some outliers can be detected by reviewing descriptive statistics. The minimum and maximum values might reveal data that exceeds the possible values that the data can take. For example, it is known that the values of the iq variables can reasonably range from around 40 to 160. Any value outside that range is improbable and must be addressed. One way to address such illegal values is to replace them with a missing value indicator. In **R**, missing data are indicated by the characters NA. This replacement can be automated by a procedure within the *psych* package:

BOX 8.8   SUMMARY STATISTICS WITH REPLACEMENT VALUES FROM *PSYCH* PACKAGE

```
## Review descriptive statistics of iq variables using psych package
## Use na.rm = TRUE or = FALSE to handle missing data
> describe(iq)
         vars   n    mean     sd median trimmed   mad min max range  skew kurtosis   se
vocab1      1 152   97.50 17.34     98   98.19 14.83  55 137    82 -0.31    -0.05 1.41
designs1    2 152   97.65 14.47     97   98.03 13.34  58 130    72 -0.21    -0.06 1.17
similar1    3 152  103.59 17.26    104  104.39 16.31  55 145    90 -0.45     0.26 1.40
matrix1     4 152   99.53 16.61    102  100.42 14.83  55 134    79 -0.52     0.07 1.35
veranal2    5 152  101.51 14.77    104  102.39 11.86  57 134    77 -0.62     0.34 1.20
vocab2      6 152  100.63 16.42    102  101.78 13.34  37 144   107 -0.80     1.72 1.33
matrix2     7 152  101.45 16.17    103  102.21 14.83  49 137    88 -0.57     0.78 1.31
designs2    8 152  100.64 13.92    102  101.03 11.86  45 137    92 -0.45     1.30 1.13
## new data set with vocab2 variable value lower than 40 set to missing
> newiq=scrub(iq,where="vocab2",isvalue=37)
## new data set with vocab2 value lower than 40 set to 40
> newiq=scrub(iq,where="vocab2",isvalue=37,newvalue=40)
```

Other outliers might be detected with plots as illustrated with the boxplot in Figure 8.4. That plot clearly displays data points that are more than 1.5 times the interquartile range. That might be a somewhat liberal standard given that some experts suggest that 2.2 times the interquartile range be used (Streiner, 2018). Nevertheless, those values are within plausible ranges and their cause is not clear. Additionally, they are univariate outliers and EFA is a multivariate procedure that necessitates that the multidimensional position of each data point be considered.

The Mahalanobis distance (D^2) is a measure of the distance of each data point from the mean of all data points in multidimensional space. Higher D^2 values represent observations farther removed from the general distribution of observations in multidimensional space and high values are potential multivariate outliers. D^2 values can be tested for statistical significance but "it is suggested that conservative levels of significance (e.g., .005 or .001) be used as the threshold value for designation as an outlier" (Hair et al., 2019, p. 89). Unfortunately, extreme outliers may negatively influence the accuracy of D^2 values so robust D^2

estimation techniques have been recommended (DeSimone et al., 2015) and are available in the *faoutlier* package.

BOX 8.9 ROBUST MAHALANOBIS DISTANCE FROM *FAOUTLIER* PACKAGE

```
## enable the faoutlier package
> library(faoutlier)
## create a new object to contain the results of D² computation
## and print those results
> out = robustMD(iq,method="mcd")
> print(out)
          mah        p  sig
121 34.96549 0.00003 ****
142 29.60457 0.00025  ***
12  23.82218 0.00245   **
122 23.60945 0.00266   **
94  23.10827 0.00323   **
124 22.90432 0.00349   **
152 21.22326 0.00658   **
131 20.81564 0.00765   **
28  19.39578 0.01288    *
23  19.16297 0.01401    *
## plot the results for a visual representation
> plot(out)
## Outlier identification through D² in psych package as an
## alternative to faoutlier package
out = outlier(iq)
plot(out)
```

Using $p < .001$ as the threshold (as suggested by Hair et al., 2019 as well as Tabachnick & Fidell, 2019), cases 121 and 142 are potential outliers. Those cases are also visible in the Robust MD graph   (Figure 8.6) and a Q-Q plot (Figure 8.7).

An examination of case 121 shows that it contains the previously identified aberrant value of 37 for the vocab2 variable. However, all of the variable values for this case are very low (45 to 58) and consistent with impaired intellectual functioning. Given this consistency, there is no good reason to delete or modify the value of this case. Case 142 is not as easily understood. Some of its values are lower than average (e.g., 85) and others are higher than average (e.g., 127). There is no obvious explanation for why these values are discrepant.

The *psych* package also contains an outlier function that can compute and display Mahalanobis distance (D^2) measures.

BOX 8.10 MAHALANOBIS DISTANCE FROM *PSYCH* PACKAGE

```
## Identification of outliers with psych package
> out=outlier(iq,bad=5,plot=T,na.rm=T,bg=c("red"),pch=21,ylab="D2",
  cex=.75,ylim=c(0,25))
## Display D2 values for every case if desired
> print(out,digits=3)
```

Robust MD

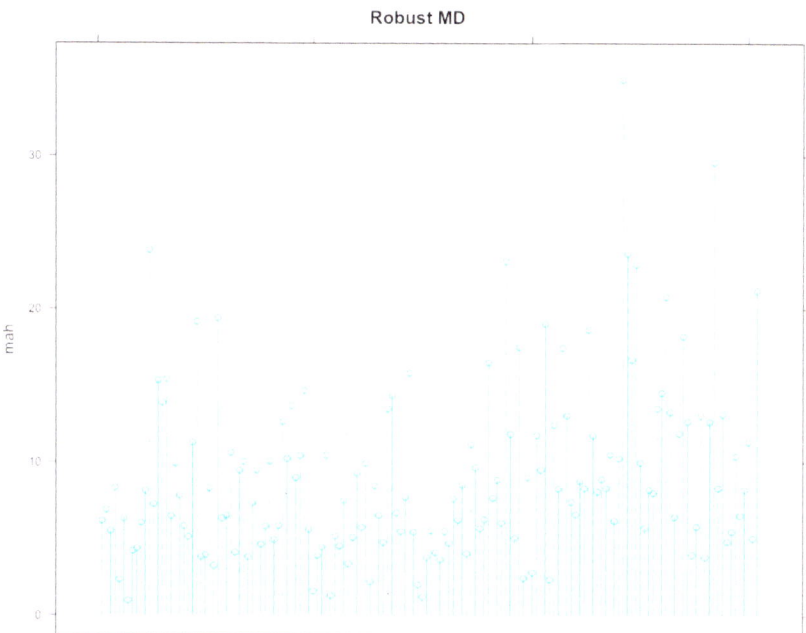

FIGURE 8.6   Robust MD Graph

It is important to articulate an outlier policy prior to data analysis (Leys et al., 2018). Not to do so makes the researcher vulnerable to interpreting this ambiguous information inconsistent with best statistical practice (Simmons et al., 2011). Although there is considerable debate among statisticians as to the advisability of deleting outliers, Goodwin and Leech (2006) suggested that "the researcher should first check for data collection or data entry errors. If there were no errors of this type and there is no obvious explanation for the outlier—the outlier cannot be explained by a third variable affecting the person's score—the outlier should not be removed" (p. 260). Hair et al. (2019) expressed similar sentiments about outliers: "they should be retained unless demonstrable proof indicates that they are truly aberrant and not representative of any observations in the population" (p. 91). Alternative suggestions for identifying and reducing the effect of outliers have been offered (e.g., Tabachnick & Fidell, 2019). Regardless, extreme values might drastically influence EFA results so it is incumbent upon the researcher to perform a sensitivity analysis. That is, conduct EFAs with and without outlier data to verify that the results are robust (Bandalos & Finney, 2019; Leys et al., 2018; Tabachnick & Fidell, 2019; Thompson, 2004).

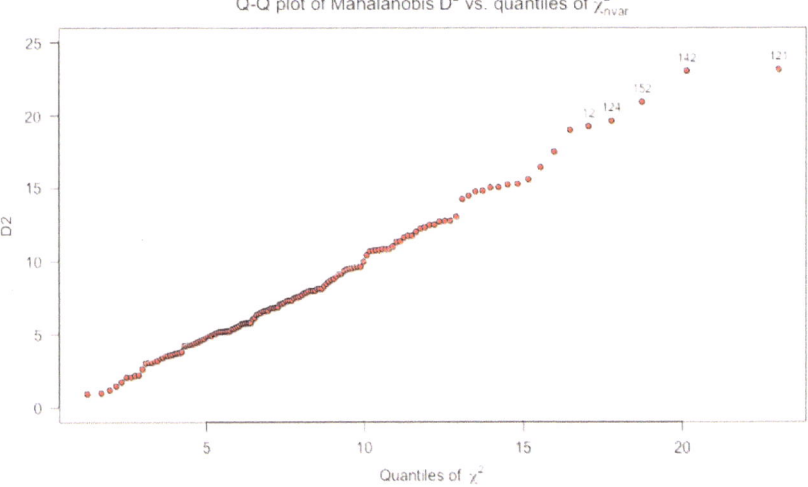

FIGURE 8.7   Mahalanobis Distance (D^2) Plot to Identify Potential Outliers in IQ Data

Missing Data

Ideally, there will be no missing data. In practice, there often are: people sometimes skip items on tests or survey, are absent on exam day, etc. First described by Rubin (1976), it is now well accepted that the treatment of missing data is contingent on the mechanism that caused the data to be missing. Data that is missing completely at random (MCAR) is entirely unsystematic and not related to any other value on any measured variable. For example, a person may accidently skip one question on a test. Data missing at random (MAR), contrary to its label, is not missing at random. Rather, it is a situation where the missingness can be fully accounted for by the remainder of the data. For instance, nonresponse to self-esteem questions might be related to other questions, such as gender and age. Finally, missing not at random (MNAR) applies when the missing data is related to the reason that it is missing. For example, an anxious person might not respond to survey questions dealing with anxiety.

It is useful to look for patterns at both variable and participant levels when considering missing data (Fernstad, 2019). For example, the first variable in the first illustration in Figure 8.8 seems to be problematic whereas the final participant is problematic in the second illustration. The third illustration reveals relatively random missingness. Generally, randomly scattered missing data is less problematic than other patterns (Tabachnick & Fidell, 2019).

Researchers tend to rely on two general approaches to dealing with missing data: discard a portion of the data or replace missing values with estimated or imputed values. When discarding data, the entire case can be discarded if one or

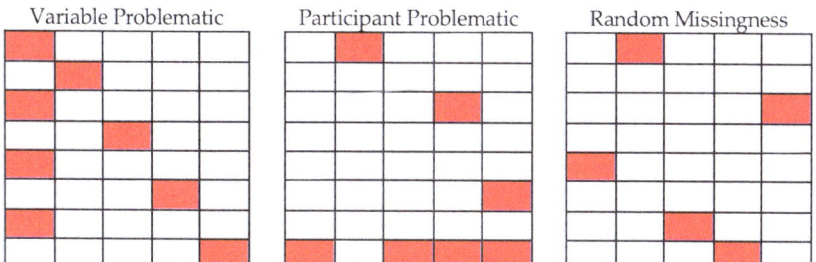

FIGURE 8.8   Missing Data Patterns

more of its data values are missing (listwise deletion). Alternatively, only the actual missing values can be discarded (pairwise deletion). Most statistical programs offer these two missing data methods. Both methods will reduce power and may result in statistical estimation problems and biased parameter estimates (Zygmont & Smith, 2014).

A wide variety of methods have been developed to estimate or impute missing data values (Hair et al., 2019; Roth, 1994; Tabachnick & Fidell, 2019) that range from simple (replace missing values with the mean value of that variable) to more complex (predict the missing data value using nonmissing values via regression analysis) to extremely complex (multiple imputation and maximum likelihood estimation). Baraldi and Enders (2013) suggested that "researchers must formulate logical arguments that support a particular missing data mechanism and choose an analysis method that is most defensible, given their assumptions about missingness" (p. 639).

Unfortunately, there is no infallible way to statistically verify the missing data mechanism and most methods used to deal with missing data values rely, at a minimum, on the assumption of MAR. Considerable simulation research has suggested that the *amount* of missing data may be a practical guide to dealing with missing data. In general, if less than 5% to 10% of the data are missing in a random pattern across variables and participants then any method of deletion or imputation will be acceptable (Chen et al., 2012; Hair et al., 2019; Lee & Ashton, 2007; Roth, 1994; Tabachnick & Fidell, 2019; Xiao et al., 2019). When more than 10% of the data are missing, Newman (2014) suggested that complex multivariate techniques, such as multiple imputation or maximum likelihood estimation, be used. As with outliers, extensive missing data requires a sensitivity analysis where the EFA results from different methods of dealing with missing data are compared for robustness (Goldberg & Velicer, 2006; Hair et al., 2019; Tabachnick & Fidell, 2019). Additionally, the amount and location of missing data at variable and participant levels should be transparently reported.

Missing Data in R. R is relative inflexible in its use of missing data indicators in data files. The only recognizable missing data indicator is the two-letter NA combination. Other statistical packages allow the user to select one or more indicators and many researchers have developed habits in this regard. For example, assigning -9 to missing values without apparent cause, -99 to missing values where the survey respondent refused to answer, and -999 when the question did not apply. Data with missing data indicators other than NA can be edited before they are analyzed in **R**. This can be accomplished in EXCEL, SPSS, SAS, Stata, etc. or by using software such as StatTransfer (https://stattransfer.com) that automatically "translates" between more than 30 file formats. Alternatively, the import data window in RStudio allows the specification of a missing data indicator (that specification was illustrated with -9 in the Importing Raw Data section).

Given this inflexibility, it is important that data be carefully screened to verify that missing values are appropriately indicated and handled. The iq data set does not contain any missing data, but a version of that data set was created with 10 random missing values (all indicated with -999) and imported via the menu sequence of *File > Import Dataset > From Excel* to illustrate the use of missing data commands in **R**. Note that the -999 indicators have been converted to NA in the new data frame object.

BOX 8.11   AS.DATA.FRAME AND ATTACH COMMANDS

```
## Specify as data frame and make variable names visible to R
> iq = as.data.frame(iqmiss)           ##152 cases of 8 observations
> attach(iq)
```

The optional missing data command in many **R** functions allows either pairwise or listwise deletion. For comparison, the mean of the vocab1 variable in the original data was 97.500.

BOX 8.12   LISTWISE AND PAIRWISE DELETION OF MISSING DATA VALUES

```
## Remove missing values and compute mean of vocab1 variable
> mean(vocab1,na.rm=TRUE)
[1] 97.533
## Compute correlation matrix with listwise deletion
> cor(iq,use="complete.obs")
## Compute correlation matrix with pairwise deletion
> cor(iq,use="pairwise.complete.obs")
```

It may be easier to delete all missing values from the data file before conducting an analysis.

BOX 8.13   COUNT AND DISPLAY CASES WITH MISSING DATA

```
## Count of missing cases in data frame
> table(complete.cases(iq))
## see which cases are complete (TRUE)without missing data (FALSE)
> complete.cases(iq)
## see the opposite, cases that are missing (TRUE) versus complete
(FALSE)
> is.na(iq)
## the number of cases missing a value for one variable
> sum(is.na(vocab1))
[1] 2
## the number of cases missing any value
> sum(is.na(iq))
[1] 10
## Display cases with a missing value
> iq[!complete.cases(iq),]
1      NA    124    118    122    116    115    127    105
6      88     NA     89    110     96     88    109    111
10    125    122    122     NA    122    124    132    111
15     95     94    107     92     NA    101     96     73
19     91     94     85    107    100    108     NA    102
33     86    100     97    121    114    100    111     NA
123    95     61    103     NA     94     93     88     67
131    61     68     88     61     98     73     NA     69
138    76     NA     82     83     87     77     88     87
152    NA    101     82     80     79     88     49    100
## create a new data frame with complete cases (listwise deletion)
> newiq=na.omit(iq)              ##142 cases of 9 observations
```

The *psych* package contains a variety of missing data procedures that may be more useful for EFA than the native **R** procedures for handling missing data.

BOX 8.14   IMPUTE MISSING DATA VALUES WITH MAXIMUM LIKELIHOOD METHOD FROM *PSYCH* PACKAGE

```
## After data loaded into iq object and psych activated
## Count of pairwise observations per variable
> pairwiseCount(iq)
         vocab1 designs1 similar1 matrix1 veranal2 vocab2 matrix2 designs2
vocab1      150      148      150     148      149    150     148      149
designs1    148      150      150     148      149    150     148      149
similar1    150      150      152     150      151    152     150      151
matrix1     148      148      150     150      149    150     148      149
veranal2    149      149      151     149      151    151     149      150
vocab2      150      150      152     150      151    152     150      151
matrix2     148      148      150     148      149    150     150      149
designs2    149      149      151     149      150    151     149      151
## Impute missing data values for missing correlation pairs with
## maximum likelihood estimation method. Output is a correlation matrix.
> newiq = corFiml(iq)
## Display that new correlation matrix rounded to two digits
> print (round(newiq,digits=2))
         vocab1 designs1 similar1 matrix1 veranal2 vocab2 matrix2 designs2
vocab1     1.00     0.58     0.79    0.61     0.69   0.82    0.56     0.51
designs1   0.58     1.00     0.57    0.66     0.51   0.54    0.59     0.66
similar1   0.79     0.57     1.00    0.59     0.70   0.74    0.58     0.55
matrix1    0.61     0.66     0.59    1.00     0.54   0.56    0.72     0.63
veranal2   0.69     0.51     0.70    0.54     1.00   0.71    0.65     0.53
vocab2     0.82     0.54     0.74    0.56     0.71   1.00    0.58     0.53
matrix2    0.56     0.59     0.58    0.72     0.65   0.58    1.00     0.63
designs2   0.51     0.66     0.55    0.63     0.53   0.53    0.63     1.00
```

If desired, the imputed correlation matrix may be used in future EFA analyses in place of the original raw data. Alternatively, the raw data can be submitted to the EFA procedure with the specification that mean or median values be imputed for missing values.

A visual depiction of the data set may also be useful in recognizing the extent and pattern of missing data values. This can be accomplished with the *Amelia* package (Figure 8.9).

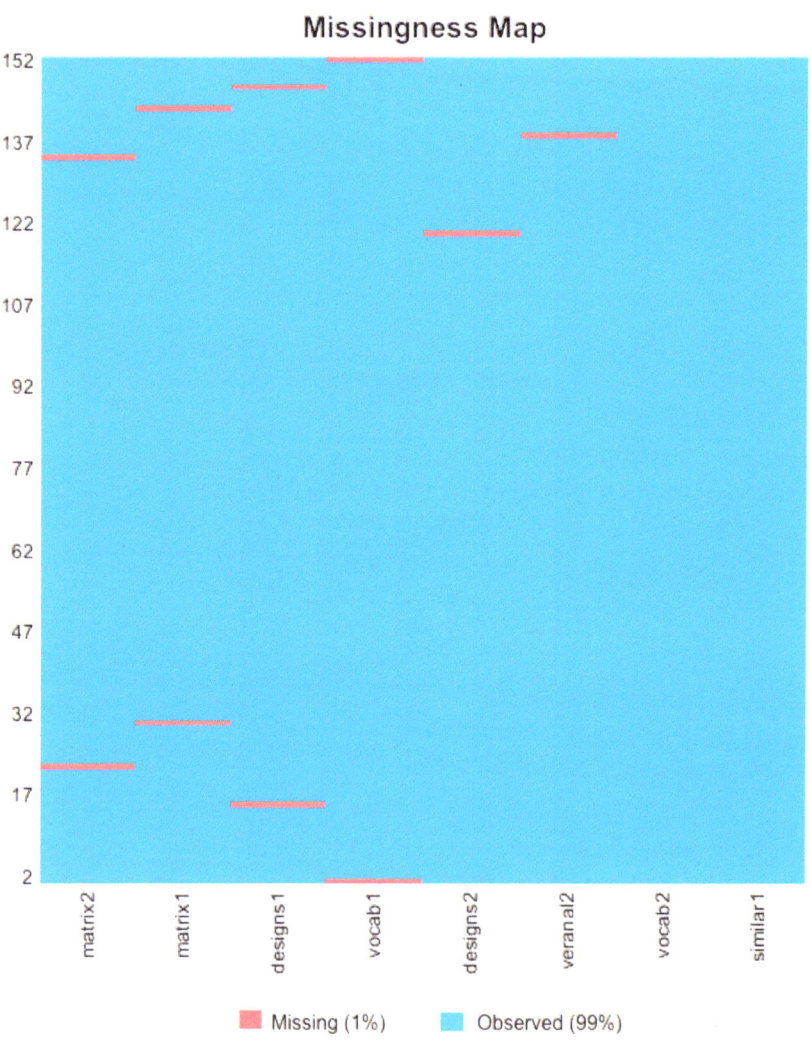

FIGURE 8.9   Missingness Map

BOX 8.15   INSTALL *AMELIA* PACKAGE FOR MISSING DATA

```
> install.packages("Amelia")
> library("Amelia")
> missmap(iq)
```

More complex presentations of missing data can be obtained from the *VIM* package.

BOX 8.16   INSTALL *VIM* PACKAGE FOR MISSING DATA

```
> install.packages("VIM")
> library("VIM")
> miss=aggr(iqmiss,plot=FALSE)
> print(miss)
 Missings in variables:
 Variable Count
   vocab1     2
 designs1     2
  matrix1     2
 veranal2     1
  matrix2     2
 designs2     1
> plot(miss,numbers=TRUE,cex.numbers=.8)
```

As illustrated in the *VIM* output in Figure 8.10, 93.42% of the values are NOT missing. At the measured variable level, vocab1 is missing 1.32% of its values whereas veranal2 is missing .66% of its values, and vocab2 is missing 0% of its values.

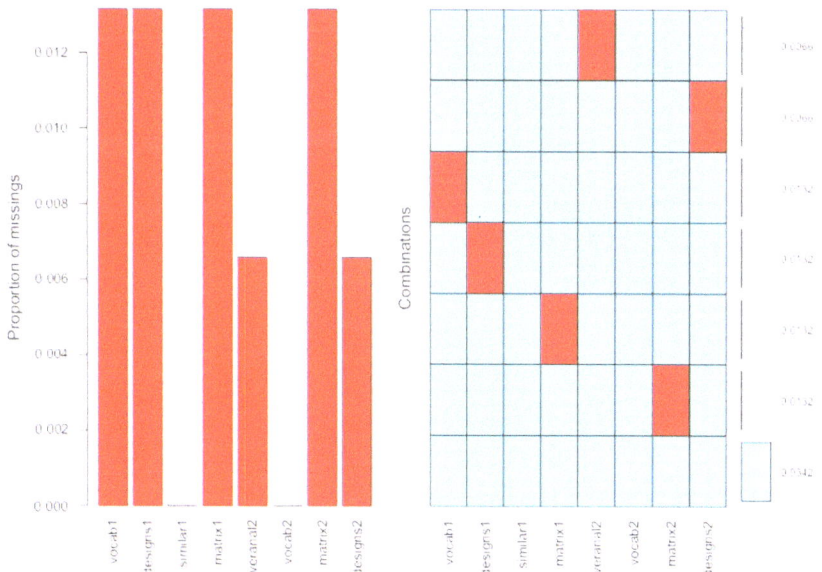

FIGURE 8.10   Missing Data Display from *VIM* Package

Currently, maximum likelihood and multiple imputation are the most appropriate methods to apply when there is more than a trivial amount of missing data (Enders, 2017). The maximum likelihood estimation method within the *psych* package, as illustrated previously, is one option available in **R**. There are several other **R** packages that might be employed if a multiple imputation method is desired. These include the *Amelia*, *MICE*, and *mitml* packages. See Enders (2017) for a tutorial on multiple imputation with the *mitml* package.

Report

Scatterplots revealed that linear relationships exist between the variables. Measures of univariate and multivariate normality indicated an underlying normal data distribution (Curran et al., 1996; Finney & DiStefano, 2013; Mardia, 1970). There was no evidence that restriction of range or outliers substantially affected the scores and there was no missing data. Therefore, a Pearson product-moment correlation matrix was submitted for EFA.

9

STEP 4

Is Exploratory Factor Analysis Appropriate

Given that exploratory factor analysis (EFA) is based on the correlation matrix, it seems reasonable that the correlation matrix should contain enough covariance to justify conducting an EFA (Dziuban & Shirkey, 1974). First, the correlation matrix can be visually scanned to ensure that there are several coefficients $\geq .30$ (Hair et al., 2019; Tabachnick & Fidell, 2019). Scanning a large matrix for coefficients $\geq .30$ can be laborious, but can be visualized with a graph from the *qgraph* package.

BOX 9.1 CREATE CORRELATION GRAPH WITH QGRAPH PACKAGE

```
## graph correlation matrix to visualize those > .30. Value can be
## changed in command.
> library(qgraph)
> qgraph(cor(iq),cut=.30,details=TRUE,posCol="orangered3",
  negCol="green",labels=names(iq))
```

The resulting graph (Figure 9.1) displays correlations above .30 with line becoming wider as the correlations rise above .30. This graph also displays the maximum correlation found among the variables. In this case, .82. Coefficients $\geq .40$ or $\geq .50$ can be specified by changing the cut value accordingly.

The exact number of correlations above .30 can be determined with a series of **R** commands.

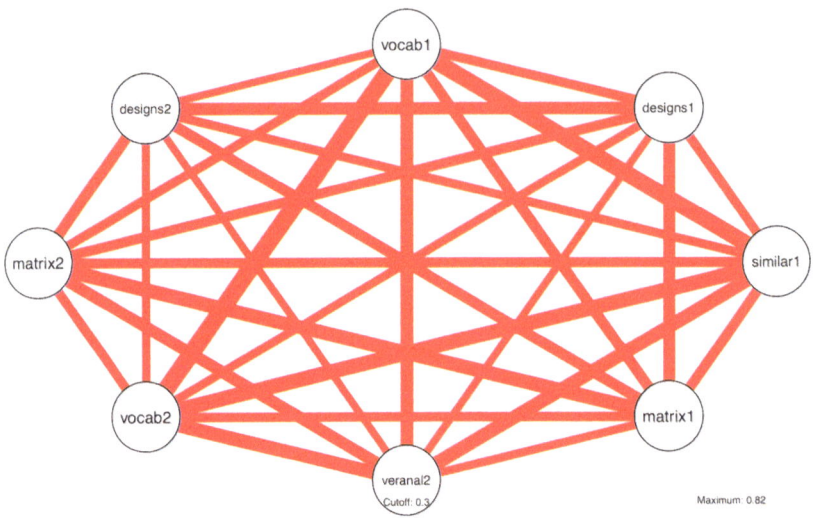

FIGURE 9.1 Correlation Graph from *qgraph* Package

BOX 9.2 DETERMINE NUMBER OF CORRELATIONS ABOVE .30

```
## create correlation matrix from raw data
> riq = cor(iq)
## Compute number of coefficients ≥ .30 off-diagonal
> BigR=sum(riq >= abs(.30) & riq < abs(1.0), na.rm=T) / 2
> print(BigR)
[1] 28
## Total number of off-diagonal elements in the data matrix
> totR=length(iq)*(length(iq)-1)/2
> print(totR)
[1] 28
## Percent of off-diagonal elements > .05 in data matrix
print((BigR/totR)*100)
[1] 100
```

A potential statistical problem can arise in EFA when correlations among the measured variables are too high. Singularity is the term used when measured variables are linearly dependent on each other like the verbal, nonverbal, and total (verbal + nonverbal) scores from a cognitive test. These linearly dependent variables cannot be included in an EFA. Other examples of inappropriate variables are "right" and "wrong" and ipsative scores. Extreme multicollinearity may also cause a problem during matrix computations akin to dividing by zero in arithmetic. Tabachnick and Fidell (2019) suggested that correlations above .90 among measured variables indicate multicollinearity. This may result in an error message (nonpositive definite matrix) from the software (Wothke, 1993). Statistically, singularity prevents the matrix operations needed for EFA to be performed and multicollinearity causes those matrix operations to produce unstable results. The likelihood of a multicollinearity problem can be checked by ascertaining the determinant of the correlation matrix. If the determinant is greater than .00001 then multicollinearity is probably not a problem (Field et al., 2012).

BOX 9.3 COMPUTE DETERMINANT OF A CORRELATION MATRIX

```
## Determinant of a full correlation matrix to assess likelihood
## of multicollinearity
> det(cor(iq))
[1] 0.002444148
```

A second assessment of the appropriateness of the correlation matrix for EFA is provided by Bartlett's test of sphericity (1950), which tests the null hypothesis that the correlation matrix is an identify matrix (ones on the diagonal and zeros on the off-diagonal) in the population. That is, it is random. Bartlett's test is sensitive to sample size and should be considered a minimal standard (Nunnally & Bernstein, 1994).

A final assessment of the appropriateness of the correlation matrix for EFA is offered by the Kaiser-Meyer-Olkin (KMO) measure of sampling adequacy (Kaiser, 1974). KMO values range from 0 to 1, only reaching 1 when each variable is perfectly predicted by the other variables. A KMO value is a ratio of the sum of squared correlations to the sum of squared correlations plus the sum of squared partial correlations. Essentially, partial correlations will be small and KMO values large if the items share common variance. Kaiser (1974) suggested that KMO values <.50 are unacceptable but other measurement specialists recommended a minimum value of .60 (Mvududu & Sink, 2013; Watson, 2017) for acceptability with values ≥ .70 preferred (Hoelzle & Meyer, 2013). KMO values for each variable as well as the total sample should be reviewed.

Bartlett's test and the KMO index can be computed with procedures included in the *psych* package after importing the iq data into RStudio.

BOX 9.4 CALCUALTE BARTLETT'S TEST AND KMO VALUES

```
> iq = as.data.frame(iq)
> attach(iq)
> library(psych)
> KMO(iq)
Kaiser-Meyer-Olkin factor adequacy
Call: KMO(r = iq)
Overall MSA =  0.9
MSA for each item =
  vocab1 designs1 similar1  matrix1 veranal2   vocab2  matrix2 designs2
    0.87     0.92     0.93     0.90     0.92     0.90     0.89     0.91
> cortest.bartlett(iq,n=152)
$chisq
[1] 887.0736

$p.value
[1] 1.007166e-168

$df
[1] 28
```

Report

A visual scan of the correlation matrix for the data revealed that all of the coefficients were ≥.30, but none exceeded .90 (Tabachnick & Fidell, 2019). Bartlett's test of sphericity (1950) rejected the hypothesis that the correlation matrix was an identity matrix (chi-square of 887.1 with 28 degrees of freedom). The KMO measure of sampling adequacy was acceptable with values of .90 for the total model and .87 to .93 for each of the measured variables (Kaiser, 1974). Altogether, these measures indicate that the correlation matrix is appropriate for EFA (Hair et al., 2019; Tabachnick & Fidell, 2019).

10

STEP 5

Factor Analysis Model

Two major models must be considered: principal components analysis (PCA) and common factor analysis (EFA). Researchers sometimes claim that an EFA was conducted when a PCA model was actually applied (Osborne & Banjanovic, 2016). However, PCA and EFA have different purposes and might, given the number and type of measured variables, produce different results.

EFA is based on the common factor model described in the Introduction (Fabrigar & Wegener, 2012). The purpose of EFA is to explain as well as possible the correlations among measured variables. In EFA, measured variables are thought to correlate with each other due to underlying latent constructs called factors. The direction of influence from factor to measured variables is signified by the arrows in the path diagram in Figure 10.1. It also assumes that unique

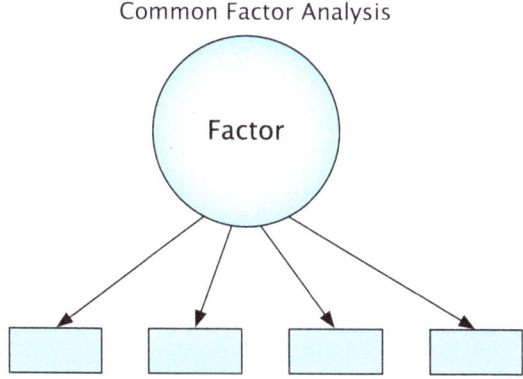

Common Factor Analysis

Factor

Observed Variable · Measured Variable · Manifest Variable · Reflective Indicator

FIGURE 10.1 Common Factor Analysis Model

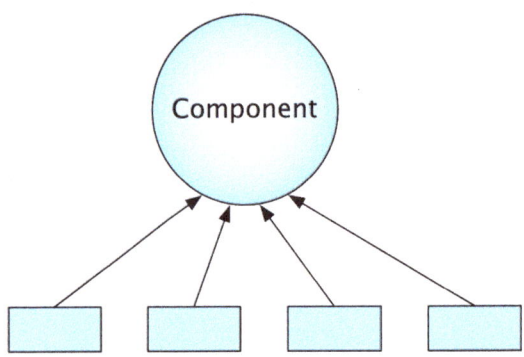

Observed Variable · Measured Variable · Manifest Variable · Formative Indicator

FIGURE 10.2 Principal Components Analysis Model

factors explain some variance beyond that explained by common factors. Conceptually, unique factors are composed of specific variance (systematic variance specific to a single measured variable) and error variance (unreliable error of measurement).

The purpose of PCA is to take the scores on a large set of observed variables and reduce them to scores on a smaller set of composite variables that retain as much information as possible from the original measured variables. The direction of influence in PCA is from measured variables to factors, which is signified by the arrows in the path diagram in Figure 10.2. PCA attempts to explain as much variance as possible and does not differentiate between common (shared) variance and unique (systematic and error) variance. PCA evaluates variance, not covariance. Therefore, principal components are *not* latent variables. Linear functions are properly called components, not factors.

As summarized in Figure 10.3, the common factor model (called EFA for our purposes) is composed of common variance (general variance shared by all measured variables plus variance shared by a subset of the measured variables) plus unique variance (variance specific to a single measured variable plus error). In contrast, the PCA model does not distinguish common variance from unique

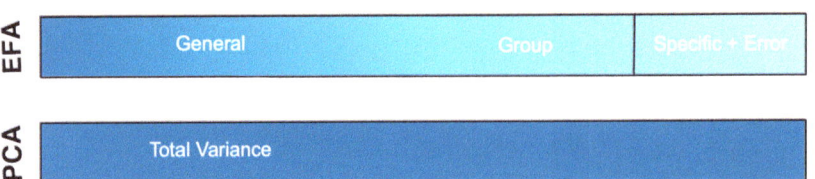

FIGURE 10.3 Variance Decomposition of EFA and PCA

variance, analyzing the total variance of the measured variables similar to multiple regression.

The relative advantages and disadvantages of EFA and PCA models have long been debated. Widaman (1993) found more bias in PCA estimates than in EFA estimates and Gorsuch (1990) recommended that EFA "should be routinely applied as the standard analysis because it recognizes we have error in our variables, gives unbiased instead of inflated loadings, and is more elegant as a part of the standard model" (p. 39). Other methodologists have argued that EFA and PCA tend to produce similar results so it does not matter which is used (Hoelzle & Meyer, 2013; Velicer & Jackson, 1990).

In truth, PCA and EFA may sometimes produce similar results. However, that is dependent on the number of variables involved in the analysis and the amount of common variance shared by the measured variables. The computation of PCA and EFA differs in how the diagonal of the correlation matrix is handled. In PCA, the correlations of 1.00 between each variable and itself is used. In contrast, EFA begins by replacing the 1s on the diagonal with an estimate of the communality or common variance. This is called a reduced correlation matrix. Thus, PCA considers all the variance (common and error) whereas EFA considers only the common variance. Because it is only the diagonal elements of the correlation matrix that differ, the number of diagonal elements influences the difference between EFA and PCA results. For example, there are 8 diagonal elements and 28 nonredundant off-diagonal elements for 8 measured variables (22%) but 20 diagonal elements and 190 nonredundant off-diagonal elements for 20 measured variables (10%). Thus, EFA and PCA results will tend to be more similar when there are more measured variables in the analysis (10% versus 22% different correlation elements).

As noted, the common factor model recognizes the presence of error in all measurements and therefore substitutes estimates of variable communalities (instead of 1s) in the diagonal of the correlation matrix. Unfortunately, it is not possible to know the communality of variables before conducting an EFA. The solution to this unknown is to estimate the communalities based on some aspect of the data. Potential solutions include the reliability of the variables, partial correlations, multiple correlations, etc. Over time, it has become accepted that a good solution is to initially estimate communalities with the squared multiple correlation of each variable with all other variables (SMC) and then systematically refine that estimate through a series of iterations until a stable estimate is reached (Fabrigar & Wegener, 2012; Pett et al., 2003; Tabachnick & Fidell, 2019).

As summarized by Widaman (2018), "PCA should never be used if the goal is to understand and represent the latent structure of a domain; only FA techniques should be used for this purpose" (p. 829). Similar opinions were expressed by Bandalos (2018); Bandalos and Boehm-Kaufman (2009); Carroll (1978, 1985); Fabrigar et al. (1999); Fabrigar & Wegener, 2012; Finch (2013); Haig (2018);

Hair et al. (2019); Preacher and MacCallum (2003); Russell (2002); and Schmitt (2011).

Report

The purpose of this study was to uncover the latent structure underlying these eight measured variables. Accordingly, a common factor model (EFA) was selected (Widaman, 2018). Squared multiple correlations (SMC) were used for initial communality estimates (Tabachnick & Fidell, 2019).

11

STEP 6

Factor Extraction Method

After selecting the common factor model, the next step in EFA is to choose an extraction method. This might also be called the model fitting procedure or the parameter estimation procedure (Fabrigar & Wegener, 2012). In simple terms, this is the mathematical process of deriving the underlying factors from the correlation matrix.

In current practice, the EFA software applies mathematical routines to complete factor extraction. Before computers, however, extraction was completed by humans who used a geometric approach. That approach retains conceptual clarity and a simple case of two variables will be used for illustration purposes.

Beginning with a correlation matrix, a scatterplot can be used to display the relationship between X and Y variables in two-dimensional space as displayed in Figure 11.1. Each data point represents an individual's unit standardized scores on variables X and Y (i.e., z scores). The center is now the mean of both variables. Notice that X–Y score pairs fall into four quadrants. Score pairs which fall into quadrants 1 and 3 tend toward positive correlations, those in quadrants 2 and 4 tend toward negative, and if evenly distributed across all four quadrants then correlation will be zero. This is a geometric display of what could be called data space. More variables would necessitate a view of multidimensional space that is difficult to visualize.

One geometric way to identify the factor(s) underlying a correlation matrix is to convert from data space to factor space as illustrated in Figure 11.2. The first step in conversion to factor space is to identify the one straight line that lies closer to all the data points than any other line. This is called the "least squares best-fitting line" because the sum of the squared deviations of each of the data points from one and only one straight line is minimum. This particular best-fitting line is the first principal component if extracted from the full correlation

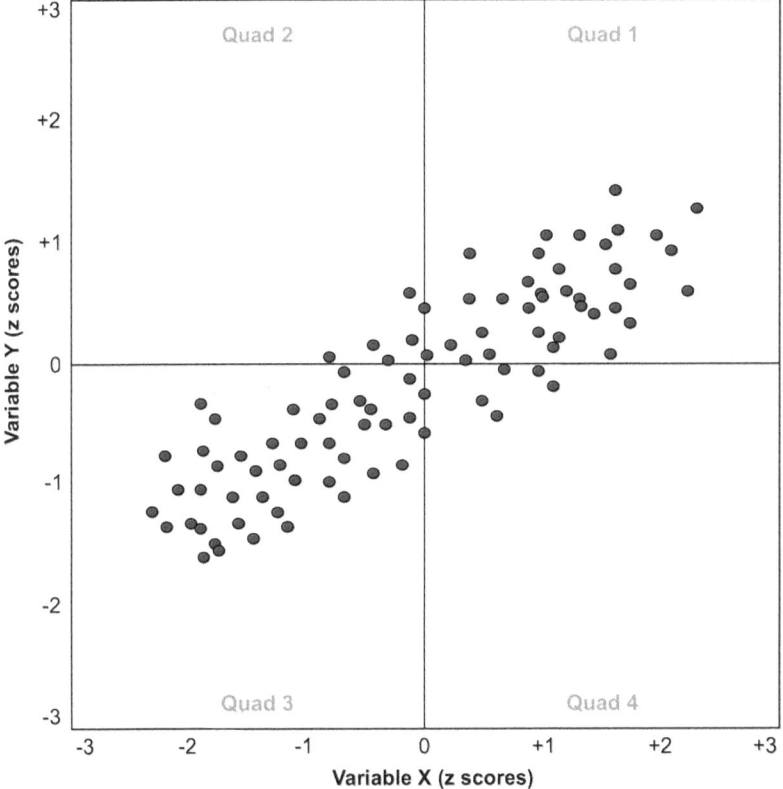

FIGURE 11.1 Two Variables in Data Space

matrix and the first principal factor if extracted from the reduced correlation matrix. This first component or factor "accounts for" more of the variance common to variables X and Y than any other possible component or factor. This best-fitting line is designated by the Roman numeral I. By convention, these lines are scaled from −1.00 to +1.00.

Each individual X–Y data point can be converted from its X–Y location in data space to a location in factor space by connecting the data point to line I with an orthogonal projection. As depicted in Figure 11.2, the new location is approximately .77 on Factor I.

The second principal component or factor, labeled II, is defined as a straight line at a right angle to the first principal component/factor. It too is a best-fitting straight line, and it accounts for that part of the total variance of the test score that was *not* accounted for by the first principal component/factor. Being at right angles, the two lines are uncorrelated. The X–Y data point is converted to a location on Factor II by connecting the data point to line II with an orthogonal projection. The Factor II location appears to be

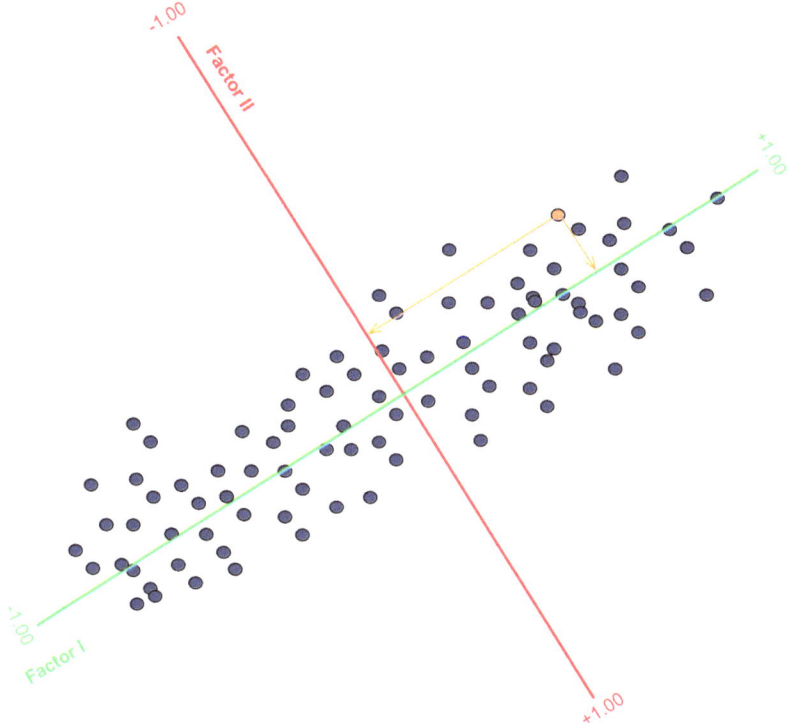

FIGURE 11.2   Two Variables in Factor Space

near −.43. If this analysis had included additional measured variables, additional factors would have been extracted with each succeeding factor accounting for a smaller proportion of variance analogous to wringing water from a wet towel.

In this simplest conceptual example of the principal components or principal axis variant of factor analysis, one set of references (X and Y) was exchanged for another set of references (I and II). The same amount of variance (in this case, the total or reduced variance of X and Y) is accounted for by both sets of references. The only difference is that X and Y are correlated variables, whereas I and II are uncorrelated components or factors. For now, the factor space references will be called factor loadings.

Theoretically, as many factors as measured variables can be extracted. Each variable can be located in factor space with its unique factor loadings. Typically, this information is presented in a table where the factors, conventionally identified with Roman numerals, and measured variables are entered in columns and rows, respectively. In practice, parsimony often suggests that most of the variance can be accounted for by only a few factors, for example, where two factors are sufficient to account for the majority of variance in five measured variables.

BOX 11.1 VARIANCE DECOMPOSITION FROM UNROTATED FACTORS

| | Unrotated Factors | | |
	I	II	h^2
Variables			
A	.73	.54	.825
B	.82	.49	.913
C	.72	.69	.995
D	.77	-.43	.778
E	.84	-.44	.899
Eigenvalue	3.02	1.39	4.41
% Total variance	60.40	27.80	88.20
Cumm % total var	60.40	88.20	
% Common variance	68.48	31.52	

The proportion of each variable's variance accounted for by a factor is the square of that variable's loading on the factor (e.g., Variable A loading of $.73^2 = .533$ for Factor I and $.54^2 = .292$ for Factor II). Communality is symbolized by h^2. It is the proportion of variance in each variable that is accounted for by all factors (e.g., .533 + .292 = .825). An eigenvalue is an algebraic solution for the percentage of variance a factor contributes. Sometimes called the latent root or characteristic root, the eigenvalue is the sum of the factor's squared loadings (e.g., $.73^2 + .82^2 + .72^2 + .77^2 + .84^2 = 3.02$). An eigenvalue is one measure of the relative importance of each factor. Mathematically, the total variance of a set of variables is equal to the total number of variables. Thus, the total variance for this five variable EFA is 5.00. Based on this sum, the proportion of the total variance contributed by a factor is its eigenvalue divided by the total variance (e.g., $3.02 \div 5.00 = .604$ or 60.40%). The proportion of common variance contributed by a factor is its eigenvalue divided by the sum of eigenvalues (e.g., $3.02 \div 4.41 = .6848$ or 68.48%).

Methodologists have devised a great number of extraction methods since Spearman (1904) first imagined EFA. These include image analysis, alpha analysis, non-iterated principal axis (PA), iterated principal axis (IPA), maximum likelihood (ML), unweighted least squares (ULS), weighted least squares (WLS), generalized least squares (GLS), minimum residual (MINRES), etc. Some extraction methods are identical yet were given different names. For example, ULS, OLS, and MINRES all refer to the same extraction method (Flora, 2018). Further, an IPA extraction will converge to an OLS solution (Briggs & MacCallum, 2003; MacCallum, 2009). Mathematically, extraction methods differ in the way they go about locating the factors that will best reproduce the original correlation matrix, whether they attempt to reproduce the sample correlation matrix or the population correlation matrix, and in their definition of the best way to measure closeness of the reproduced and original correlation matrices.

The most significant distinction between extraction methods is between ML and least squares methods (OLS, PA, and IPA). ML attempts to reproduce the population matrix that most likely generated the sample correlation matrix, whereas the least squares methods attempt to reproduce the sample correlation matrix. The population focus of ML extraction leaves it dependent on two critical assumptions: (a) the data are a random sample of some population, and (b) the measured variables have an underlying multivariate normal distribution. In contrast, the least squares methods have no distributional assumptions (Fabrigar & Wegener, 2012).

Simulation research has compared ML and least squares extraction methods in terms of factor recovery under varying levels of sample size and factor strength (Briggs & MacCallum, 2003; de Winter & Dodou, 2012; MacCallum et al., 2007; Ximénez, 2009). In general, least squares methods have outperformed ML when the factors were relatively weak (i.e., the factor accounted for ≤16% of the variance of a measured variable), the model was wrong (too many factors were specified), and the sample size was small ($N = 100$). Given these results, Briggs and MacCallum (2003) recommended "use of OLS in exploratory factor analysis in practice to increase the likelihood that all major common factors are recovered" (p. 54). Thus, ML may be appropriate for larger samples with normal data (i.e., univariate skew ≤ 2.0 and kurtosis ≤ 7.0; multivariate kurtosis ≤ 5.0) and strong factors, whereas least squares methods may be preferable for smaller samples with nonnormal data or weak factors (MacCallum et al., 2007; Watson, 2017).

Some researchers prefer ML extraction because it attempts to generalize to the population and it allows computation of statistical tests of model parameters (Fabrigar et al., 1999; Fabrigar & Wegener, 2012; Matsunaga, 2010). Other researchers prefer least squares extraction methods because they have no distributional assumptions and are sensitive to weak factors (Carroll, 1985, 1993; McCoach et al., 2013; Pett et al., 2003; Russell, 2002; Widaman, 2012). Osborne and Banjanovic (2016) concluded that "there is a general consensus in the literature that ML is the preferred choice for when data exhibits multivariate normality and iterated PAF or ULS for when that assumption is violated" (p. 26). Other researchers have endorsed that conclusion (Bandalos & Gerstner, 2016; Costello & Osborne, 2005; Sakaluk & Short, 2017; Schmitt, 2011). However, different extraction methods tend to produce similar results in most cases (Tabachnick & Fidell, 2019).

Regardless of extraction method, researchers must be cautious of improper solutions. That is, solutions that are mathematically impossible. For example, communality values greater than 1.00. Researchers must also be aware that extraction may fail with iterative estimators such as IPA. This happens because EFA software will try to arrive at an optimal estimate of the correlation matrix before some maximum number of estimation iterations has been completed. If an optimal estimate has not been computed at that point, an error message mentioning nonconvergence will be produced. In that case, the researcher may increase the maximum number of iterations and rerun the analysis. If nonconvergence persists after >100 iterations then the results, like those from an improper solution, should not be interpreted (Flora, 2018). "Improper solutions and nonconvergence are more likely to occur when there is a linear dependence among observed variables, when the model includes too many common factors, or when the sample size is too small" (Flora, 2018, p. 257). Alternatively, another extraction method could be employed (i.e., a sensitivity analysis) to ensure that the results are robust to extraction method.

Report

The multivariate normal distribution of the data and substantial reliability of the measured variables indicated that a ML extraction method would be appropriate. Nevertheless, the robustness of ML results will be verified by applying an IPA method to ensure that weak factors are not overlooked (Briggs & MacCallum, 2003; de Winter & Dodou, 2012).

12

STEP 7

How Many Factors to Retain

As many factors as measured variables can be extracted for exploratory factor analysis (EFA), but it is usually possible to explain the majority of variance with a smaller number of factors. For example, using the *psych* package to specify eight factors with ML extraction with the iq data, the measured variables all loaded zero on the final four factors as displayed in Box 12.1. Thus, the first four factors can explain the variance among these eight variables.

BOX 12.1 PATTERN MATRIX FOR SOLUTION WITH EIGHT FACTORS FROM *PSYCH* PACKAGE.

```
> attach(iq)
> library(psych)
## An 8 factor ML initial solution. Pairwise deletion of missing data
## is default.
> f8=fa(iq,nfactors=8,SMC=TRUE,min.err=.001,max.iter=100,fm="ml",
  rotate="none",n.obs=152)
> print(f8,digitis=2)
Standardized loadings (pattern matrix) based upon correlation matrix
          ML1    ML2    ML3    ML4 ML5 ML6 ML7 ML8   h2   u2 com
vocab1    0.87 -0.24 -0.07 -0.03   0   0   0   0 0.81 0.19 1.2
designs1  0.72  0.28 -0.16  0.04   0   0   0   0 0.62 0.38 1.4
similar1  0.84 -0.15 -0.02  0.02   0   0   0   0 0.73 0.27 1.1
matrix1   0.76  0.30 -0.04 -0.08   0   0   0   0 0.68 0.32 1.3
veranal2  0.79 -0.10  0.19  0.04   0   0   0   0 0.68 0.32 1.2
vocab2    0.85 -0.23 -0.01  0.00   0   0   0   0 0.77 0.23 1.1
matrix2   0.76  0.29  0.17 -0.03   0   0   0   0 0.69 0.31 1.4
designs2  0.70  0.33 -0.06  0.08   0   0   0   0 0.61 0.39 1.5
```

The problem arises in determining the *exact* number of factors to retain for interpretation. Methodologists have observed that this is probably the most important decision in EFA because there are serious consequences for selecting either too few or too many factors (Benson & Nasser, 1998; Fabrigar et al., 1999; Glorfeld, 1995; Hoelzle & Meyer, 2013; Preacher et al., 2013), whereas the options for other EFA decisions tend to be fairly robust (Hayton et al., 2004; Tabachnick & Fidell, 2019). Retaining too few factors can distort factor loadings and result in solutions in which common factors are combined, thereby obscuring the true factor solution. Extracting too many factors can focus on small, unimportant factors that are difficult to interpret and unlikely to replicate (Hayton et al., 2004). "Choosing the number of factors is something like focusing a microscope. Too high or too low an adjustment will obscure a structure that is obvious when the adjustment is just right" (Hair et al., 2019, p. 144).

"In the end, the overriding criteria for choosing a particular number of factors are interpretability and theoretical relevance because a factor solution is useful only if it can be interpreted in a meaningful way" (Bandalos, 2018, p. 324). A delicate balance between *comprehensiveness* and *parsimony* is needed to achieve an interpretable solution. Unfortunately, no infallible method to determine the "true" number of factors to retain has been discovered (Bandalos, 2018; Barrett & Kline, 1982; Cattell, 1966; Comrey & Lee, 1992; Fabrigar & Wegener 2012; Gorsuch, 1983; Nunnally & Bernstein, 1994; Pett et al., 2003; Preacher et al., 2013; Rummel, 1970; Widaman, 2012). It appears that the nature of the data (e.g., the number of indicators per factor, communality level, factor inter-correlations, complex loadings, sample size, etc.) differentially affects each method. Given this uncertainty, methodologists have recommended that both empirical evidence and theoretical knowledge be applied to determine the number of factors to retain for interpretation (Bandalos, 2018; Finch, 2020a; Hair et al., 2019; Osborne, 2014; Pituch & Stevens, 2016). Additionally, it has generally been agreed that underextraction is more dangerous than overextraction, so it may not be a bad strategy to risk the overextraction of one or two factors (Cattell, 1978; Fava & Velicer, 1992, 1996; Gorsuch, 1983; Kline, 2013; MacCallum et al., 2001; Stewart, 1981; Wood et al., 1996).

Empirical Guidelines

A variety of simulation studies have provided empirical guidelines for determining the number of factors to retain. Based on these simulations, some empirical methods have been found to perform better than others. For example, the parallel analysis (PA) criterion of Horn (1965) has generally performed well (Auerwald & Moshagen, 2019; Finch, 2020b; Peres-Neto et al., 2005; Ruscio & Roche, 2012; Velicer et al., 2000; Zwick & Velicer, 1986). Conceptually, PA requires the factor analyst to generate a set of random data with the same number of variables and participants as the real data and then compare the mean eigenvalues from multiple sets of random data with the corresponding eigenvalues from the real data. In this comparison, only factors with eigenvalues that are above the mean of those from the random data should be retained. PA has remained accurate with nonnormal data and non-Pearsonian correlations (Buja & Eyuboglu, 1992; Dinno, 2009; Garrido et al., 2013) and has performed better than modified PA versions (Lim &

Jahng, 2019). Some methodologists have noted that PA tends to overextract by one or two factors and recommended that the upper 95th or 99th percentile of each eigenvalue be retained rather than the mean (Glorfeld, 1995; Hoyle & Duvall, 2004). However, Crawford et al. (2010) found that PA tended to underextract if there was a strong general factor and Caron (2019) reported that PA also tended to underextract if there were correlated factors. Given these competing results, it seems reasonable to compare mean eigenvalues rather than risk underextraction. PA is easily computed with modern computers so it is recommended that at least 100 random datasets be generated (Hoelzle & Meyer, 2013).

A second empirical guidelines that has been found to be relatively accurate in simulation studies is the minimum average partial (MAP) method of Velicer (1976). A matrix of partial correlations is calculated after each principal component is extracted. The average of the squared off-diagonal partial correlations is computed from each matrix. This average is expected to reach a minimum when the correct number of components is extracted. The logic of this procedure is that as common variance is partialled out of the matrix, the MAP criterion will decrease. At the point where the common variance has been removed and only unique variance remains, the MAP criterion will begin to rise. Thus, the MAP criterion separates common and unique variance and retains only components consisting of common variance.

A third, more subjective, method relies on graphing the eigenvalues derived from extraction and using visual analysis to detect any abrupt change in their slope. Developed by Cattell (1966), this scree graph plots the eigenvalues on the Y-axis against their extraction order on the X-axis. The concept is that the eigenvalues for the "true" common factors tend to form a more or less straight line, whereas the error factors form another line with a different, smaller slope (analogous to the scree or rubble at the base of a cliff). This assumes that as succeeding factors are extracted from the factor matrix, error variance will begin to predominate and will represent only minor, random fluctuations. To follow the geology analogy, this will separate important early factors (bedrock) from the rubble (scree) of random error.

To analyze a scree plot, draw a straight line through the smallest eigenvalues. The eigenvalues above and to the left of the straight line are the factors to retain (Pett et al., 2003). An ideal scree plot, as illustrated in Figure 12.1, may be relatively easy to accurately interpret. The three largest eigenvalue are clearly above the trajectory of the straight line. However, most scree plots are more ambiguous and researchers tend to be unreliable when using scree plots to determine the number of factors to retain (Streiner, 1998).

Attempts have been made to interpret scree plots more objectively via empirical methods. These include the optimal coordinates method (Raîche et al., 2013) that uses eigenvalues as predictors in a multiple regression and identifies the cut point when an observed eigenvalue exceeds its estimated value. Another empirical approach is the acceleration factor (Yakovitz & Szidarovszky, 1986) that identifies

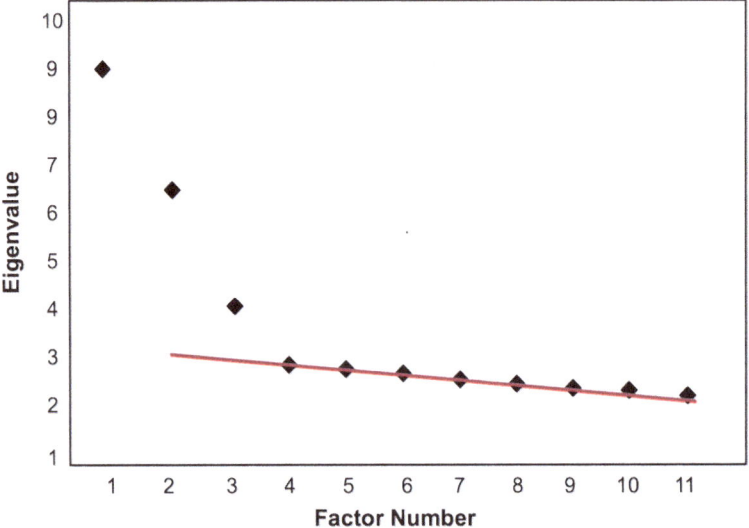

FIGURE 12.1 Simplified Scree Plot

where the slope in the curve of the scree plot changes abruptly. Finally, the standard error scree (Zoski & Jurs, 1996) is based on the standard error of the estimate of each eigenvalue. Unfortunately, results from simulation studies have been inconsistent and it is not clear if any empirical scree method is superior (Nasser et al., 2002; Raîche et al., 2013).

Numerous other empirical guidelines have been suggested by researchers. For example, innovative network graphing methods (Golino & Epskamp, 2017; Golino et al., 2020), a very simple structure (VSS) approach that minimizes factor complexity (Revelle & Rocklin, 1979), the Hull method that attempts to balance goodness-of-fit and parsimony (Lorenzo-Seva et al., 2011), and model fit indices commonly used in confirmatory factor analysis (Clark & Bowles, 2018; Finch, 2020b). Sufficient evidence has not accumulated as yet to justify the use of these methods. There are several methods of determining the number of factors to retain that are *not* supported and should be ignored. These include the so-called "Eigenvalue 1" rule as well as the chi-square test with ML extraction (Flora, 2018; Hayashi et al., 2007; Russell, 2002; Velicer et al., 2000).

Velicer et al. (2000) recommended that a combination of PA and MAP should be employed, with scree reserved as a potentially useful adjunct. Other methodologists have also recommended PA and/or MAP (Bandalos, 2018; DeVellis, 2017; Fabrigar & Wegener, 2012; Fabrigar et al., 1999; Ford et al., 1986; Hair et al., 2019; Hayton et al., 2004; Hoelzle & Meyer, 2013; Howard, 2016; Hoyle & Duvall, 2004; Kanyongo, 2005; Lawrence & Hancock, 1999; Osborne, 2014; Sakaluk & Short, 2017), noting that PA tends to slightly overextract whereas MAP tends to slightly underextract.

BOX 12.2   PARALLEL ANALYSIS WITH *PSYCH* PACKAGE

```
> attach(iq)
> library(psych)
## Parallel analysis with 500 repetitions
## For correlation matrix the n.obs must be added: n.obs=152
> pariq = fa.parallel(iq,fa="pc",n.iter=500,ylab="Eigenvalues",
  quant=.50)
> print(pariq)
Parallel analysis suggests that the number of components =   1
 eigen values of components
[1] 5.33 0.84 0.47 0.40 0.32 0.27 0.22 0.15
 eigen values of simulated components
[1] 1.36 1.22 1.11 1.03 0.95 0.87 0.78 0.68
```

PA can be accomplished using the *psych* package. Note that the PCA extraction method has been specified (fa = "pc") in the **R** command language. PA can also be conducted with the eigenvalues extracted from a reduced correlation matrix by specifying a common factor extraction method (fa = "fa") and some researchers prefer this approach (Crawford et al., 2010). However, the unreduced correlation matrix was used in the development of PA (Horn, 1965) and in much of the simulation research (Velicer et al., 2000; Zwick & Velicer, 1986) and has been found more accurate than results from the reduced matrix (Auerswald & Moshagen, 2019; Garrido et al., 2013; Lim & Jahng, 2019). Additionally, the unreduced matrix was the foundation for development of both MAP and scree so it seems reasonable to "use it to determine the spread of variance across the factors and as the basis for deciding on the number of factors to be extracted for the next stage" (Child, 2006, p. 153).

In this example, the number of simulated data sets is controlled by the n.iter command and the comparison standard by the quant command (i.e., 50th percentile). By comparing the actual eigenvalues with the simulated eigenvalues, respectively, it appears that only one component is sufficient (actual eigenvalue of 5.33 versus simulated eigenvalue of 1.36). This command also produces a plot of the actual versus simulated eigenvalues.

The MAP criterion can be obtained from the VSS command within the *psych* package.

BOX 12.3   MAP WITH *PSYCH* PACKAGE

```
## Compute MAP
> VSS(iq,rotate="promax",fm="pc",plot=FALSE,n.obs=152)
The Velicer MAP achieves a minimum of NA   with   2   factors
Statistics by number of factors
  vss1 vss2   map
1 0.96 0.00 0.070
2 0.96 0.98 0.063  <------smallest map value
3 0.90 0.95 0.095
4 0.83 0.94 0.170
5 0.93 0.97 0.324
6 0.91 0.97 0.510
7 0.97 0.99 1.000
8 0.99 1.00   NA
```

The MAP value sequentially drops from .070 to .063 and then increases to .095. The lowest MAP value identifies the number of factors to retain. In this case, MAP reaches a minimum at two factors.

BOX 12.4 SCREE PLOT WITH *PSYCH* PACKAGE

```
## Display scree plot from both unreduced and reduced
## correlation matrices
> scree(iq,pc=TRUE,factors=TRUE,hline="-1",main="Scree Plot")
```

Finally, the scree plot can be displayed as an adjunct decision tool.

The scree plot (from both reduced and unreduced correlation matrices) also indicates that two factors should be retained (Figure 12.2).

BOX 12.5 PCA WITH *FACTOMINER* PACKAGE

```
## Install FactoMineR package (if not previously installed) for PCA
> install.packages("FactoMineR")
## Activate the FactoMineR package
> library (FactoMineR)
## Conduct PCA analysis and generate vector graph
> pca=PCA(iq)
```

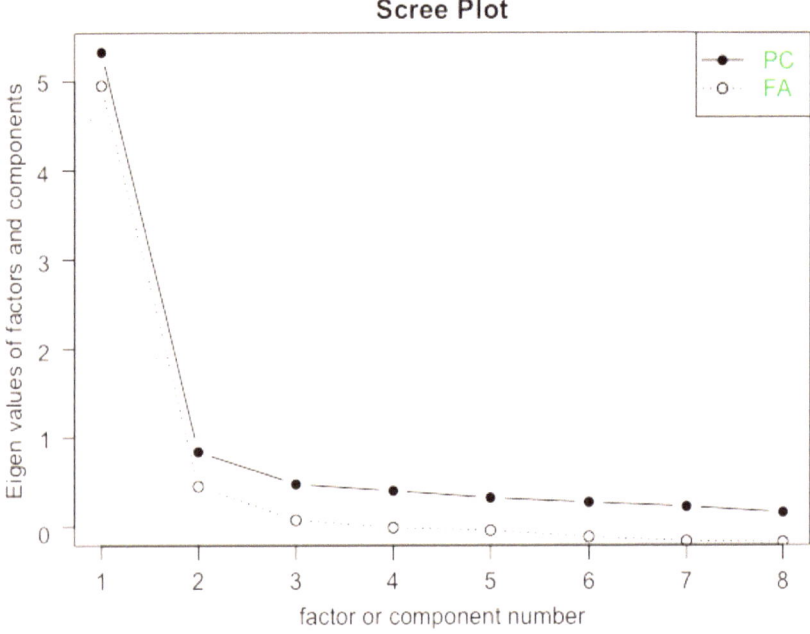

FIGURE 12.2 Scree Plot of IQ Data

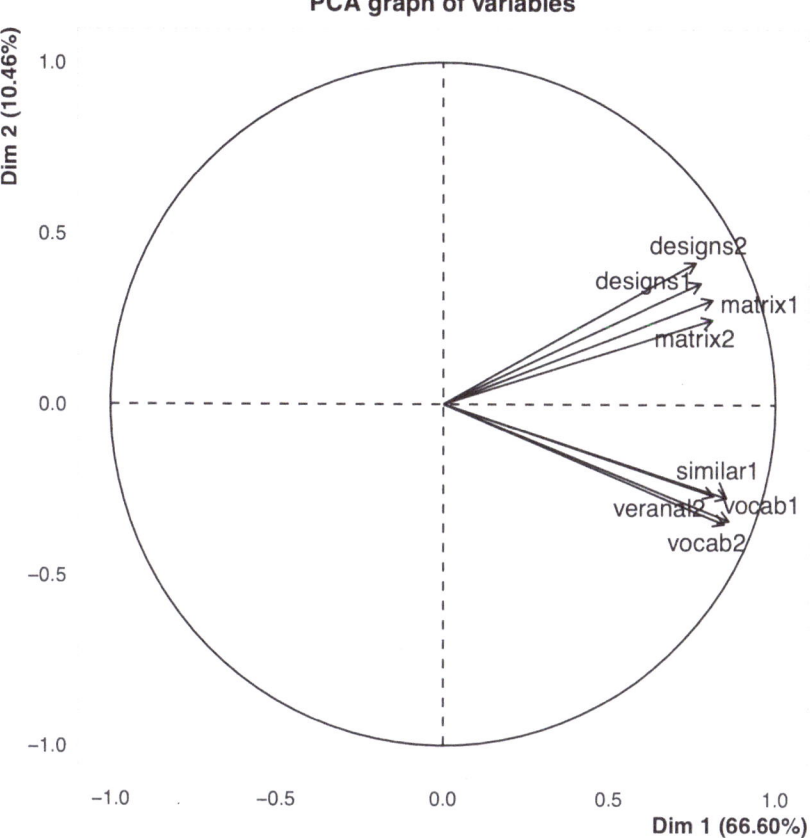

FIGURE 12.3   Vector Graph of IQ Data

More detailed information can be obtained from other **R** packages.

The PCA command within the *FactoMineR* package generates a vector plot that visually illustrates the PCA structure (Figure 12.3).

BOX 12.6 AUGMENTED SCREE PLOT WITH *FACTOEXTRA* PACKAGE

```
## Install factoextra package (if not previously installed)
> install.packages("factoextra")
## Activate the factoextra package
> library(factoextra)
## Create augmented scree plot
## Using results of prior PCA analysis using FactoMineR package
> fviz_eig(pca,addlabels=TRUE,ylim=c(0,70))
```

The augmented scree plot generated by the *factoextra* package (Figure 12.4) includes the percentage of variance allocated to each dimension.

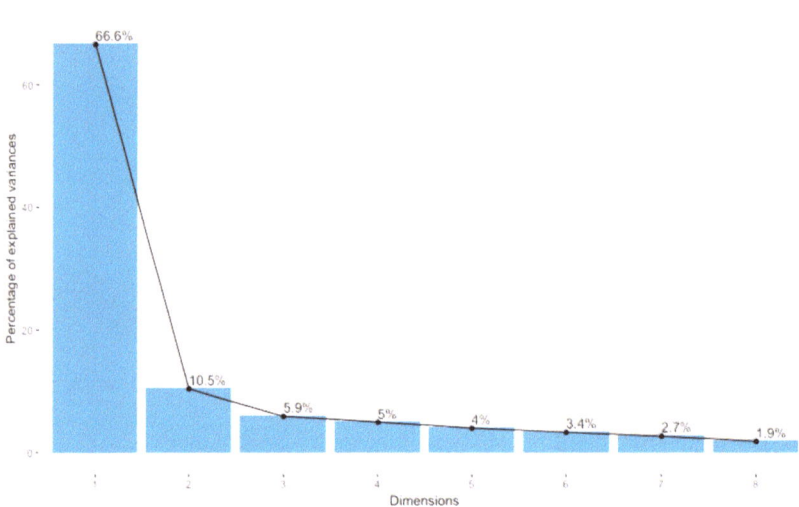

FIGURE 12.4 Augmented Scree Plot of IQ Data

Some methodologists supplement the scree with a minimum variance guideline, but these guidelines are subjective (e.g., 40% to 75%) and unlikely to be reasonable for social science research (Beavers et al., 2013; Reio & Shuck, 2015).

Empirical scree tests can be conducted with the *nFactors* package.

BOX 12.7 EMPIRICAL SCREE TESTS WITH *NFACTORS* PACKAGE

```
## Empirical scree methods
## Activate nFactors package
> library(nFactors)
## Compute eigenvalues
> e=eigenComputes(iq)
> print(e)
[1] 5.3280352 0.8370123 0.4743501 0.3989081 0.3203761 0.2683994 0.2193804 0.1535386
## Standard error scree
> ses=nSeScree(e,model="components")
> ses$nFactors[1]
se
 1
## Other empirical scree methods
## noc = Optimal coordinates, naf = acceleration factor
> ee=nScree(x=e,model="components")
## Optimal coordinates
> ee$Components$noc
[1] 1
## Acceleration factor
> ee$Components$naf
[1] 1
```

All three empirical scree methods indicated that one factor would be sufficient. Thus, all of the empirical guidelines indicated that one or two factors are sufficient for an optimal balance between comprehensiveness and parsimony.

Theoretical Knowledge

Although empirical guidelines are useful, there is no guarantee that they are correct (Bandalos, 2018; Cattell, 1966; Fabrigar & Wegener, 2012; Gorsuch, 1983; Pett et al., 2003; Preacher et al., 2013; Widaman, 2012). The accuracy of empirical guidelines is more likely to be compromised when factors are highly correlated, factor loadings are low, the number of factors is large, and the sample size is small (Lim & Jahg, 2019). Given this fundamental uncertainty, methodologists have recommended that multiple criteria, including relevant theory and previous research, be used to determine the number of factors to retain (Bandalos, 2018; Bandalos & Boehm-Kaufman, 2009; Bandalos & Finney, 2019; Basto & Pereira, 2012; Brown, 2015; Fabrigar et al., 1999; Finch, 2013, 2020a, 2020b; Flora, 2018; Hoelzle & Meyer, 2013; McCoach et al., 2013; Norman & Streiner, 2014; Nunnally & Bernstein, 1994; Osborne, 2014; Pituch & Stevens, 2016; Preacher & MacCallum, 2003; Preacher et al., 2013; Reio & Shuck, 2015; Velicer & Fava, 1998; Widaman, 2012). There is no prior research with these eight measured variables, but research with similar verbal and nonverbal measures have suggested two factors and development of these tests was guided by that theoretical expectation.

Model Selection

Given that there is no infallible method to identify the "true" number of factors, Cattell (1978) said that, "taking out the right number of factors does not mean in most cases a number correct in some absolute sense but in the sense of not missing any factor of more than trivial size" (p. 61). This suggests a strategy of "selecting from among a set of competing theoretical explanations the model that best balances the desirable characteristics of parsimony and fit to observed data" (Preacher et al., 2013, p. 29). Each candidate model contains a different numbers of factors and is judged on its interpretability and conceptual sense (Bandalos, 2018; Carroll, 1993; Cudeck, 2000; Fabrigar & Wegener, 2012; Fabrigar et al., 1999; Finch, 2013; Flora, 2018; Ford et al., 1986; Gorsuch, 1983, 1988, 1997; Hair et al., 2019; Hoelzle & Meyer, 2013; Kahn, 2006; McCoach et al., 2013; Nunnally & Bernstein, 1994; Osborne, 2014; Osborne & Banjanovic, 2016; Pituch & Stevens, 2016; Preacher & MacCallum, 2003; Preacher et al., 2013; Schmitt et al., 2018; Tabachnick & Fidell, 2019; Velicer et al., 2000; Widaman, 2012). Of course, a model that is generalizable to other samples is scientifically desirable but requires new samples and multiple EFAs (Preacher et al., 2013).

Report

Velicer et al. (2000) recommended that a combination of PA (Horn, 1965) and MAP (Velicer, 1976) methods should be employed for determining the number of factors to retain for rotation, with scree reserved as a potentially useful adjunct. Using these three criteria, it appeared that one or two factors would be sufficient for an optimal balance between comprehensiveness and parsimony. Two factors were also signaled as sufficient by prior research and theory. To ensure that underextraction did not occur, a model with three factors might also be plausible (Cattell, 1978). Therefore, models with three, two, and one factor(s) will be sequentially evaluated for their interpretability and theoretical meaningfulness.

13

STEP 8

Rotate Factors

Factor extraction methods have been mathematically optimized to account for the covariance among measured variables but they do not take interpretability into account (Bandalos, 2018; Comrey & Lee, 1992; DeVellis, 2017; Nunnally & Bernstein, 1994; Pituch & Stevens, 2016). As previously described, the orientation of the factor axes is fixed in factor space during factor extraction. Those axes can be rotated about their origin to make the loadings more interpretable without changing the underlying structure of the data (Tabachnick & Fidell, 2019). The rotated structure accounts for the same proportion of variance as the unrotated structure but it distributes that variance across factors differently. Rotation is akin to taking a photograph of a person from multiple angles. The person remains the same but some of the photographs better represent the person than others. DeVellis (2017, pp. 171–176) described several other analogies to help understand the concept of rotation.

For a simple example, the two-factor initial (unrotated) solution for the iq data was obtained and conceptually plotted on a two-dimensional graph in factor space. It is apparent that the variables tend to form two clusters in multidimensional space but they are not particularly well aligned with the factor axes (Figure 13.1).

Perhaps the factor axes could be rotated about their origin to bring them closer to the center of the variable clusters (Osborne & Banjanovic, 2016). As displayed in gray in Figure 13.2, the Factor II axis is now closer to the cluster of three variables but that has moved the axis of Factor I away from the second variable cluster. This is called an orthogonal rotation because the factor axes have been restrained to right angles. Due to this restraint, the two factors also remain uncorrelated.

Alternatively, the factor axes could be rotated independent of each other to bring each of them closer to the centroids of the variable clusters, that is, rotation of the axes without constraining them to orthogonality. Independent rotation of the

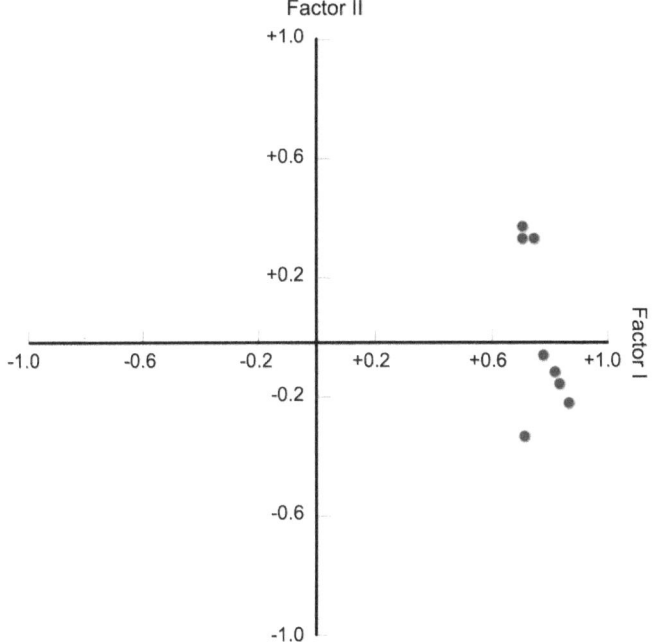

FIGURE 13.1 Unrotated Factor Plot

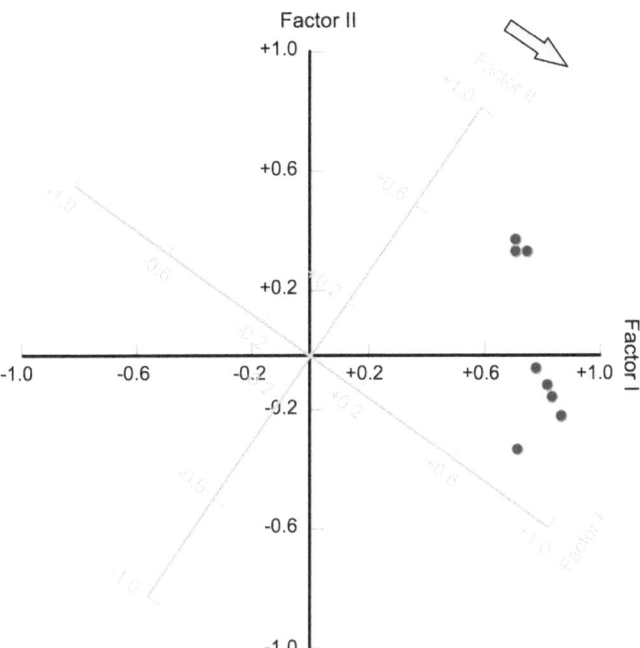

FIGURE 13.2 Orthogonally Rotated Factor Plot

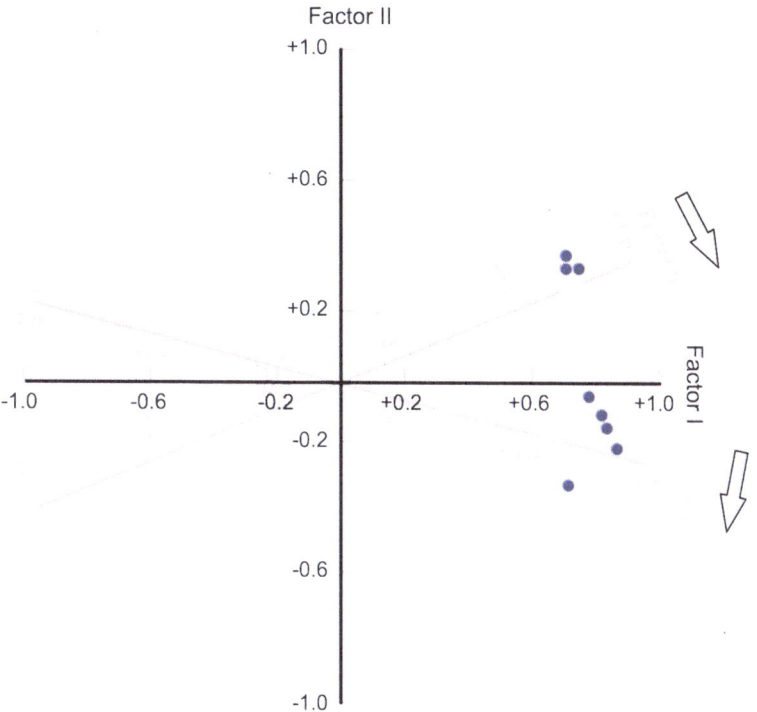

FIGURE 13.3 Obliquely Rotated Factor Plot

axes is called oblique rotation. This allows the factors to become correlated if that results in improved simplicity of loadings. As displayed in gray in Figure 13.3, this has brought both axes closer to the variable clusters.

These geometric representation of factor rotation have been only approximate, sufficient for illustration of the concept of rotation but not precise enough for use in practice. They also intimate that "there is an infinite number of equally fitting ways those factors may be oriented in multidimensional space" (Sakaluk & Short, 2017, p. 3), which is called rotational indeterminacy (Fabrigar & Wegener, 2012). Rotational indeterminacy is an additional reason that methodologists stress that factor models must be judged on their interpretability and theoretical sense (Bandalos, 2018; Cudeck, 2000; Fabrigar & Wegener, 2012; Fabrigar et al., 1999; Ford et al., 1986; Gorsuch, 1983, 1988; Hair et al., 2019; Kahn, 2006; Nunnally & Bernstein, 1994; Osborne, 2014; Preacher & MacCallum, 2003; Preacher et al., 2013; Tabachnick & Fidell, 2019; Velicer et al., 2000; Widaman, 2012).

Orthogonal versus Oblique Rotation

Researchers differ on their preference for orthogonal or oblique rotations. Those who prefer orthogonal rotations cite simplicity and ease of interpretation

(Mertler & Vannatta, 2001). Other researchers prefer oblique rotations due to their accuracy and to honor the reality that most variables are correlated to some extent (Bandalos & Boehm-Kaufman, 2009; Bandalos & Finney, 2019; Brown, 2013, 2015; Costello & Osborne, 2005; Cudeck, 2000; Fabrigar & Wegener, 2012; Fabrigar et al., 1999; Finch, 2013; Flora, 2018; Flora et al., 2012; Ford et al., 1986; Gorsuch, 1983; McCoach et al., 2013; Meehl, 1990; Mulaik, 2010, 2018; Osborne, 2014; Pett et al., 2003; Pituch & Stevens, 2016; Preacher & MacCallum, 2003; Reio & Shuck, 2015; Reise et al., 2000; Rummel, 1967; Russell, 2002; Sakaluk & Short, 2017; Sass, 2010; Widaman, 2012; Worthington & Whittaker, 2006; Zhang & Preacher, 2015).

Some researchers suggest using oblique rotation only if the correlation between factors exceeds .20 (Finch, 2020a) or .32 (Roberson et al., 2014; Tabachnick & Fidell, 2019), whereas others believe there is no compelling reason to select one type of rotation over another so both should be applied (Child, 2006; Hair et al., 2019). Nonetheless, the arguments in favor of oblique rotations are compelling. As articulated by Schmitt (2011), "because oblique rotation methods generally produce accurate and comparable factor structures to orthogonal methods even when interfactor correlations are negligible, it is strongly recommend that researchers only use oblique rotation methods because they generally result in more realistic and more statistically sound factor structures" (p. 312).

In practice, rotation is accomplished with algebraic algorithms (analytic rotations). The most prominent orthogonal rotation is varimax (Kaiser, 1958). Others include quartimax, equamax, and parsimax. The most popular oblique rotations are promax (Hendrickson & White, 1964) and oblimin (Jennrich & Sampson, 1966). Other oblique rotations include geomin, maxplane, orthoblique, direct quartimin, bigquartmin, promin, and covarimin. Technical reviews of analytic rotations are available if further details are desired (Browne, 2001; Sass & Schmitt, 2010; Schmitt & Sass, 2011). In many cases, different rotations within the orthogonal and oblique categories are likely to produce similar results (Bandalos & Finney, 2019; Nunnally & Bernstein, 1994; Sass & Schmitt, 2010).

Many methodologists have recommended that varimax be selected if an orthogonal rotation is employed (Child, 2006; Gorsuch, 1983, 2003; Kline, 1994; Nunnally & Bernstein, 1994). It is not clear whether there is a superior oblique method (Schmitt & Sass, 2011). Methodologists have variously recommended oblimin (Child, 2006; Flora, 2018; McCoach et al., 2013; Mulaik, 2018), geomin (Hattori et al., 2017), and promax (Finch, 2006; Gorsuch, 1983, 1988, 2003; Matsunaga, 2010; Morrison, 2009; Russell, 2002; Sass, 2010; Thompson, 2004). These oblique rotations require that a parameter be set that specifies the extent to which the factors are allowed to be correlated. That parameter is referred to as delta in oblimin, k or kappa in promax, and ε in geomin. Oblimin and geomin solutions seem to be very sensitive to the parameter setting, whereas promax is relatively insensitive to the k setting (Gorsuch, 2003; Tataryn et al., 1999). For oblimin rotations, Howard (2016) noted that delta values of zero were preferred. For geomin rotations, ε values of .01 and .05 were recommended by Hattori et al. (2017) and Morin et al. (2020), respectively. Unfortunately, geomin may converge on solutions that are not optimal (Hattori et al., 2017). For promax rotations, a *k* value of four will probably be adequate (Gorsuch, 2003; Tataryn et al., 1999). Given this choice among oblique rotations, many methodologists recommend that results from another rotation method be compared to the initial choice to ensure that results are robust to rotation method (Finch, 2020a; Hattori et al., 2017). Promax and oblimin would be the obvious choice for this comparison.

Factor Loadings

To this point, factor loadings have been specified as quantifications of the relationship between measured variables and factors. By allowing factors to correlate, oblique rotations produce two types of factor loadings: pattern coefficients and structure coefficients. Pattern coefficients quantify the relationship between a measured variable and its underlying factor, after the effects of the other variables have been taken into account or "partialled out". Pattern coefficients are regression-like weights and may occasionally be greater than ±1.00. In contrast, structure coefficients reflect the simple correlation of a measured variable with its underlying factor and ignore the effects of other factors and must range from −1.00 to +1.00. Consequently, it is no longer sufficient to refer to factor loadings after an oblique rotation has been applied. Rather, the appropriate coefficient *must* be identified (pattern or structure).

Pattern and structure coefficients will be identical if the factors are perfectly uncorrelated with each other and will increasingly deviate from each other as the factor intercorrelations increase. Methodologists typically recommend that both pattern and structure coefficients should be interpreted (Gorsuch, 1983; Matsunaga, 2010; McClain, 1996; McCoach et al., 2013; Nunnally & Bernstein, 1994; Pett et al., 2003; Reio & Shuck, 2015; Thompson, 2004) because that "increases the interpretative insights gained from a factor analysis" (Hetzel, 1996, p. 183). However, pattern coefficients and factor intercorrelations should receive primary attention during the model evaluation process (Bandalos, 2018; Brown, 2015; Cattell, 1978; Fabrigar & Wegener, 2012; Flora, 2018; Hair et al., 2019; McCoach et al., 2013; Mulaik, 2010; Pituch & Stevens, 2016; Rencher & Christensen, 2012; Roberson et al., 2014; Sakaluk & Short, 2017). Comrey and Lee (1992) suggested that loadings greater than .70 are excellent, .63 are very good, .55 are good, .45 are fair, and .32 are poor. Morin et al. (2020) concluded that loadings ≥.50 are "fully satisfactory" (p. 1052). Structure coefficients can be consulted after the final model has been tentatively accepted to ensure that the factors have been named appropriately and that anomalous results have not been inadvertently accepted (Kahn, 2006).

Eigenvalues and Variance Extracted

The unrotated and rotated factor solutions will explain the same amount of total variance (computed with eigenvalues) but rotation spreads that variance across the factors to improve interpretation and parsimony. For example, the first two unrotated factors in the iq data explain 62.3% and 7.3% of the total variance, respectively, but after rotation those same two factors explain 36.6% and 33.0% of the total variance. Given this redistribution of variance across factors, it is necessary to identify whether the unrotated or rotated solution is referenced when considering the proportion of total variance that was attributed to each factor.

Report

An oblique rotation was selected because it honors the ubiquity of intercorrelations among social science variables (Meehl, 1990). Among the potential oblique analytic rotations, promax was chosen because it is an oblique modification of the widely accepted varimax procedure (Gorsuch, 1983; Thompson, 2004). To ensure stability across extraction methods, oblimin extraction was also employed (Finch, 2020a).

14

STEP 9

Interpret Exploratory Factor Analysis Results

Model Selection Guidelines

Models with different numbers of factors should be sequentially judged for their interpretability and theoretical meaningfulness (Fabrigar & Wegener, 2012; Finch, 2020a; Flora, 2018). There are a variety of guidelines that can be used to judge models. It is crucial that the researcher explicitly detail the judgment guidelines that will be applied *prior* to implementation. This a priori explanation will reduce the possibility of self-serving judgments (Rubin, 2017; Simmons et al., 2011). Following is an enumerated list of guidelines that are most likely to be helpful.

1. Establish a threshold at which factor loadings (pattern coefficients for oblique rotations) will be considered meaningful (Worthington & Whittaker, 2006). Conventionally, loadings that meet this threshold are characterized as *salient*. It is common to arbitrarily consider factor loadings of .30, .32, or .40 as salient (Child, 2006; Comrey & Lee, 1992; Hair et al., 2019; Pituch & Stevens, 2016), that is, variables with around 9%, 10%, or 16% (factor loading squared) of their variance explained by the factor. Some researchers consider .30 or .32 salient for exploratory factor analysis (EFA) and .40 salient for principal components analysis (PCA). These thresholds honor practical significance but ignore statistical significance. That is, a loading of .32 could account for 10% of a variable's variance but it might not be statistically significantly different from zero, thereby calling into question its stability (Schmitt & Sass, 2011; Zhang & Preacher, 2015). Norman and Streiner (2014) suggested an approximation based on Pearson correlation coefficients to compute the statistical significance ($p = .01$) of factor loadings: $\frac{5.152}{\sqrt{N-2}}$. For the iq data, statistical significance ($p = .01$) would equate to $5.152 \div 12.25 = .42$. A more relaxed $p = .05$ standard would modify the numerator: $\frac{3.92}{\sqrt{N-2}}$ or $3.92 \div 12.25 = .32$.

Alternatively, confidence intervals (CIs) for the factor loadings can be estimated by the statistical software. Thus, establish a threshold for salience that is both practically and statistically significant.

2. Respect the concept of simple structure (Thurstone, 1947). Variables with salient loadings on more than one factor are said to cross-load and are called complex variables. Complex loadings might be appropriate for some structures, but will complicate interpretation. Simple structure solutions will probably be more interpretable and more likely to replicate. Conceptually, simple structure implies that each variable will exhibit salient loadings on a few factors (the fewer the better) and weak loadings on all other factors (Pituch & Stevens, 2016). At its simplest, several variables will saliently load onto each factor and each variable will saliently load onto only one factor. In practice, a reasonable approximation of simple structure is the goal (Morin et al., 2020). Simple structure recognizes "the purpose of science [which] is to uncover the relatively simple deep structure principles or causes that underlie the apparent complexity observed at the surface structure level" (Le et al., 2010, p. 112) and embodies the scientific principle of parsimony (Harman, 1976).

3. If the measured variables are items or are otherwise meant to be combined into a scale, the alpha reliability (Cronbach, 1951) of each factor should exceed the threshold established for the use of such scales (Pett et al., 2003). For example, reliability coefficients in the .90s are excellent and likely sufficient for clinical decisions (DeVellis, 2017), coefficients in the .80s are good and sufficient for non-critical decisions, coefficients in the .70s are adequate for group experimental research, and coefficients less than .70 are inadequate for most applications (Hunsley & Mash, 2007; Kline, 2013).

4. Measures of model fit, including

   a. Residuals: The difference between the actual correlation matrix and a correlation matrix reproduced by the model. The *psych* package provides the root mean squared residual (RMSR), which is an average of overall residual misfit. The smaller the RMSR value the better with values ≤.08 preferred (Brown, 2015). RMSR values will continue to decrease as more factors are extracted, so several models may exhibit RMSR values of ≤.08. The goal is to select the model where RMSR is substantially smaller than a model with one more factor but does not appreciably decrease when another factor is removed.

   Additionally, individual residual correlations should be considered. Ideally, the proportion of non-redundant residual correlations greater than the absolute value of .05 should be small (Basto & Pereira, 2012; Finch, 2020a; Garson, 2013; Johnson & Morgan, 2016; Maydeu-Olivares, 2017), with absolute residuals of >.10 more strongly indicating the presence of another factor (Cudeck, 2000; Flora, 2018; Kline, 2013; McDonald, 2010). If the residuals "are not both small and without apparent pattern, additional factors may be present in the data" (Nunnally & Bernstein, 1994, p. 471).

Maydeu-Olivares (2017) found that RMSRs from samples tended to be higher than RMSRs from populations and suggested that the standard of close fit should be an overall value of .05 with no individual residual larger than .10. As summarized by Flora (2018), "although there is no concrete guideline or cut-off for how small residual correlations should be, I suggest that any residual correlation > .10 is worthy of further consideration with respect to potential model misfit" (p. 255).

b. Bayesian information criterion (BIC; Schwarz, 1978): An index that balances model simplicity versus goodness of fit. There is no absolute good or bad BIC value: the model with the lowest BIC value is preferred. The BIC was designed to detect the "true" model if it is among the set of candidate models and emphasizes parsimony by including a penalty for model complexity (Burnham & Anderson, 2004). Unfortunately, the BIC tends to overestimate the number of factors as sample size increases (Schmitt et al., 2018) and has received little research attention for use with EFA models.

c. Indices of model fit used in CFA, including the comparative fit index (CFI), Tucker-Lewis index (TLI), root mean square error of approximation (RMSEA), etc. Similar to the BIC, these indices have received little research attention in the EFA context. However, one study found that they were of "questionable utility" for determining the number of factors in EFA (Clark & Bowles, 2018, p. 544) although CFI/TLI values of ≥.95 might protect against underfactoring. Another study found that RMSEA difference values of ≥.015 might be helpful in determining the number of factors to retain (Finch, 2020b). Garrido et al. (2016) found that all fit indices were influenced by the properties of the data and model, making them less accurate than parallel analysis.

5. Symptoms of model misfit due to overfactoring:

a. Factors with only one (singlet) or two (doublet) salient loadings. Such factors are relatively weak and unlikely to replicate (Bandalos, 2018; Bandalos & Finney, 2019; Benson & Nasser, 1998; Brown, 2015; Fabrigar & Wegener, 2012; Nunnally & Bernstein, 1994; Preacher & MacCallum, 2003; Velicer & Fava, 1998). Factors with at least three salient loadings are preferred (Comrey & Lee, 1992; Garson, 2013; Johnson & Morgan, 2016; Mulaik, 2010, 2018; Reio & Shuck, 2015; Velicer & Fava, 1998) because "no meaningful component can be identified unless each factor is overdetermined with three or four or more tests" (Thurstone, 1937, p. 75). Singlet and doublet variables will likely exhibit low communality (Fabrigar & Wegener, 2012) and therefore little explanatory power.

b. Factors that are very highly correlated. Interfactor correlations that exceed .80 or .85 might be a sign of overfactoring and pose a threat to discriminant validity (Brown, 2015; Finch, 2020a; McCoach et al., 2013; Schmitt et al., 2018), whereas interfactor correlations >.90 probably mean that "the two factors are clearly not distinct" (Kline, 2013, p. 185).

    c.   Factors based on similarities in variable distributions rather than similarity of variable content (Bandalos, 2018).

    d.   Unreasonable parameter estimates called Heywood cases (e.g., communalities > 1.00) or a failure of iterations to converge on a factor extraction solution may indicate a misspecified factor model (Flora, 2018; Pituch & Stevens, 2016).

    e.   Factor splitting: Measured variables that are known to load on a single factor in the population are split onto multiple factors after rotation (Wood et al., 1996).

6.   Symptoms of model misfit due to underfactoring:

    a.   Measured variables that saliently load on a factor do not seem to reflect a common unifying theme. This may indicate that two or more factors have collapsed onto the same factor (Fabrigar & Wegener, 2012).

    b.   Poor model fit indices and modest loadings of measured variables on all factors or many complex loadings (Benson & Nasser, 1998; Zhang, 2014).

7.   Robustness of results across extraction and rotation methods. As suggested by Gorsuch (1983), "factor the data by several different analytic procedures and hold sacred only those factors that appear across all the procedures used" (p. 330).

Report

Models with three, two, and one factor(s) will be sequentially evaluated for their interpretability and theoretical meaningfulness using several guidelines. Given the oblique rotation, pattern coefficients and factor intercorrelations will receive primary attention during the model evaluation process (Bandalos, 2018; Hair et al., 2019). To ensure both practical (10% variance explained) and statistical significance ($p < .05$) of pattern loadings, the threshold for salience will be set at .32 (Norman & Streiner, 2014) with a goal of approximate simple structure (Thurstone, 1947). The models will be compared on two indexes of residual model fit: (a) the proportion of residual coefficients that exceed absolute values of .05 and .10 (Nunnally & Bernstein, 1994); and (b) RMSR values ≤.08 (Brown, 2015). Additionally, the alpha reliability of scales created from the salient variables of each factor should approach .90 given the intended clinical use of these scales (DeVellis, 2017). Finally, each model will be examined for symptoms of overextraction such as statistically inadmissible solutions, fewer than three salient loadings, technical factors, etc. and symptoms of underextraction such as no common unifying theme, many complex loadings, etc. (Bandalos, 2018; Fabrigar & Wegener, 2012).

Model Evaluation

Given the many matrices created during an EFA, results are more easily managed and interpreted by creating several **R** objects rather than attempting to produce, interpret, and print the entire model in one **R** command. Some of the voluminous **R** output has been omitted for readability. Each model is subsequently generated and described.

Model 3

BOX 14.1   EFA WITH THREE FACTORS FROM THE *PSYCH* PACKAGE

```
## 3 factor model, promax rotation, ML extraction, save residuals
## Missing data can be imputed with mean (impute="mean") or median
## (impute="median")
## Default values for iteration (max.iter) and initial communality
## estimate (SMC)
> f3=fa(iq,nfactors=3,rotate="promax",residuals=TRUE,SMC=TRUE,
  missing=FALSE,fm="ml",n.obs=152)
## 3-factor solution printed with precision to 3 decimals and sorted
## from high to low
> print(f3,digits=3,sort=TRUE)
Standardized loadings (pattern matrix) based upon correlation matrix
          item    ML3    ML1    ML2    h2     u2  com
matrix1     4  0.821  0.130 -0.110 0.715 0.2848 1.09  Pattern coefficients with
designs2    8  0.796 -0.051  0.029 0.607 0.3929 1.01  salient in bold. h2 is
designs1    2  0.736  0.132 -0.082 0.609 0.3910 1.09  communality, u2 is uniqueness.
matrix2     7  0.713 -0.101  0.263 0.698 0.3024 1.31  com is factor complexity of each
vocab1      1 -0.017  1.035 -0.075 0.941 0.0586 1.01  variable with 1.0 indicating
vocab2      6  0.048  0.715  0.150 0.750 0.2504 1.10  perfect simple structure for VSS.
similar1    3  0.157  0.595  0.161 0.712 0.2876 1.29
veranal2    5 -0.028  0.127  0.882 0.919 0.0808 1.04

                        ML3    ML1    ML2   ← order of factors is unimportant
SS loadings           2.574  2.276  1.101  ← eigenvalues after rotation
Proportion Var        0.322  0.284  0.138  ← % total variance for each factor after rotation
Cumulative Var        0.322  0.606  0.744  ← cumulative % total variance after rotation
Proportion Explained  0.433  0.382  0.185  ← % common variance after rotation
Cumulative Proportion 0.433  0.815  1.000  ← cumulative % common variance after rotation

 With factor correlations of
       ML3    ML1    ML2
ML3 1.000  0.725  0.676  ← factor intercorrelation matrix
ML1 0.725  1.000  0.724
ML2 0.676  0.724  1.000

The root mean square of the residuals (RMSR) is  0.019
BIC =  -22.985
## Off-diagonal residuals
> resd=residuals(f3,diag=FALSE,na.rm=TRUE)
> print(resd)
          vocb1 dsgn1 smlr1 mtrx1 vrnl2 vocb2 mtrx2 dsgn2
vocab1      NA
designs1   0.00    NA
similar1   0.00  0.01    NA
matrix1    0.00 -0.01  0.00    NA
veranal2   0.00  0.00  0.00  0.00    NA
vocab2     0.00 -0.01  0.01 -0.02  0.00    NA
matrix2    0.00 -0.04 -0.02  0.04  0.00  0.00    NA
designs2  -0.01  0.06  0.02 -0.03  0.00  0.02 -0.01    NA
## Display a histogram of the residuals if desired
> hist(resd,col="red",main="",xlab="Residuals")
## Print structure matrix if desired
> print(sort=TRUE,digits=3,cut=0,f3$Structure)
## Display list of contents of an object if desired
> names(f3)
## Display name of one item in the contents list by directly addressing
## its $name
> print(f3$rms)
[1] 0.01858966
```

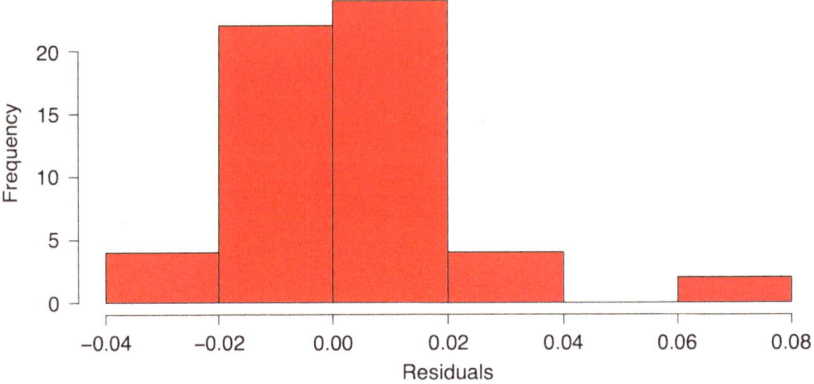

FIGURE 14.1   Histogram of Residuals of Three-factor Model

Note that a new entry appears in the RStudio **Environment** pane as this factor model object (f3) is produced. Clicking on the small "magnification" icon next to that object will display a list of that object's contents in the top left pane of the RStudio display.

It was hypothesized that the three-factor model would exhibit symptoms of overextraction (Figure 14.1). A review of the output confirms that hypothesis: the third factor had only one salient variable loading (veranal2). This singlet factor disqualifies the three-factor model from further consideration.

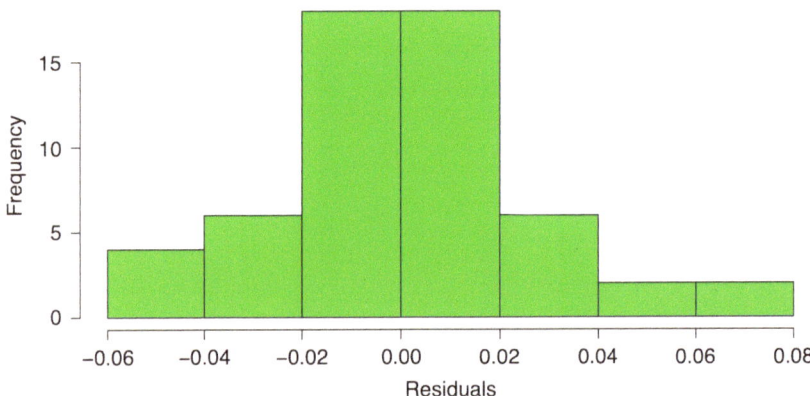

FIGURE 14.2   Histogram of Residuals of Two-factor Model

Model 2

BOX 14.2 EFA WITH TWO FACTORS FROM THE *PSYCH* PACKAGE

```
## 2 factor model, promax rotation, ML extraction, save residuals
## Missing data can be imputed with mean (impute="mean") or median
## (impute="median"). Default values for iteration (min.err, max.iter)
## and initial communality estimate (SMC)
> f2=fa(iq,nfactors=2,rotate="promax",residuals=TRUE,SMC=TRUE,
  missing=FALSE,fm="ml",n.obs=152)
> print(f2,digits=3,sort=TRUE)
Standardized loadings (pattern matrix) based upon correlation matrix
          item   ML1    ML2     h2    u2   com
vocab1       1  0.959 -0.047 0.855 0.145 1.00
vocab2       6  0.896 -0.011 0.787 0.213 1.00
similar1     3  0.752  0.130 0.731 0.269 1.06
veranal2     5  0.616  0.211 0.621 0.379 1.23
designs2     8 -0.024  0.799 0.611 0.389 1.00
matrix2      7  0.056  0.779 0.677 0.323 1.01
matrix1      4  0.077  0.770 0.688 0.312 1.02
designs1     2  0.088  0.705 0.598 0.402 1.03


                          ML1   ML2
SS loadings             2.926 2.641
Proportion Var          0.366 0.330
Cumulative Var          0.366 0.696
Proportion Explained    0.526 0.474
Cumulative Proportion   0.526 1.000
 With factor correlations of
       ML1   ML2
ML1 1.000 0.758
ML2 0.758 1.000


The root mean square of the residuals (RMSR) is  0.028
BIC =  -34.316
> resd=residuals(f2,diag=FALSE,na.rm=TRUE)
> print(resd)
          vocb1 dsgn1 smlr1 mtrx1 vrnl2 vocb2 mtrx2 dsgn2
vocab1      NA
designs1  0.02    NA
similar1  0.01  0.00    NA
matrix1   0.02  0.01 -0.01    NA
veranal2 -0.02 -0.04  0.03 -0.05    NA
vocab2    0.00 -0.01 -0.02 -0.02  0.02    NA
matrix2  -0.02 -0.05 -0.01  0.03  0.08  0.01    NA
designs2 -0.01  0.06  0.01 -0.03 -0.01  0.02 -0.02    NA
## Display a histogram of the residuals if desired
> hist(resd,col="blue",main="",xlab="Residuals")
## Use the structure to create a scale for each factor and obtain
## its alpha reliability
## Note that errors may occur if packages other than psych are active
> s1 = data.frame(vocab1,vocab2,similar1,veranal2)
> alpha(s1)
 lower alpha upper     95% confidence boundaries
   0.9 0.92 0.94
> s2 = data.frame(designs2,matrix2,matrix1,designs1)
> alpha(s2)
 lower alpha upper     95% confidence boundaries
  0.84 0.88 0.91
## Structure matrix
> print(sort=TRUE,digits=3,cut=0,f2$Structure)
Loadings:
          ML1   ML2
vocab1    0.924 0.680
similar1  0.851 0.700
veranal2  0.776 0.678
vocab2    0.887 0.667
designs1  0.622 0.771
matrix1   0.660 0.828
matrix2   0.647 0.822
designs2  0.582 0.781
```

Model 2 converged properly, produced reasonable parameter estimates, and exhibited four salient loadings at good to excellent levels (Comrey & Lee, 1992) on each factor in a simple structure configuration. Communalities were robust (.60 to .85; Watson, 2017), only two off-diagonal residual coefficients exceeded the absolute value of .05 (Figure 14.2), and the RMSR value was low at .028 (Brown, 2015). When the variables that saliently loaded each factor were combined to create a scale, their internal consistency reliability estimates were .92 and .88. Reliability coefficients of this magnitude are generally considered to be strong and useful for clinical decisions (DeVellis, 2017). The interfactor correlation of .76 was somewhat elevated but that might be due to a strong general factor that permeates all the variables (Gorsuch, 1983). Additionally, the measured variables were distributed across the two factors as predicted by prior theory (verbal versus nonverbal measures) and the structure was interpretable and theoretically meaningful.

The structure coefficients for each factor were strong (.58 to .92) and there was no evidence of a suppression effect (Thompson, 2004), that is, a structure coefficient around zero but a high pattern coefficient or vice versa, or pattern and structure coefficients of different signs (Graham et al., 2003). A review of the correlation matrix revealed strong bivariate correlations between the measured variables, making it improbable that this result was simply a mathematical artifact. The two-factor model was robust to different extraction and rotation methods as very similar results were obtained when iterated principal axis extraction and direct oblimin rotation were employed. In sum, the two-factor model appears to be a good EFA solution and offers the optimum balance between comprehensiveness (accounting for the most variance) and parsimony (with the fewest factors).

BOX 14.3 UNROTATED PCA EIGENVALUES AND VARIANCE

```
## Determine unrotated PCA eigenvalues and variance
> pcaiq=pca(iq,nfactors=8,rotate="none",residuals=TRUE,SMC=TRUE,
  missing=FALSE,fm="pca",n.obs=152)
> print (pcaiq,cut=0,digits=3)
:::::::::::::::::::::::::::::::::::::::::::::::::::::::::::::::::::::::::
                        PC1   PC2   PC3   PC4  PC5   PC6   PC7   PC8
SS loadings           5.328 0.837 0.474 0.399 0.32 0.268 0.219 0.154
Proportion Var        0.666 0.105 0.059 0.050 0.04 0.034 0.027 0.019
Cumulative Var        0.666 0.771 0.830 0.880 0.92 0.953 0.981 1.000
Proportion Explained  0.666 0.105 0.059 0.050 0.04 0.034 0.027 0.019
Cumulative Proportion 0.666 0.771 0.830 0.880 0.92 0.953 0.981 1.000

## Determine total and common variance of 2 factors before rotation
>
f2nr=fa(iq,nfactors=2,rotate="none",residuals=TRUE,SMC=TRUE,missing=FALSE,
  fm="ml",n.obs=152)
> print(f2nr,cut=0,digits=3)
::::::::::::::::::::::::::::::::::
                        ML1   ML2
SS loadings           4.985 0.583
Proportion Var        0.623 0.073
Cumulative Var        0.623 0.696
Proportion Explained  0.895 0.105
Cumulative Proportion 0.895 1.000
```

Using SPSS output format as a model, the total variance apportionment of Model 2 could be illustrated as in Box 14.4.

BOX 14.4   VARIANCE APPORTIONMENT OF THE TWO-FACTOR MODEL

	Initial (Unrotated) PCA			ML Extraction Unrotated			ML Extraction Rotated		
Factor	Eigen-values	% of Variance	Cumul-ative %	Eigen-values	% of Variance	Cumul-ative %	Eigen-values	% of Variance	Cumul-ative %
1	5.328	66.6	66.6	4.99	62.3	62.3	2.93	36.6	36.6
2	0.837	10.5	77.1	0.58	7.3	69.6	2.64	33.0	69.6
3	0.474	5.9	83.0						
4	0.399	5.0	88.0						
5	0.320	4.0	92.0						
6	0.268	3.4	95.3						
7	0.219	2.7	98.1						
8	0.154	1.9	100						

Note that PCA extracted 100% of the total variance when eight factors were extracted, whereas the reduced model with two factors accounted for 70% of the total variance. This is a vivid demonstration of parsimony: two factors explained 70% of the variance of eight measured variables. Also, note that the unrotated and rotated ML solutions explained the same amount of total variance (70%) but rotation spread that variance across the two factors differently (62% and 7% for the unrotated versus 37% and 33% for the rotated factors). Common variance was also redistributed across the two factors during rotation (90% and 10% for the unrotated versus 53% and 47% for the rotated factors). Given this redistribution of variance across factors, it is necessary to identify whether the unrotated or rotated solution is referenced while reporting the proportion of total variance that was attributed to each factor.

BOX 14.5   PATH DIAGRAM AND FACTOR LOADING PLOT FROM *PSYCH* PACKAGE

```
## Set-up graphics window for 2 graphs
> par(mfrow=c(1,2))
## Path diagram
> fa.diagram(f2,sort=TRUE,cut=0,digits=3,main="Model 2",cex=.75)
## Factor loading plot
> plot(f2)
```

The *psych* package also allows a simple path diagram of a factor model to be generated as well as a factor loading plot. Those two graphs can be placed in a single output window as shown in Figure 14.3.

Additionally, CIs of the factor loadings and factor intercorrelations can be generated through bootstrap sampling.

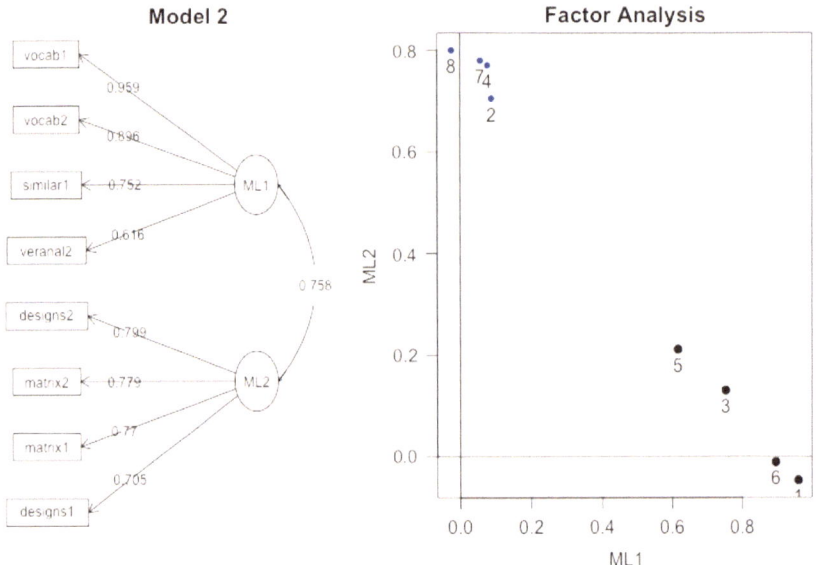

FIGURE 14.3 Path Diagram and Factor Loading Plot of Two-factor Model

BOX 14.6 BOOTSTRAP SAMPLING OF CONFIDENCE INTERVALS FOR PATTERN COEFFICIENTS FROM *PSYCH* PACKAGE

```
## Confidence intervals computed with n.iter command for 1,000
bootstrapped samples
> f2iter=fa(iq,nfactors=2,rotate="promax",residuals=T,missing=F,fm="ml",
  n.obs=152,n.iter=1000)
> print(sort=TRUE,digits=3,cut=0,f2iter)
 Coefficients and bootstrapped confidence intervals
           low    ML1 upper    low    ML2 upper
vocab1    0.788  0.959 1.107 -0.204 -0.047 0.184
designs1 -0.080  0.088 0.312  0.510  0.705 0.877
similar1  0.583  0.752 0.906 -0.004  0.130 0.326
matrix1  -0.124  0.077 0.311  0.547  0.770 0.996
veranal2  0.410  0.616 0.842 -0.001  0.211 0.447
vocab2    0.748  0.896 1.036 -0.144 -0.011 0.171
matrix2  -0.118  0.056 0.299  0.529  0.779 1.008
designs2 -0.212 -0.024 0.232  0.575  0.799 0.986

 Interfactor correlations and bootstrapped confidence intervals
         lower estimate upper
ML1-ML2 0.675    0.758 0.817
```

Bootstrap sampling is a method of estimating the properties of a distribution (in this case, CIs of factor loadings) based on sample data without making assumptions about that distribution (Hancock & Liu, 2012). In this example, the idea is to mimic taking 1,000 samples of size 152 from a population and computing CIs for the factor loadings from that distribution (see Diaconis and Efron (1983) for a basic description of bootstrapping). Efron (1987) demonstrated that 1,000 replications would produce CIs with a coefficient of variation of 4%. If time permits, 2,000 or more replications might be specified to ensure greater accuracy.

Model 1

BOX 14.7   EFA WITH ONE FACTOR FROM THE *PSYCH* PACKAGE

```
## 1 factor model, promax rotation, ML extraction, save residuals
## Missing data can be imputed with mean (impute="mean") or median
## (impute="median"). Default values for iteration (min.err, max.iter)
## and initial communality estimate (SMC)
> f1=fa(iq,nfactors=1,rotate="promax",residuals=TRUE,SMC=TRUE,
  missing=FALSE,fm="ml",n.obs=152)
> print(f1,digits=3,sort=TRUE)
Standardized loadings (pattern matrix) based upon correlation matrix
            V   ML1    h2    u2 com
vocab1    1 0.875 0.765 0.235   1
vocab2    6 0.855 0.731 0.269   1
similar1  3 0.853 0.728 0.272   1
veranal2  5 0.797 0.636 0.364   1
matrix1   4 0.744 0.553 0.447   1
matrix2   7 0.740 0.548 0.452   1
designs1  2 0.703 0.494 0.506   1
designs2  8 0.680 0.462 0.538   1

The root mean square of the residuals (RMSR) is  0.077
BIC =  15.787
## Residual matrix
> resd=residuals(f1,diag=FALSE,na.rm=TRUE)
> print(resd,digits=3)
          vocab1 dsgns1 simlr1 matrx1 vernl2 vocab2 matrx2 dsgns2
vocab1        NA
designs1  -0.039     NA
similar1   0.042 -0.030     NA
matrix1   -0.033  0.127 -0.036     NA
veranal2  -0.008 -0.052  0.021 -0.060     NA
vocab2     0.076 -0.062  0.006 -0.070  0.025     NA
matrix2   -0.084  0.066 -0.050  0.164  0.058 -0.055     NA
designs2  -0.087  0.183 -0.030  0.113 -0.028 -0.051  0.121     NA
## Next,count of number of residuals > .05. Can be changed to .10
> BigR=sum(resd>abs(.05),na.rm=T)
> print(BigR)
[1] 16
## Total number of off-diagonal elements in the data matrix
> totR=length(iq)*(length(iq)-1)/2
> print(totR)
[1] 28
## Proportion of off-diagonal elements > .05 in residual matrix
> sum(BigR/totR*100)
[1] 57.14286
## Largest residual in residual matrix
> max(abs(resd),na.rm=TRUE)
[1] 0.1834762
## Structure matrix if desired
> print(sort=TRUE,digits=3,cut=0,f2$Structure)
## Pattern matrix separated from remainder of output if desired
> print(sort=TRUE,digits=3,cut=0,f1$loadings)
Loadings:
[1] 0.875 0.703 0.853 0.744 0.797 0.855 0.740 0.680

                ML1
SS loadings    4.917
Proportion Var 0.615
```

Model 1 converged properly, produced reasonable parameter estimates, and exhibited eight salient loadings on its single factor. However, communalities were relatively weak in comparison to Model 2 and its RMSR value was near its acceptable limit of .08 (Brown, 2015). Further, 57% of the off-diagonal residual coefficients exceeded .05 and 18% exceeded .10 (Figure 14.4). These residual values suggest that another factor might be extracted.

Most critically, the single factor does not seem to reflect a common unifying theme because it encompasses both verbal and nonverbal reasoning variables. This is evidence that two factors have collapsed onto one (Fabrigar & Wegener, 2012). Thus, the measures of model fit as well as theoretical convergence remove this model from consideration, leaving Model 2 as the preferred solution.

Additional useful information can be extracted from the EFA models.

BOX 14.8 EFA INFORMATION FROM *PSYCH* PACKAGE

```
## Initial eigenvalues (PCA)
> print(digits=3,cut=0,f2$e.values)
[1] 5.328 0.837 0.474 0.399 0.320 0.268 0.219 0.154
## Alternative method to obtain initial eigenvalues
> eigen(cor(iq))$values
[1] 5.3280352 0.8370123 0.4743501 0.3989081 0.3203761 0.2683994
    0.2193804 0.1535386
## Eigenvalues from an initial EFA model
> print(digits=3,cut=0,f2$values)
[1]   5.0316   0.5402   0.1307   0.0715   0.0216 -0.0422 -0.0701 -0.1160
## Squared multiple correlations (SMC)
> smc(iq)
   vocab1  designs1  similar1   matrix1  veranal2    vocab2   matrix2  designs2
0.7695082 0.5599797 0.6924306 0.6329851 0.6298663 0.7268670 0.6360395 0.5491816
## Pattern coefficients from a factor model
> print(f2$loadings,sort=TRUE,cut = 0)
Loadings:
          ML1    ML2
vocab1    0.959 -0.047
similar1  0.752  0.130
veranal2  0.616  0.211
vocab2    0.896 -0.011
designs1  0.088  0.705
matrix1   0.077  0.770
matrix2   0.056  0.779
designs2 -0.024  0.799
## Correlation matrix internally computed for factor analysis
> print(digits=3,cut=0,f2$r)
## Principal components analysis without rotation
> pca8=principal(iq,nfactors=8,rotate="none",n.obs=152)
> print(pca8,digits=3)
Standardized loadings (pattern matrix) based upon correlation matrix
          PC1    PC2    PC3    PC4    PC5    PC6    PC7    PC8 h2        u2  com
vocab1   0.859 -0.340  0.154 -0.155 -0.063  0.073 -0.011 -0.298  1 4.44e-16 1.76
designs1 0.775  0.355  0.352 -0.027  0.379  0.051 -0.052  0.024  1 3.00e-15 2.43
similar1 0.851 -0.273  0.105 -0.013 -0.055 -0.392 -0.149  0.103  1 1.33e-15 1.80
matrix1  0.810  0.306 -0.116 -0.403 -0.110 -0.058  0.237  0.061  1 7.77e-16 2.13
veranal2 0.815 -0.267 -0.274  0.271  0.239 -0.044  0.239 -0.014  1 6.66e-16 2.16
vocab2   0.845 -0.350  0.087  0.003 -0.118  0.311 -0.032  0.213  1 2.00e-15 1.87
matrix2  0.809  0.247 -0.446 -0.018  0.028  0.073 -0.277 -0.041  1 1.55e-15 2.09
designs2 0.760  0.415  0.144  0.371 -0.293 -0.009  0.055 -0.047  1 1.78e-15 2.56


                         PC1   PC2   PC3   PC4  PC5   PC6   PC7   PC8
SS loadings            5.328 0.837 0.474 0.399 0.32 0.268 0.219 0.154
Proportion Var         0.666 0.105 0.059 0.050 0.04 0.034 0.027 0.019
Cumulative Var         0.666 0.771 0.830 0.880 0.92 0.953 0.981 1.000
Proportion Explained   0.666 0.105 0.059 0.050 0.04 0.034 0.027 0.019
Cumulative Proportion  0.666 0.771 0.830 0.880 0.92 0.953 0.981 1.000
```

Although these models were created with raw data as input, identical results can be obtained with correlation matrix input. For this normally distributed data, Pearson correlations were chosen but Kendall's *tau* and Spearman's *rho* matrices can also be obtained from procedures in the *stats* package.

BOX 14.9   EFA FROM CORRELATION MATRIX

```
## Compute the Pearson correlation matrix from raw data
## Compute Kendall or Spearman matrices (method="kendall" or
method="spearman")
> iqcorr=cor(iq,method="pearson")
> print(iqcorr,digits=2)
         vocab1 designs1 similar1 matrix1 veranal2 vocab2 matrix2 designs2
vocab1    1.00    0.58     0.79    0.62     0.69    0.82    0.56    0.51
designs1  0.58    1.00     0.57    0.65     0.51    0.54    0.59    0.66
similar1  0.79    0.57     1.00    0.60     0.70    0.74    0.58    0.55
matrix1   0.62    0.65     0.60    1.00     0.53    0.57    0.71    0.62
veranal2  0.69    0.51     0.70    0.53     1.00    0.71    0.65    0.51
vocab2    0.82    0.54     0.74    0.57     0.71    1.00    0.58    0.53
matrix2   0.56    0.59     0.58    0.71     0.65    0.58    1.00    0.62
designs2  0.51    0.66     0.55    0.62     0.51    0.53    0.62    1.00
## Verify that results are identical by recomputing the 2 factor model
> f2c=fa(iqcorr,nfactors=2,rotate="promax",residuals=T,SMC=TRUE,
  missing=F,fm="ml",n.obs=152)
> print(f2c,digits=3,sort=TRUE)
```

As demonstrated earlier, the *psych* package computes the 95% CI for alpha reliability coefficients. For the first factor in the two-factor solution, it computed coefficient alpha at .92 with 95% CI. What if the 99% CI was desired? The MBESS package can be utilized to obtain bootstrapped CIs at any confidence level (Kelley & Pornprasertmanit, 2016).

BOX 14.10   BOOTSTRAPPED CONFIDENCE INTERVALS FOR ALPHA COEFFICIENTS FROM *MBESS* PACKAGE

```
## Install MBESS package if needed
## Make MBESS package available
> library(MBESS)
## Identify components of first factor
> s1 = data.frame(vocab1,vocab2,similar1,veranal2)
## Compute bootstrapped alpha CI at 99% level
> ci.reliability(data=s1,N=152,type="alpha",interval.type="bca",
  B=1000,conf.level=.99)
$est
[1] 0.9191956

$se
[1] 0.0135079

$ci.lower
[1] 0.879541

$ci.upper
[1] 0.9469119

$conf.level
[1] 0.99

$type
[1] "alpha"

$interval.type
[1] "bca bootstrap"
```

Thus, alpha ranged from .90 to .94 at the 95% CI but from .88 to .95 at the 99% CI.

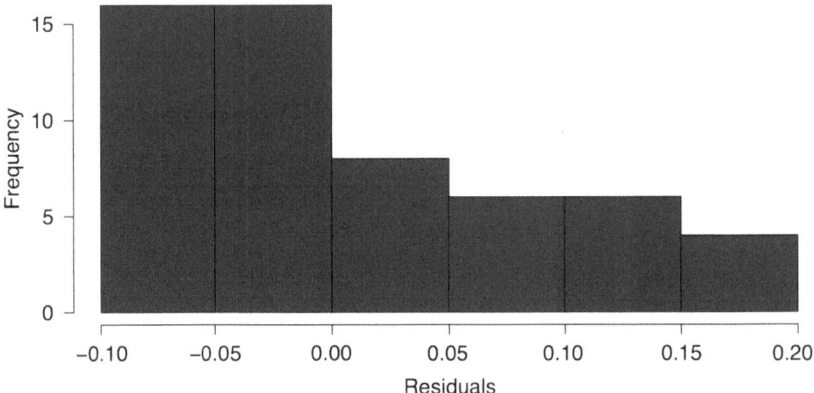

FIGURE 14.4 Histogram of Residuals of One-factor Model

Factor Names

For convenience, researchers typically name the factors identified through EFA. Names can be given to factors to facilitate the communication of results and advance cumulative knowledge. Rummel (1967) suggested that factors can be named symbolically, descriptively, or causally. Symbolic names are without any substantive meaning, for example, F1 and F2 or A, B, and C. These names merely denote the factors without adding any meaning. Descriptive names are clues to factor content that can categorize the factor in terms of its apparent contents. For example, measures of word meaning, synonyms, and paragraph comprehension might be described as verbal. Causal names involve reasoning from the salient loadings to the underlying influences that caused them. Given that a factor is a construct operationalized by its factor loadings, the researcher tries to understand the underlying dimension that unifies the variables that define the factor. "Thus, the naming of a factor is based on its conceptual underpinnings" (Reio & Shuck, 2015, p. 20). For example, measures of word meaning, synonyms, and paragraph comprehension might be described as a verbal reasoning factor.

To reduce the possibility of confusion between measured variables and factors, the factors should *not* be named after measured variables (Thompson, 2004). Factors are typically named by considering what their most salient measured variables have in common with higher loadings receiving greater consideration (Kahn, 2006; Thompson, 2004). Although both pattern and structure coefficients are considered, structure coefficients may be more useful for naming when the interfactor correlations are modest because they reflect the simple relationship between a variable and a factor without the confounding effect of other factors (Kahn, 2006). With high interfactor correlations, the pattern coefficients might become more useful.

Factor naming is a subjective process (Watson, 2017), and the researcher must avoid the construct identity fallacy (Larsen & Bong, 2016). That is, assuming that two factors are the same because they have the same name (jingle fallacy) or different because they have different names (jangle fallacy). In either case, the unwary might be tempted to accept an inaccurate factor label. Likewise, it would be inappropriate to reify a factor label (Cliff, 1983; Kline, 2013). That is, assume that it is a real, physical thing rather than an explanatory latent construct. As explained by Carroll (1995b), "merely because it is convenient to refer to a factor (like g), by use of a noun does not make it a physical thing. At the most, factors should be regarded as sources of variance, dimensions, intervening variables, or latent traits that are useful in explaining manifest phenomena, much as abstractions such as gravity, mass, distance, and force are useful in describing physical events" (p. 126). There is ample evidence that jingle-jangle fallacies are widespread in practice and have resulted in construct proliferation and empirically redundant measures (Le et al., 2010; Shaffer et al., 2016)

Report

Three plausible models were evaluated. It was hypothesized that the three-factor model would exhibit symptoms of overextraction. This hypothesis was confirmed by a factor with only one salient loading. In contrast, the one-factor model exhibited symptoms of underextraction: weak communalities and failure to reflect a common unifying theme (Fabrigar & Wegener, 2012). Additionally, 57% of the off-diagonal absolute residuals exceeded .05 and 18% exceeded .10 in Model 1, strongly indicating the presence of another factor (Cudeck, 2000). Model 2 converged properly, produced reasonable parameter estimates, and exhibited four salient loadings on each factor in a simple structure configuration. Communalities were robust (.60 to .85), only one off-diagonal residual coefficient exceeded the absolute value of .05, and the RMSR value was low at .028. When the variables that saliently loaded each factor were combined to create a scale, their internal consistency reliability was .92 and .88.

The four measured variables that saliently loaded on the first factor contained verbal content and seemed to require reasoning with that content: defining words, describing how words are similar, and explaining verbal analogies. The four measured variables that saliently loaded on the second factor contained nonverbal content that involved analysis for patterns, inductive discovery of relationships, and deductive identification of missing components. Thus, the first factor might be called verbal reasoning and the second nonverbal reasoning. Performance on the verbal measures is obviously affected by experience, learning, and acculturation, whereas performance on the nonverbal measures is less affected by prior learning and experience. These attributes can be found in the taxonomy of cognitive abilities elucidated by Carroll (1993) and are probably better labeled crystalized and fluid ability, respectively, to reduce construct redundancy (Le et al., 2010; Shaffer et al., 2016). The high interfactor correlation of .76 is also consistent with Carroll's (1993) model of a general ability that accounts for the correlation between cognitive factors (Carretta & Ree, 2001; Gorsuch, 1983).

15

STEP 10

Report Exploratory Factor Analysis Results

As previously documented, many published exploratory factor analysis (EFA) employ inappropriate methods and are deficient in detail (Conway & Huffcutt, 2003; Fabrigar et al., 1999: Ford et al., 1986; Gaskin & Happell, 2014; Henson & Roberts, 2006; Howard, 2016; Izquierdo et al., 2014; Lloret et al., 2017; McCroskey & Young, 1979; Norris & Lecavalier, 2010; Park et al., 2002; Roberson et al., 2014; Russell, 2002; Sakaluk & Short, 2017). EFA reports should provide a clear presentation of the decisions made and a comprehensive presentation of the results. In other words, the EFA process must be made transparent (Flake & Fried, 2020). Enough detail must be provided to allow "informed review, replication, and cumulation of knowledge" (Ford et al., 1986, p. 307) yet remain succinct enough for journal presentation. Ideally, "the description of the methods used in the analysis should be sufficiently clear that a reader could replicate the study exactly" (Finch, 2020a, p. 94). The Report paragraphs in prior sections are preliminary models of how each decision step could be reported.

The EFA report should echo the previously enumerated decision steps. Following is an outline for the EFA report:

1. Describe the measured variables and justify their inclusion.
2. Describe the participants and justify their adequacy in terms of number and representativeness.
3. Present descriptive statistics. Ensure that linearity, outliers, and normality are addressed. Report extent of missing data and how it was addressed. Report correlation matrix if journal space allows. If not, present in a supplemental table.

4. Verify that data are appropriate for EFA with Bartlett's test of sphericity, KMO sampling adequacy, and magnitude of coefficients in the correlation matrix.
5. Justify model: principal components or common factor analysis.
6. Detail the method of factor extraction and justify its use with the data. Report method of estimating communalities if applicable. Report and justify type of correlation matrix employed (Pearson, Spearman, polychoric, etc.).
7. Describe *a priori* criteria for determination of how many factors to retain for interpretation. Ensure multiple criteria are applied within a model testing approach. Report results of each criterion.
8. Identify rotation method (orthogonal or oblique) and type (varimax, promax, oblimin, etc.). Justify selection.
9. Interpret each model using a priori guidelines for acceptability (including salience of loadings, scale reliability, model fit standards, symptoms of over- and underextraction). For the final model, present all pattern coefficients (do not omit non-salient values), communalities, and factor intercorrelations. Also present structure coefficients if journal space allows. If not, present in a supplemental table.

Factor Scores

It is possible to weight variable scores according to their relationship to each factor and thereby create factor score estimates for each participant that can subsequently be included in other investigations. Conceptually, a factor score is an estimate of the latent variable that underlies the measured variables. Unfortunately, "an infinite number of ways for scoring the individuals on the factors could be derived that would be consistent with the same factor loadings" (Grice, 2001, p. 431). Consequently, numerous ways to compute factor scores have been developed over the years but none have been found to be superior in all circumstances (Finch, 2013; Gorsuch, 1983). Some methodologists prefer complex computations involving multiple regression and maximum likelihood estimation (Comrey & Lee, 1992; Hair et al., 2019). Others believe that simple unit weights (e.g., adding the scores from variables that saliently load) may be superior (Carretta & Ree, 2001; Gorsuch, 2003; Kline, 1994; Russell, 2002; Wainer, 1976). Given the current state of knowledge about factor score indeterminacy (Rigdon et al., 2019), it is best to be cautious about the use of factor scores (Osborne & Banjanovic, 2016).

If factor scores are estimated, Nunnally and Bernstein (1994) suggested that they should exhibit strong multiple correlations with the variables that comprise each factor and should not correlate with other factor scores beyond the underlying factor intercorrelations. Mulaik (2018) recommended that factor scores be avoided unless the R^2 for predicting the common factors exceeds .95. Gorsuch (1983) recommended that the factor score correlations with factors should, at a minimum, exceed .80. An extended discussion of the benefits and liabilities of factor scores was provided by DiStefano et al. (2009).

The output from each EFA conducted with the *psych* package terminates with estimates of the adequacy of factor scores. Additionally, the *psych* package offers four alternatives for complex computation of factor scores that are described by Revelle (2016).

BOX 15.1   FACTOR SCORES FROM *PSYCH* PACKAGE

```
## Adequacy of factor scores at end of EFA output
> f2=fa(iq,nfactors=2,rotate="promax",residuals=TRUE,SMC=TRUE,missing=FALSE,fm="ml",n.obs=152)
> print(f2,digits=3,sort=TRUE)
Standardized loadings (pattern matrix) based upon correlation matrix
          item    ML1    ML2    h2     u2   com
vocab1       1  0.959 -0.047 0.855 0.145 1.00
vocab2       6  0.896 -0.011 0.787 0.213 1.00
similar1     3  0.752  0.130 0.731 0.269 1.06
veranal2     5  0.616  0.211 0.621 0.379 1.23
designs2     8 -0.024  0.799 0.611 0.389 1.00
matrix2      7  0.056  0.779 0.677 0.323 1.01
matrix1      4  0.077  0.770 0.688 0.312 1.02
designs1     2  0.088  0.705 0.598 0.402 1.03
::::::::::::::::::::::::::::::::::::::::::::::::::::::::::::::::
Measures of factor score adequacy
                                                    ML1   ML2
Correlation of (regression) scores with factors   0.967 0.944
Multiple R square of scores with factors          0.935 0.891
Minimum correlation of possible factor scores     0.871 0.781
## Factor scores can be computed from results of EFA
> factor.scores(iq,f2,method="tenBerge")
$scores
             ML1          ML2
  [1,]  1.01231369  1.466749239
  [2,]  0.36387256  0.336601249
  [3,]  1.22476361  1.303838287
:::::::::::::::::::::::::::::::::::::::
[150,] -0.51766709 -0.762459764
[151,] -0.10374816  0.286792061
[152,] -1.24392421 -1.447019456
$weights
                  ML1          ML2
vocab1     0.461311165 -0.040298580
designs1   0.015320629  0.221584168
similar1   0.194727821  0.061391651
matrix1    0.017331893  0.312119185
veranal2   0.113327953  0.070517254
vocab2     0.293302606 -0.006547303
matrix2    0.012300432  0.304498067
designs2  -0.004183442  0.259649970

$r.scores
         ML1       ML2
ML1 1.0000000 0.7575612
ML2 0.7575612 1.0000000

$R2
      ML1       ML2
0.9665415 0.9414390
```

Cautions

Factor analysis only provides models of the world. By definition, models cannot capture the complexities of the real world. "At best, they can provide an approximation of the real world that has some substantive meaning and some utility" (MacCallum, 2003, p. 115). Therefore, the researcher should not fall prey to the nominalistic fallacy or the construct identity fallacy, nor should they reify factors (Cliff, 1983; Kline, 2013; Larsen & Bong, 2016). That is, believe that naming a factor means that the factor is a real physical entity, well understood, or even correctly named.

A basic premise of the philosophy of science is that data do not confirm a model, they can only fail to disconfirm it (Popper, 2012). Thus, "factor analysis is not an end in itself but a prelude to programmatic research on a particular psychological construct" (Briggs & Cheek, 1986, p. 137). Factor analysis addresses only one type of construct validity evidence: the internal structural aspect that "appraises the fidelity of the scoring structure to the structure of the construct domain" (Messick, 1995, p. 745). "Strong factorial evidence is necessary, but not sufficient, for establishing evidence of validity" (McCoach et al., 2013, p. 111).

The value of factors must be judged by their replicability across samples and methods and by the meaningfulness of their relationships with external criteria (Comrey & Lee, 1992; Goldberg & Velicer, 2006; Gorsuch, 1983; Mulaik, 2018; Nunnally & Bernstein, 1994; Preacher et al., 2013). Replication is critical because results that cannot be reproduced cannot contribute to the cumulative grown of knowledge necessary for scientific progress (Open Science Collaboration, 2015). Of course, replication with independent samples would be ideal but is not always possible. If the sample is sufficiently large, it can be randomly split into two samples and EFA results compared across those replication samples (Osborne & Fitzpatrick, 2012). A variety of cross-validation techniques that might be implemented with a single sample were presented by Koul et al. (2018). Absent replication, the researcher should employ alternative extraction and rotation methods to ensure that the EFA results are robust across those methods (Gorsuch, 1983).

It is essential that a construct validation program be implemented to delineate the external ramifications of replicated structural validity studies (Comrey & Lee, 1992; Goodwin, 1999; Gorsuch, 1983; Lubinski & Dawis, 1992; Rencher & Christensen, 2012). See Benson (1998) and Simms and Watson (2007) for tutorials on construct validation programs and Messick (1995) for a discussion of construct validity.

16

EXPLORATORY FACTOR ANALYSIS WITH CATEGORICAL VARIABLES

The measured variables in the original application of exploratory factor analysis (EFA) by Spearman (1904) were scores on tests of math, spelling, etc. Thus, each variable was the sum of multiple math or spelling items called a scale and EFA was developed for the analysis of such scales (Gorsuch, 1997). Scales are more reliable than items because they rely on the aggregation principle whereby common variance accumulates whereas measurement error, being random, does not (Lubinski & Dawis, 1992). Additionally, response options for items often take the form of a set of ordered categories rather than a continuous range of values. For ability and achievement items, responses may allow only two categories: correct or incorrect. For attitude items, 3- to 7-category Likert-type responses (*strongly agree* to *strongly disagree*) are often used with five alternatives the most common (Likert, 1932). These ordered categorical responses constitute ordinal variables (Stevens, 1946). The psychometric characteristics of items (compared to scales) require careful consideration when conducting an EFA (Gorsuch, 1997; Nunnally & Bernstein, 1994; Reise et al., 2000; Widaman, 2012).

Data

After importing the sdq.xls file, a new object will be displayed under the **Environment** tab. As imported, it is a table object containing 425 observations and 30 variables.

BOX 16.1   CONVERT TABLE OBJECT TO DATA FRAME OBJECT

```
## Convert sdq table to a data frame
> sdq=as.data.frame(sdq)
## Variables in sdq data frame made directly available
> attach(sdq)
```

That table object can be converted to a data frame and then the variables made directly available to **R**. For convenience, the data can be saved as an **R** Workspace through the menus: *Session* > *Save Workspace As* > *sdq.RData*. In the future, the sdq data frame can be accessed through the menus: *Session* > *Load Workspace* > *sdq.RData*.

Participants

Participants were 425 elementary school children. The communality of the variables under study is unknown, but prior international research and the ordinal nature of the response scale indicate that it would be reasonable to estimate communality to be in the low range (Mucherah & Finch, 2010). With 30 items and three anticipated factors, the number of items per factor is 10. Rouquette and Falissard (2011) simulated typical attitudinal scale data and reported that scales with that item to factor ratio required a sample of 350 to 400 participants. The ratio of participants to measured variables is 14 to 1, exceeding the recommendations of several measurement specialists (Child, 2006; Gorsuch, 1983). Given these considerations, the current sample size of 425 participants was judged to be adequate.

Data Screening

Pearson correlations assume normality, which requires continuous scores. Thus, categorical scores are not, by definition, normally distributed (Bandalos, 2018; Hancock & Liu, 2012; Puth et al., 2015; Walsh, 1996). In addition, categorization of continuous scores causes imprecise estimation of Pearson correlations. For example, Bollen and Barb (1981) used simulated data and demonstrated the effect of categorizing two continuous scores with a correlation of .90. As demonstrated in Figure 16.1 the reduction in precision is relatively modest for seven categories, falling from .90 to .85. However, the fewer the categories, the more imprecise the correlation estimates. With only two categories, the estimated correlation dropped to .72, a reduction of 20%. Additionally, the Pearsonian correlation for dichotomous items (phi) is strongly

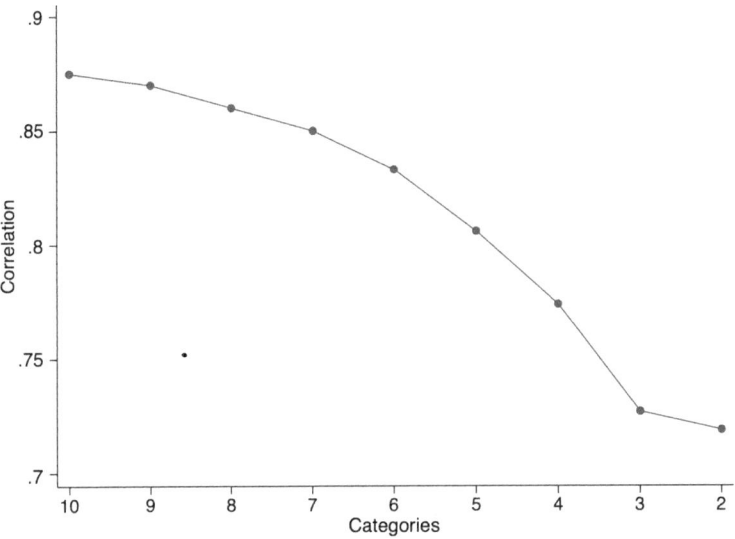

FIGURE 16.1   Effect on Correlation Coefficient of Categorizing Continuous Variables

influenced by differences in item endorsement frequencies. Rummel (1970) suggested deleting dichotomous variables with ≥ 90 to 10 splits between categories because the correlation coefficients between these variables and others are truncated and because the scores for the cases in the small category are more influential than those in the category with numerous cases. Of course, imprecise correlation estimates impact EFA results.

Given that EFA is conducted on a correlation matrix, it is important to utilize the optimal type of correlation for ordinal data. Bollen and Barb (1981) suggested "that under certain conditions it may be justifiable to use Pearson correlations and analyze categorical data as if it were continuous" (p. 232). Lozano et al. (2008) conducted a statistical simulation study and found that four response categories were minimal and seven optimal to ensure adequate factorial validity. Other methodologists have suggested the use of Pearson correlations when there are at least five ordered categories (DiStefano, 2002; Mueller & Hancock, 2019).

However, nonnormality, especially kurtosis, can bias Pearson correlation estimates and thereby bias EFA results (Cain et al., 2017; DeCarlo, 1997; Greer et al., 2006). The extent to which variables can be nonnormal and not substantially affect EFA results has been addressed by several researchers. Curran et al. (1996) opined that univariate skew should not exceed 2.0 and univariate kurtosis should not exceed 7.0. Other measurement specialists have agreed with those guidelines (Bandalos, 2018; Fabrigar et al., 1999; Wegener & Fabrigar, 2000). In terms of multinormality, multivariate kurtosis values > 3.0 to 5.0 might bias factor analysis results (Bentler, 2005; Finney & DiStefano, 2013; Mueller & Hancock, 2019). Thus, Pearson correlations might not be appropriate for ordinal data with five to seven categories if the variables are severely nonnormal.

In fact, some methodologists recommend that "it is often not appropriate to pretend that categorical variables are continuous" (Flora et al., 2012, p. 12) and have studied the characteristics of alternative types of correlation coefficients for factor analysis of ordinal data. These alternatives include the nonparametric correlations of Kendall and Spearman (Revelle, 2016) as well as polychoric and tetrachoric correlations (Basto & Pereira, 2012; Choi et al., 2010; McCoach et al., 2013). Polychoric correlations assume that a normally distributed continuous, but unobservable, latent variable underlies the observed ordinal variable and are a maximum likelihood estimate of the Pearson correlations for those underlying normally distributed continuous variables (Basto & Pereira, 2012). A tetrachoric correlation is a special case of the polychoric correlation applicable when the observed variables are dichotomous (Panter et al., 1997). Although some researchers prefer Spearman correlations for kurtotic distributions or when outliers are present (de Winter et al., 2016), factor analysis results based on polychoric correlations have better reproduced the measurement model than Pearson correlations (Barendse et al., 2015; Carroll, 1961; Choi et al., 2010; Flora et al., 2012; Flora & Flake, 2017; Holgado-Tello et al., 2012; Lloret et al., 2017; van der Eijk & Rose, 2015; Zhang & Browne, 2006). In fact, Flora and Curran (2004) found that polychoric correlations tended to be robust to violations of univariate nonnormality until nonnormality became extremely severe (skew = 5.0, kurtosis = 50.0). Nevertheless, polychoric correlations would not be appropriate if the assumption of an underlying normally distributed latent variable is not tenable.

Given the ordinal nature of the sdq data, it was anticipated that nonnormality would be readily apparent. Screening of the sdq data begins with a review of the univariate descriptive statistics. First, load the sdq data into RStudio through the **Session > Load Workspace > sdq.RData** menus. Next, make its variables directly available to **R** and enable the *psych* package.

BOX 16.2 DESCRIPTIVE STATISTICS FROM THE *PSYCH* PACKAGE

```
> attach(sdq)
> library(psych)
> describe(sdq)
        vars   n mean   sd median trimmed  mad min max range  skew kurtosis   se
sdq1       1 425 4.17 1.80      5    4.33 1.48   1   6     5 -0.57    -1.06 0.09
sdq2       2 425 4.83 1.37      5    5.07 1.48   1   6     5 -1.20     0.70 0.07
sdq3       3 425 4.82 1.42      5    5.03 1.48   1   6     5 -0.96    -0.20 0.07
sdq4r      4 425 3.82 1.92      4    3.90 2.97   1   6     5 -0.24    -1.49 0.09
sdq5r      5 425 5.32 1.27      6    5.63 0.00   1   6     5 -1.95     2.85 0.06
sdq6       6 425 4.00 1.81      4    4.13 2.97   1   6     5 -0.45    -1.18 0.09
sdq7       7 425 4.05 1.80      4    4.19 2.97   1   6     5 -0.48    -1.14 0.09
sdq8       8 425 4.77 1.38      5    5.01 1.48   1   6     5 -1.21     0.79 0.07
sdq9r      9 425 4.86 1.58      6    5.16 0.00   1   6     5 -1.27     0.37 0.08
sdq10r    10 425 4.79 1.58      6    5.07 0.00   1   6     5 -1.16     0.12 0.08
sdq11r    11 425 5.02 1.29      6    5.26 0.00   1   6     5 -1.39     1.26 0.06
sdq12     12 425 4.44 1.48      5    4.62 1.48   1   6     5 -0.83    -0.23 0.07
sdq13     13 425 3.85 1.87      4    3.93 2.97   1   6     5 -0.31    -1.35 0.09
sdq14     14 425 4.77 1.38      5    5.02 1.48   1   6     5 -1.28     0.99 0.07
sdq15r    15 425 5.14 1.46      6    5.48 0.00   1   6     5 -1.65     1.48 0.07
sdq16r    16 425 4.30 1.80      5    4.49 1.48   1   6     5 -0.67    -0.97 0.09
sdq17r    17 425 4.96 1.59      6    5.30 0.00   1   6     5 -1.44     0.76 0.08
sdq18     18 425 4.19 1.79      5    4.36 1.48   1   6     5 -0.57    -1.04 0.09
sdq19     19 425 4.24 1.69      5    4.42 1.48   1   6     5 -0.62    -0.88 0.08
sdq20     20 425 4.81 1.45      5    5.08 1.48   1   6     5 -1.26     0.72 0.07
sdq21r    21 425 5.04 1.53      6    5.38 0.00   1   6     5 -1.52     1.06 0.07
sdq22r    22 425 4.87 1.66      6    5.20 0.00   1   6     5 -1.33     0.40 0.08
sdq23r    23 425 5.13 1.47      6    5.47 0.00   1   6     5 -1.66     1.58 0.07
sdq24     24 425 4.46 1.55      5    4.68 1.48   1   6     5 -0.87    -0.24 0.08
sdq25     25 425 3.97 1.78      4    4.08 1.48   1   6     5 -0.47    -1.16 0.09
sdq26     26 425 5.52 1.01      6    5.77 0.00   1   6     5 -2.76     8.14 0.05
sdq27r    27 425 3.82 1.88      4    3.90 2.97   1   6     5 -0.17    -1.50 0.09
sdq28r    28 425 4.68 1.76      6    4.98 0.00   1   6     5 -1.03    -0.41 0.09
sdq29r    29 425 5.58 0.96      6    5.84 0.00   1   6     5 -2.59     6.26 0.05
sdq30     30 425 4.71 1.45      5    4.96 1.48   1   6     5 -1.11     0.36 0.07
```

The minimum and maximum values all items range from one to six, indicating no illegal values. There is no missing data as the *n* for each item is 425. The mean and median values are high (many in the five to six range for a scale with a maximum score of six). Univariate skew reflects that distributional tilt. Several variables exhibited high skew and kurtosis (-2.76 and 8.14, respectively), indicating univariate nonnormality.

BOX 16.3 MULTIVARIATE NORMALITY AND OUTLIER IDENTIFICATION FROM THE *PSYCH* PACKAGE

```
> mardia(sdq,na.rm=TRUE, plot=TRUE)
Mardia tests of multivariate skew and kurtosis
Use describe(x) the to get univariate tests
n.obs = 425   num.vars =   30
b1p = 168.94   skew = 11966.43  with probability =  0
  small sample skew = 12056.38  with probability =  0
b2p = 1202.42   kurtosis =   57.03  with probability =  0
## Outlier identification through D2 in psych package
> out=outlier(sdq,bad=5,cex=.5,plot=T,na.rm=TRUE,bg=c("blue"),
  pch=21,ylab="D2",ylim=c(0,100))
## The D2 value of each case can be printed if desired
> print(out,digits=3)
```

As expected from the univariate distributions, the data are not multivariate normal with Mardia's kurtosis $= 1202.42$ ($p < .001$). Thus, a polychoric correlation matrix might be more appropriate for this data because a Pearson correlation matrix could bias EFA results.

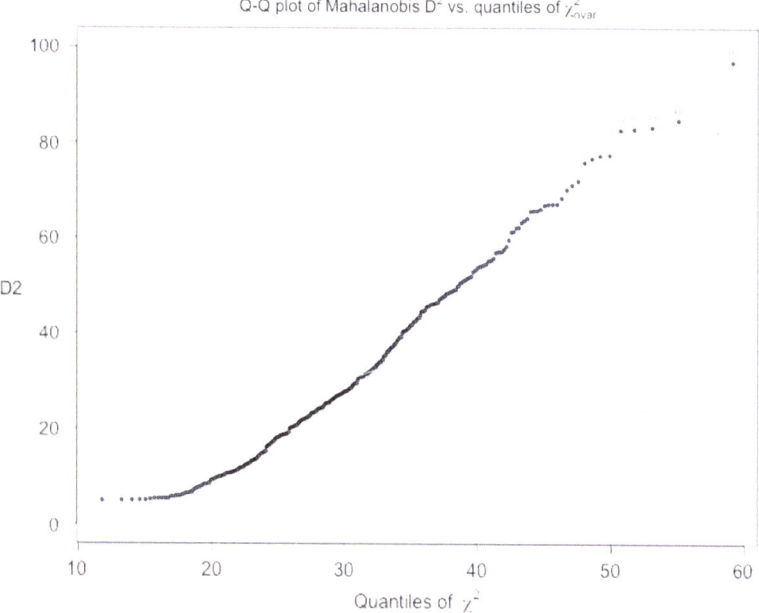

FIGURE 16.2   Mahalanobis Distance (D^2) Plot to Identify Potential Outliers in SDQ Data

Although several cases might be outliers (see Figure 16.2), none of the values are illegal or out of bounds so they will be retained. Given that these are ordinal data, it might be useful to view frequency distributions or cross-tabulations of responses (McCoach et al., 2013). Although each item has six response options, it is possible that the participants never selected one or more options, effectively reducing the actual number of response options (empirical underidentification).

BOX 16.4   FREQUENCY AND CROSS-TABS FOR ORDINAL DATA

```
## Frequency distribution of a single variable
> table(sdq1)
sdq1
   1    2    3    4    5    6
  62   25   62   51   80  145
  17   18   33   63  114  180
  11   24   56   53   78  203
:::::::::::::::::::::::::::
  44   27   34   39   51  230
   1   15    7   23   48  331
  24   20   33   69  111  168
## Cross tabulation of 2 items
> xtabs(~sdq1+sdq30,data=sdq)
     sdq30
sdq1   1   2   3   4   5   6
   1   0   4   4  10  12  32
   2   0   1   2   3   6  13
   3   2   2   7   8  20  23
   4   5   0   5  12  13  16
   5   4   7   3  11  22  33
   6  13   6  12  25  38  51
```

Items 26 and 29 had few responses for some categories, but both had at least one participant for all six options. If desired, more intelligible tables can be obtained from the CrossTable procedure within the *gmodels* package.

Ordinal scale data is often obtained from surveys that rely on respondents to provide honest and thoughtful answers. Thus, it is assumed that respondents were motivated to respond accurately and thoughtfully about their self-concept on the SDQ. Unfortunately, that assumption may not be correct and participants may provide invalid responses due to linguistic incompetence, deliberate misrepresentation, or careless inattentiveness (Curran, 2016). Linguistic incompetence is related to how the scale was constructed and its proper application to a specific sample. For example, asking preschool children to respond to a written self-concept scale would likely produce invalid responses because most of them cannot read. Misrepresentation typically involves respondents cheating or faking (either good or bad), usually on high-stakes tests or surveys (Curran, 2016) whereas carelessness is the result of responding without consideration of the content of the items (Dunn et al., 2018).

A variety of screening techniques have been developed to detect invalid responses (Curran, 2016; DeSimone et al., 2015; Dunn et al., 2018) and are included in the *careless* package.

BOX 16.5 DETECT INVALID RESPONSES WITH THE *CARELESS* PACKAGE

```
## Download & activate the careless package & activate the psych package
> library(careless)
> library(psych)
## Compute the standard deviation of all responses for each participant,
the IRV
> irv = irv(sdq)
## Display descriptive statistics of the IRV
> describe (irv)
   vars   n mean   sd median trimmed  mad min  max range  skew kurtosis
se
X1    1 425 1.44 0.47   1.47    1.46 0.49   0 2.49  2.49 -0.44    -0.05
0.02
## For each case, the average and maximum number of identical responses.
> longstring(sdq,avg=TRUE)
    longstr    avgstr
1         4  1.666667
2         3  1.111111
::::::::::::::::::::::
57       30 30.000000
::::::::::::::::::::::
423       4  1.578947
424       4  1.304348
425       5  1.764706
```

There are also several measures of internal response reliability available from the *careless* package. Unfortunately, there are no normative standards for the screening techniques provided by the *careless* package and each technique "has pros and cons, and is designed to identify a different *type* of invalid data" (Curran, 2016, p. 16). Accordingly, multiple techniques should be used to identify individual cases (Dunn et al., 2018; Curran, 2016) "for deeper examination, thoughtful consideration, and transparent exclusion or inclusion" (Curran, 2016, p. 17).

The irv and longstring commands identified four participants who selected the most positive response option to all 30 SDQ items (i.e., participants 57, 167, 244, and 295), suggesting the possibility of impression management (Curran, 2016). Thus, these four participants might be deleted. However, as with continuous data (Bandalos & Finney, 2019; Leys et al., 2018; Tabachnick & Fidell, 2019; Thompson, 2004), results with and without the outlier data should be reported (Curran, 2016; DeSimone et al., 2015; Dunn et al., 2018). Inconsistent results may raise questions about the scale or the sample whereas consistent results will allow greater confidence in the results. In this case, results did not differ when the four discrepant cases were deleted so the full data set is retained for subsequent analyses.

Given the ordinal scale and nonnormal data, polychoric correlations will be used as input for the EFA (Flora & Curran, 2004; Flora & Flake, 2017; Lloret et al., 2017; McCoach et al., 2013).

BOX 16.6   POLYCHORIC CORRELATIONS FROM THE *PSYCH* PACKAGE

```
## Convert raw data to polychoric correlation matrix for EFA analysis
> out=polychoric(sdq)
## Extract polychoric matrix from the out object
> sdqpoly=out$rho
Warning message:  313 cells were adjusted for 0 values using the
correction for continuity. Examine your data carefully.
## If desired, print sdq polychoric matrix for review
> print(sdqpoly,digits=3)
## Warning of sparseness, meaning that many contingency tables had low
## frequency cells
## Create a Pearson corr matrix to allow comparison of results
> sdqcor=cor(sdq)
```

The warning of sparseness (contingency tables with zero frequency cells) is relatively common with skewed data (Flora et al., 2012) and will be ignored in this case.

Is EFA Appropriate

The correlation matrix can be visually scanned to ensure that there are several coefficients ≥ .30 (Hair et al., 2019; Tabachnick & Fidell, 2019). Given the laborious nature of a scan of the 30 × 30 correlation matrix, a graph from the *qgraph* package might again be generated   (Figure 16.3). The *qgraph* graph displays the polychoric correlations above .30 with lines widening as the correlations increase.

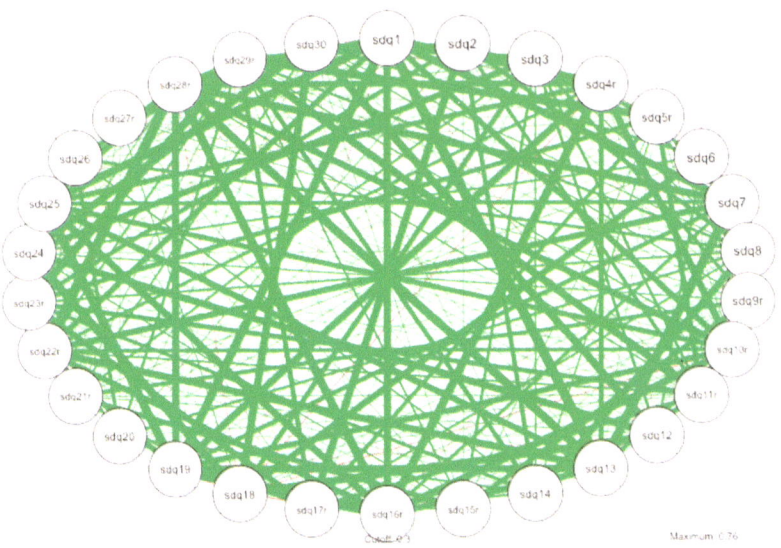

FIGURE 16.3   Visualizing Correlation Coefficients ≥ .30 in SDQ Data

BOX 16.7   CORRELATION GRAPH FROM THE *QGRAPH* PACKAGE

```
## graph correlation matrix with qgraph package to visualize
correlations > .30
> library(qgraph)
> qgraph(sdqpoly,cut=.30,details=TRUE,posCol="darkgreen",negCol="red",
  labels=names(sdq))
```

An alternative visual illustration with more detail about the size of the correlation coefficients can be generated by a correlation plot from the *psych* package as demonstrated in Figure 16.4.

BOX 16.8   CORRELATION PLOT FROM THE *PSYCH* PACKAGE

```
## correlation plot from the psych package to see correlations > .30
> corPlot(sdqpoly,diag=F,zlim=c(.3,1),upper=F,numbers=TRUE,cex.axis=.5)
```

This graph visually depicts many coefficients ≥ .30 and none that exceeded .90 (Tabachnick & Fidell, 2019). The Kaiser-Meyer-Olkin (KMO) measure of sampling adequacy (Kaiser, 1974) and Bartlett's test of sphericity (1950) were computed with procedures included in the *psych* package.

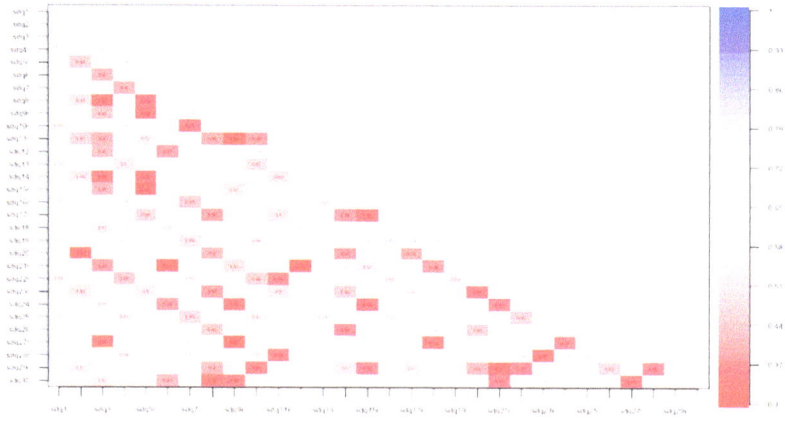

FIGURE 16.4 Correlation Plot of SDQ Data

BOX 16.9 KMO AND BARTLETT'S TEST FROM THE *PSYCH* PACKAGE

```
> KMO(sdqpoly)
Kaiser-Meyer-Olkin factor adequacy
Overall MSA =  0.87
MSA for each item =
  sdq1   sdq2   sdq3  sdq4r  sdq5r   sdq6   sdq7   sdq8  sdq9r sdq10r sdq11r  sdq12
sdq13  sdq14
  0.89   0.88   0.87   0.87   0.88   0.76   0.86   0.86   0.86   0.88   0.90   0.89
 0.89   0.85
sdq15r sdq16r sdq17r  sdq18  sdq19  sdq20 sdq21r sdq22r sdq23r  sdq24  sdq25  sdq26
sdq27r sdq28r
  0.87   0.88   0.83   0.82   0.91   0.87   0.83   0.88   0.84   0.90   0.93   0.87
 0.79   0.90
sdq29r  sdq30
  0.87   0.88
> cortest.bartlett(sdqpoly,n=425)
$chisq [1] 7956.61                     $p.value [1] 0                     $df [1] 435
## Robustness of results can be verified with Pearson matrix if desired
> KMO(sdqcor)
Overall MSA =  0.88
:::::::::::::::::::::::::::::::::::::::::::::::::::::::::::::::::::::::::::::::::::::
::::::::
> cortest.bartlett(sdqcor,n=425)
$chisq [1] 5346.271                    $p.value [1] 0                     $df [1] 435
```

The KMO measure of sampling adequacy (Kaiser, 1974) was acceptable (.87 for the total group of variables and .76 to .93 for each of the measured variables). Similar results were obtained when the Pearson correlation matrix was substituted for the polychoric matrix. Bartlett's test of sphericity (1950) statistically rejected the hypothesis that the correlation matrix was an identity matrix (chi-square of 7956.61 with 435 degrees of freedom) at $p < .001$. Altogether, these measures indicated that the both polychoric and Pearson correlation matrices are appropriate for EFA (Hair et al., 2019; Tabachnick & Fidell, 2019).

Factor Analysis Model

The purpose of this study was to uncover the latent structure underlying the 30 SDQ items. Accordingly, a common factor model (EFA) was selected (Widaman, 2018).

Factor Extraction Method

Maximum likelihood estimation can be biased in the presence of multivariate non-normality. Therefore, an estimation method with greater computational robustness and reduced sensitivity to nonnormality would be preferred (Barendse et al., 2015; Cudeck, 2000; Lee et al., 2012; Rhemtulla et al., 2012; Zhang & Browne, 2006). Accordingly, iterated principal axis extraction was conducted with initial communalities estimated by squared multiple correlations (Tabachnick & Fidell, 2019).

How Many Factors to Retain

As before, empirical guidelines include parallel analysis, minimal average partials (MAP), and scree (Velicer et al., 2000). Empirical criteria are tested on the polychoric matrix because MAP with polychoric correlations may be more accurate than with Pearson correlations (Garrido et al., 2011). However, parallel analysis with Pearson correlations has been shown to perform well with ordinal data so all criteria were repeated with the Pearson matrix to verify the robustness of results (Cho et al., 2009; Garrido et al., 2013).

BOX 16.10 PARALLEL ANALYSIS, MAP, AND SCREE PLOT FROM THE *PSYCH* PACKAGE

```
## Number of factors to retain for interpretation
## Parallel analysis
> fa.parallel(sdqpoly,n.obs=425,fa="pc",n.iter=500)
Parallel analysis suggests that the number of factors =  NA  and the
number of components =  4
## MAP
> VSS(sdqpoly,rotate="promax",fm="pc",plot=FALSE,n.obs=425)
The Velicer MAP achieves a minimum of 0.02  with  4  factors
## Visual scree plot
> scree(sdqpoly,pc=TRUE,factors=FALSE,hline="-1",main="Scree Plot")
## Check for consistency of results using sdqcor object instead of
## sdqpoly object
> fa.parallel(sdqcor,n.obs=425,fa="pc",n.iter=500)
Parallel analysis suggests that the number of factors =  NA  and the
number of components =  4
> VSS(sdqcor,rotate="promax",fm="pc",plot=FALSE,n.obs=425)
The Velicer MAP achieves a minimum of 0.01  with  4  factors
```

Both parallel analysis and MAP indicated that four factors would be sufficient with identical results for polychoric and Pearson correlation matrices.

As often happens, the scree plot is somewhat ambiguous (Mulaik, 2018; Streiner, 1998). It might indicate as many as six factors or as few as four factors (Figure 16.5).

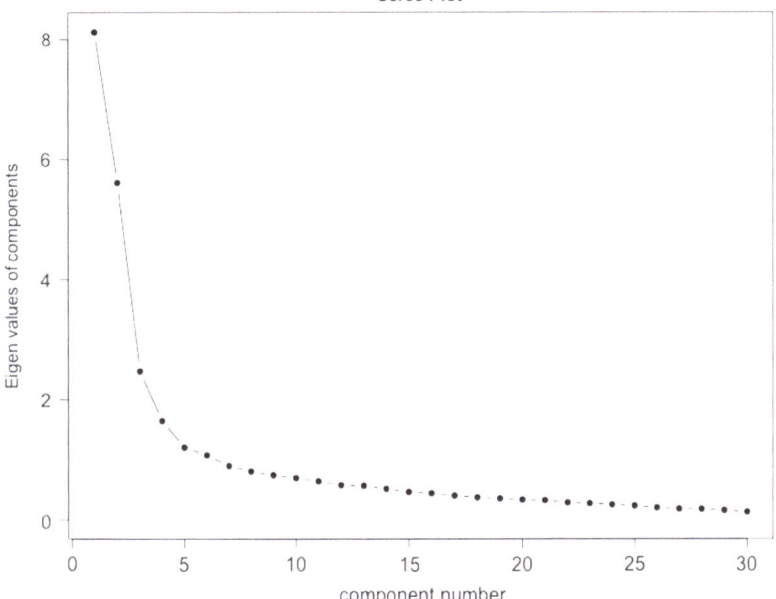

FIGURE 16.5   Scree Plot for SDQ Data

Although it has not been subjected to much empirical evaluation, it might be interesting to see the results from an innovation network graphing method (Golino & Epskamp, 2017; Golino et al., 2020). This requires the *EGAnet* package via **Packages > Install** in RStudio.

BOX 16.11   NETWORK GRAPH FROM THE *EGANET* PACKAGE

```
## download network graph package(EGAnet)
## Activate EGAnet package and generate network graph
> library(EGAnet)
> EGA(sdqpoly,n=425,plot.EGA=TRUE,steps=10)
```

The resulting network graph (Figure 16.6) suggested that three factors would be sufficient.

The instrument was designed to measure three dimensions of self-concept. Therefore, models with six (the largest estimate, obtained from the visual scree), five, four, and three factors will be sequentially evaluated for their interpretability and theoretical meaningfulness (Preacher et al., 2013).

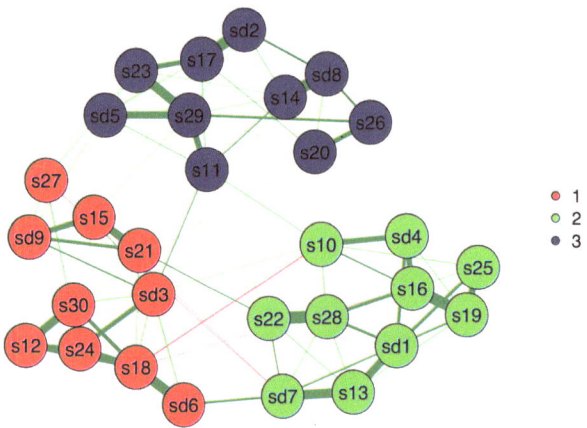

FIGURE 16.6   Network Graph of SDQ Data

Rotate Factors

An oblique rotation was selected because it honors the ubiquity of inter-correlations among social science variables (Meehl, 1990). Among the potential oblique analytic rotations, "promax rotation is almost always a good choice" (Thompson, 2004, p. 43).

Interpret Results

Given the oblique rotation, pattern coefficients and factor intercorrelations will receive primary attention during the model evaluation process (Bandalos, 2018; Hair et al., 2019). To ensure both practical (10% variance) and statistical ($p < .01$) significance of pattern loadings, the threshold for salience will be set at .32 (Norman & Streiner, 2014) with a goal of approximate simple structure (Thurstone, 1947). This threshold seems reasonable given that a meta-analysis of EFA outcomes found that the average factor loading of ordinal data was around .32 (Peterson, 2000).

The four models will be compared on the root mean squared residual (RMSR), which is a measure of overall residual misfit, as well as the proportion of residual coefficients that exceed absolute values of .10. The smaller the RMSR value the better, with values ≤ .08 preferred (Brown, 2015). Likewise, the proportion of non-redundant residual correlations greater than the absolute value of .10 should be small (Finch, 2013).

The alpha reliability of scales created from the salient variables of each factor should reach .80 given that the intended use of these variables is for group re-search (DeVellis, 2017). Finally, each model will be examined for symptoms of overextraction such as inadmissible solutions, fewer than three salient loadings, technical factors, etc. as well as for symptoms of underextraction such as no common unifying theme, many complex loadings, etc. (Bandalos, 2018; Fabrigar & Wegener, 2012).

The six-, and five-factor models converged properly and produced reasonable parameter estimates. However, both models exhibited symptoms of over-extraction. For example, the final factor in the six-factor model was saliently loaded by four items but all four were complex with higher loadings on other factors. Likewise, the final factor in the five-factor model was saliently loaded by three items but all three were complex with higher loadings on other factors.

BOX 16.12 ALPHA RELIABILITY ESTIMATES FROM THE *PSYCH* PACKAGE

```
## alpha reliability of final factor of Model 6
> final = data.frame(sdq22r,sdq6,sdq7,sdq28r)
> alpha(final)
lower alpha upper     95% confidence boundaries
 0.6 0.66 0.71
## alpha reliability of final factor of Model 5
> final = data.frame(sdq13,sdq7,sdq6,sdq22r)
> alpha(final)
 lower alpha upper     95% confidence boundaries
  0.62 0.67 0.72
```

The alpha reliability of the final factors in these models was .66 and .67. Given these weak factors, these two models were not considered plausible.

Similarly, the final factor in the four-factor model was saliently loaded by four items but two were complex and the alpha reliability of this 4–item scale was only .67. One item failed to saliently load on any factor (displayed in Box 16.13 in bold red). The items containing math and general self-concept content consistently cohered across these three models whereas the items designed to tap verbal self-concept tended to split into reading versus English groupings. This is a potential indicator of overextraction and suggested that the three-factor model might be more appropriate.

BOX 16.13 EFA WITH FOUR FACTORS FROM THE *PSYCH* PACKAGE

```
## Extract and display 4 factors
> f4=fa(sdqpoly,nfactors=4,rotate="promax",residuals=T,SMC=T,
  fm="pa",n.obs=425)
> print(f4,sort=TRUE,cut=0,digits=3)
Standardized loadings (pattern matrix) based upon correlation matrix
        item    PA1    PA3    PA2    PA4    h2    u2   com
sdq1      1   0.885 -0.014  0.008 -0.139 0.755 0.245 1.05
sdq13    13   0.837  0.065  0.178 -0.231 0.715 0.285 1.26
sdq19    19   0.827 -0.102 -0.071  0.100 0.675 0.325 1.08
::::::::::::::::::::::::::::::::::::::::::::::::::::::::::::
sdq3      3  -0.022  0.109  0.451  0.358 0.516 0.484 2.04
sdq15r   15  -0.045  0.053  0.017  0.703 0.530 0.470 1.02
sdq9r     9   0.041 -0.017  0.160  0.603 0.448 0.552 1.15
sdq21r   21   0.050 -0.051  0.320  0.457 0.380 0.620 1.85
sdq27r   27  -0.007  0.102  0.221  0.302 0.237 0.763 2.10

                         PA1    PA3    PA2    PA4
SS loadings            5.949  4.522  3.472  2.119
Proportion Var         0.198  0.151  0.116  0.071
Cumulative Var         0.198  0.349  0.465  0.535
Proportion Explained   0.370  0.282  0.216  0.132
Cumulative Proportion  0.370  0.652  0.868  1.000
::::::::::::::::::::::::::::::::::::::::::::::::::::::::
The root mean square of the residuals (RMSR) is   0.044

## Polychoric correlation can be specified in fa command if desired
## Rather than creating a polychoric matrix as above
> f4=fa(sdq,nfactors=4,rotate="promax",residuals=T,SMC=T,fm="pa",
  n.obs=425,cor="poly")
> print(f4,sort=TRUE,cut=0,digits=3)
Standardized loadings (pattern matrix) based upon correlation matrix
        item    PA1    PA3    PA2    PA4    h2    u2   com
sdq1      1   0.885 -0.014  0.008 -0.139 0.755 0.245 1.05
sdq13    13   0.837  0.065  0.178 -0.231 0.715 0.285 1.26
sdq19    19   0.827 -0.102 -0.071  0.100 0.675 0.325 1.08
::::::::::::::::::::::::::::::::::::::::::::::::::::::::::::
sdq3      3  -0.022  0.109  0.451  0.358 0.516 0.484 2.04
sdq15r   15  -0.045  0.053  0.017  0.703 0.530 0.470 1.02
sdq9r     9   0.041 -0.017  0.160  0.603 0.448 0.552 1.15
sdq21r   21   0.050 -0.051  0.320  0.457 0.380 0.620 1.85
sdq27r   27  -0.007  0.102  0.221  0.302 0.237 0.763 2.10
```

The three-factor model was consistent with the theoretical underpinning of the scale with the exception of one item (sdq27r) that failed to saliently load on any factor. In total, more than 80% of the loadings were good to excellent in magnitude (Comrey & Lee, 1992) in a simple structure configuration. Interfactor correlations were low enough to pose no threat to discriminant validity (Brown, 2015) and the factors exhibited alpha reliability coefficients of .91 for the math self-concept factor, .83 for the general self-concept factor, and .82 for the verbal self-concept factor.

BOX 16.14   EFA WITH THREE FACTORS FROM THE *PSYCH* PACKAGE

```
## Extract and display 3 factors
> f3=fa(sdqpoly,nfactors=3,rotate="promax",residuals=T,SMC=T,
  fm="pa",n.obs=425)
> print(f3,sort=TRUE,cut=0,digits=3)
Factor Analysis using method =  pa
Standardized loadings (pattern matrix) based upon correlation matrix
         item    PA1     PA3    PA2    h2    u2   com
sdq1        1  0.882 -0.073 -0.050 0.742 0.258 1.02
sdq19      19  0.838 -0.064 -0.030 0.669 0.331 1.01
sdq28r     28  0.820  0.092 -0.062 0.731 0.269 1.04
sdq13      13  0.815 -0.046  0.081 0.645 0.355 1.03
sdq16r     16  0.808  0.000 -0.074 0.656 0.344 1.02
sdq25      25  0.763 -0.057 -0.005 0.554 0.446 1.01
sdq4r       4  0.718 -0.021 -0.073 0.510 0.490 1.02
sdq7        7  0.703  0.100  0.083 0.454 0.546 1.07
sdq22r     22  0.688  0.072  0.113 0.538 0.462 1.08
sdq10r     10  0.604  0.219 -0.075 0.497 0.503 1.29
sdq17r     17 -0.103  0.845 -0.203 0.533 0.467 1.15
sdq29r     29  0.034  0.840 -0.070 0.675 0.325 1.02
sdq23r     23  0.000  0.763 -0.126 0.503 0.497 1.05
sdq2        2 -0.104  0.751 -0.045 0.487 0.513 1.05
sdq5r       5  0.037  0.695 -0.093 0.448 0.552 1.04
sdq11r     11  0.072  0.669  0.034 0.512 0.488 1.03
sdq14      14 -0.014  0.626  0.033 0.407 0.593 1.01
sdq8        8 -0.083  0.572  0.141 0.399 0.601 1.16
sdq26      26  0.062  0.452  0.051 0.254 0.746 1.06
sdq20      20  0.054  0.434  0.122 0.275 0.725 1.19
sdq15r     15 -0.013  0.295  0.289 0.252 0.748 2.00
sdq18      18 -0.059 -0.244  0.940 0.729 0.271 1.14
sdq24      24 -0.044 -0.062  0.811 0.614 0.386 1.02
sdq30      30 -0.065 -0.032  0.807 0.631 0.369 1.02
sdq12      12 -0.056 -0.084  0.749 0.510 0.490 1.04
sdq6        6  0.050 -0.141  0.612 0.307 0.693 1.12
sdq3        3 -0.018  0.171  0.609 0.500 0.500 1.16
sdq21r     21  0.059  0.073  0.505 0.304 0.696 1.07
sdq9r       9  0.059  0.181  0.393 0.270 0.730 1.46
sdq27r     27  0.000  0.177  0.349 0.215 0.785 1.48

                          PA1   PA3   PA2
SS loadings             5.937 4.779 4.105
Proportion Var          0.198 0.159 0.137
Cumulative Var          0.198 0.357 0.494
Proportion Explained    0.401 0.322 0.277
Cumulative Proportion   0.401 0.723 1.000

 With factor correlations of
        PA1   PA3   PA2
PA1 1.000 0.363 0.019
PA3 0.363 1.000 0.495
PA2 0.019 0.495 1.000

The root mean square of the residuals (RMSR) is  0.057
## Display the structure matrix if desired
> print(sort=TRUE,digits=3,cut=0,f3$Structure)
## Display the initial eigenvalues from a PCA
> print(digits=3,cut=0,f3$e.values)
 [1] 8.118 5.612 2.473 1.642 1.199 1.070 0.893 0.800 0.738 0.691 0.637 0.571 0.563 0.511 0.457
[16] 0.436 0.395 0.366 0.346 0.328 0.317 0.279 0.268 0.247 0.228 0.195 0.176 0.172 0.151 0.124
## Display the initial eigenvalues from an EFA
> print(digits=3,cut=0,f3$values)
 [1]  7.6438  5.1681  2.0085  1.0275  0.6214  0.4802  0.3444  0.2888  0.1782  0.1364  0.1156
[12]  0.0807  0.0296 -0.0113 -0.0380 -0.0517 -0.0846 -0.1006 -0.1117 -0.1307 -0.1768 -0.1865
[23] -0.1914 -0.2516 -0.2684 -0.2890 -0.3055 -0.3532 -0.3587 -0.3927
```

Prior to rotation, the first factor explained 25.5% of the total variance and 51.6% of the common variance; the second factor explained 17.2% of the total variance and 34.9% of the common variance; and the third factor explained 6.7% of the total variance and 13.6% of the common variance. Altogether, the three factors accounted for 49.4% of the total variance. This three-factor structure was robust to rotation method (promax and oblimin) as well as extraction method (iterated principal axis and ordinary least squares). Additionally, results did not differ when the Pearson correlation matrix was submitted to EFA.

BOX 16.15 ANALYSIS OF RESIDUALS FROM THE *PSYCH* PACKAGE

```
## Extract and display the residual matrix if desired
> resd=residuals(f3,diag=FALSE,na.rm=TRUE)
> print(resd,digits=3)
## Display a histogram of the residuals
> hist(resd,col="maroon",main="",xlab="Residuals")
## Compute number and % of large residuals
> BigR=sum(resd>abs(.10),na.rm=T)
> print(BigR)
[1] 32
## Total number of off-diagonal elements in the data matrix
> totR=length(sdq)*(length(sdq)-1)/2
> print(totR)
[1] 435
## Proportion of off-diagonal elements > .05 in residual matrix
print((BigR/totR)*100)
[1] 7.356322
## Largest residual in residual matrix
> print(max(abs(resd),na.rm=TRUE),digits=3)
[1] 0.267
```

Analysis of the residuals matrices for the candidate models indicated that the root mean square of residuals was .031 for the six-factor model, .036 for the five-factor model, .044 for the four-factor model, and .057 for the three-factor model. All met the guideline of ≤ .08 (Brown, 2015).

More than 7% of the residuals were above the absolute value of .10 in the three-factor model (Figure 16.7), and examination of their pattern suggested three plausible explanations. First, the item that loaded equally on two factors was a source of misfit. Second, given the content of this and other items, children in elementary school may see reading proficiency as central to their general self-concept rather than a specific academic self-concept attribute. Thus, a smaller reading self-concept factor might emerge if more reading items were included. Finally, the mixture of positively and negatively worded items may be responsible because they are known to disrupt the pattern of correlations and thereby create artifactual factors (Spector et al., 1997). With these caveats, the three-factor solution appears to be the most acceptable solution.

A potential criticism of the scale in its entirety is the possibility of what Cattell (1978) called a "bloated specific". That is, items that are virtual paraphrases of each other. For example: "Do badly on math tests" and "Bad grades in math" might be perceived by young children as essentially the same question. Factors created by boated specifics are narrow and unlikely to replicate (de Winter et al.,

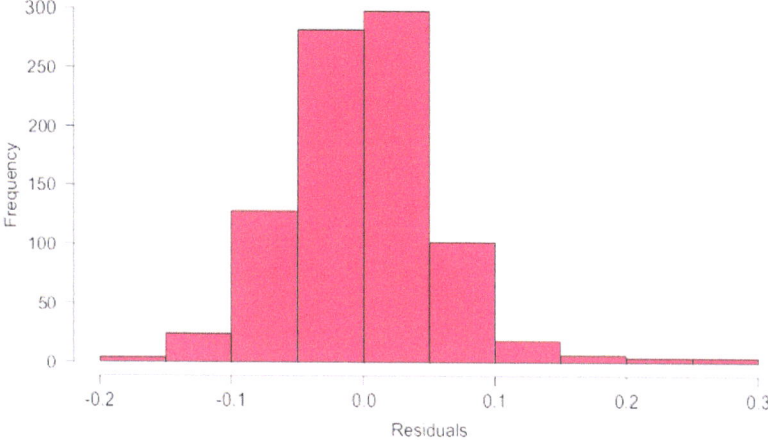

FIGURE 16.7   Histogram of Residuals of the Three-factor Model

2009). Likewise, factors created by combining items with similar vocabulary (e.g., math, reading, English) might be too narrow and unlikely to replicate (Gorsuch, 1997; Podsakoff et al., 2012). These sources of "hidden invalidity" should be considered (Hussey & Hughes, 2020, p. 166).

17

HIGHER-ORDER AND BIFACTOR MODELS

Higher-Order Models

There are situations where constructs of different conceptual breadth exist and should, therefore, be reflected in the factor model. For example, the concept of general intelligence is currently assumed to subsume narrower group factors which, in turn, subsume even narrower abilities as illustrated in Figure 17.1 (Carroll, 1993). This model reflects the theoretical belief that intelligence is comprised of subdimensions.

In this simple higher-order model (Figure 17.1), factor one through three are first-order factors (group factors) responsible for the intercorrelations of their indicator variables whereas g is a broad general factor responsible for the intercorrelations of the first-order factors.

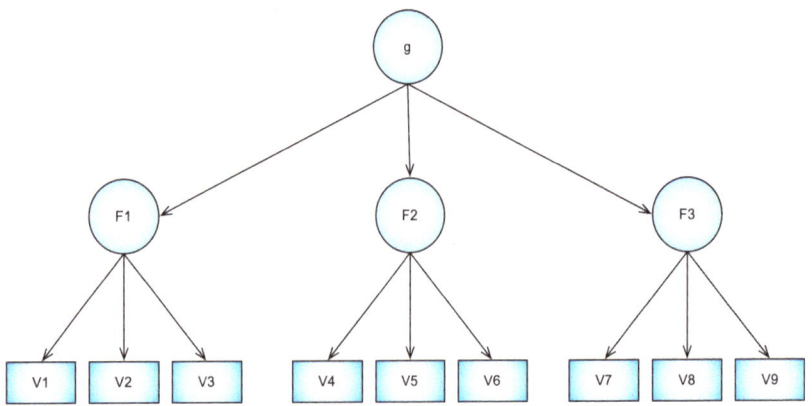

FIGURE 17.1 Simplified Higher-order Factor Model

Gorsuch (1988) maintained that "correlated factors imply the existence of higher-order factors" (p. 250) and higher-order models have been advanced as a solution for the misinterpretation of rotated factors (Carretta & Ree, 2001). When factors are rotated, variance from the first factor is distributed across the remaining factors and seems to strengthen those factors. In actuality, variance from the first factor has simply become a major source of variance in the new rotated factors. This can lead to a mistaken interpretation about the relative importance of the factors (Gignac, 2007). Similar opinions were expressed by Carroll (1983, 1989). Some researchers object to the use of exploratory factor analysis (EFA) for higher-order analyses (Osborne & Banjanovic, 2016). However, EFA higher-order models are often encountered in the research literature (e.g., Canivez & Watkins, 2010; Watkins, 2006) and should be utilized if congruous with theory (Gorsuch, 1983; Thompson, 2004).

A second-order factor analysis can be conduced with the first-order factor correlation matrix as input and should be based on at least three first-order factors for identification. This requirement rules out the iq data used in the previous example. Likewise, the sdq data is not appropriate because there is no theoretical expectation of a broader general factor (Marsh, 1990). However, there are several datasets within the *psych* package that could be used as examples.

BOX 17.1   HOLZINGER.9 DATASET FROM THE *PSYCH* PACKAGE

```
## Load dataset from psych package into RStudio
## Holzinger (1937) 9x9 correlation matrix with N = 145
## 3 spatial tests, 3 verbal tests, and 3 mental speed tests
> library(psych)
> data("Holzinger.9")
## 3 factor solution
> f3=fa(Holzinger.9,nfactors=3,rotate="promax",residuals=T,missing=F,
  fm="pa",n.obs=145)
> print(f3,cut=0,digits=3)
Standardized loadings (pattern matrix) based upon correlation matrix
             PA1     PA2     PA3    h2    u2   com
vis perc    0.048   0.056   0.632 0.466 0.534 1.03
cubes      -0.026  -0.056   0.556 0.274 0.726 1.02
lozenges    0.046  -0.074   0.716 0.505 0.495 1.03
par comp    0.860  -0.048   0.051 0.757 0.243 1.01
sen comp    0.825   0.093  -0.044 0.702 0.298 1.03
wordmean    0.812  -0.057   0.060 0.680 0.320 1.02
addition    0.114   0.806  -0.248 0.586 0.414 1.23
count dot  -0.159   0.814   0.125 0.688 0.312 1.13
s c caps    0.036   0.478   0.370 0.541 0.459 1.90

                       PA1    PA2    PA3
SS loadings          2.148  1.566  1.485
Proportion Var       0.239  0.174  0.165
Cumulative Var       0.239  0.413  0.578
Proportion Explained 0.413  0.301  0.286
Cumulative Proportion 0.413 0.714  1.000

 With factor correlations of
      PA1    PA2    PA3
PA1 1.000 0.322 0.479
PA2 0.322 1.000 0.426
PA3 0.479 0.426 1.000

The root mean square of the residuals (RMSR) is  0.021
```

Although one of the mental speed items also saliently loaded on the spatial factor (Box 17.1), the three-factor solution appears to be adequate. However, theory suggests that there is an overarching general factor that is responsible for the intercorrelations between these three first-order factors (Carroll, 1993).

BOX 17.2 HIGHER-ORDER EFA WITH *PSYCH* PACKAGE

```
## Import interfactor corr matrix (from 1st order results) via clipboard
## Be sure to separate columns with tabs, not spaces
PA1    PA2    PA3
1.000 0.322 0.479
0.322 1.000 0.426
0.479 0.426 1.000
> HOcor = as.matrix(read.clipboard(header=TRUE))
## Verify that corr matrix was correctly entered
> print(HOcor)
        PA1    PA2    PA3
[1,] 1.000 0.322 0.479
[2,] 0.322 1.000 0.426
[3,] 0.479 0.426 1.000
> f1=fa(HOcor,nfactors=1,fm="pa")
> print(f1,sort=T,digits=3,cut=0)
Standardized loadings (pattern matrix) based upon correlation matrix
      V    PA1     h2    u2 com
PA1 1 0.605 0.366 0.634    1
PA2 2 0.537 0.289 0.711    1
PA3 3 0.789 0.623 0.377    1

               PA1
SS loadings    1.278
Proportion Var 0.426
```

To conduct a higher-order factor analysis require a second analysis using the factor intercorrelation matrix as input. As described in the Importing a Correlation Matrix section, this is easily accomplished by copying the correlation matrix, including the first row that contains the variable names (but not the first column of names) to the clipboard.

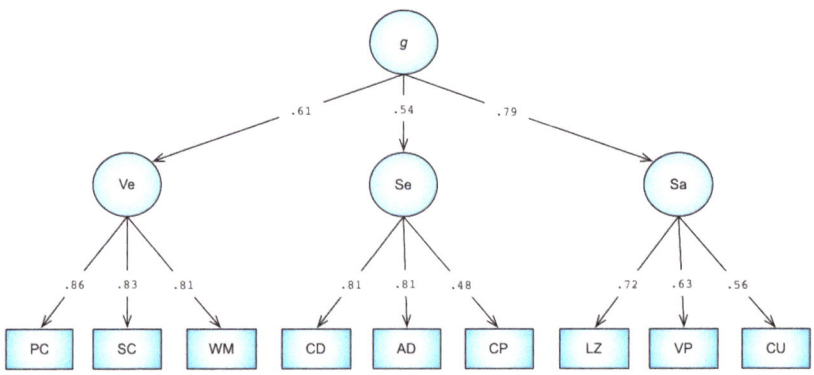

FIGURE 17.2 Higher-order Model of Holzinger Data from *Psych* Package

These two analyses can be summarized in a path diagram that displays both first- and second-order loadings (Figure 17.2). This model is conceptually more complicated than a first-order model because each measured variable is influenced by two factors, one of them far removed from the measured variables and thus more abstract and difficult to understand (Hair et al., 2019). Thompson (2004) suggested the analogy of a mountain range: first-order factors provide a close-up view that focuses on the details of the valleys and the peaks whereas the second-order factors are like looking at the mountains at a great distance, seeing them as constituents of a range. Alternatively, first- and second-order factors might be compared to viewing a mountain range through a camera's telephoto and wide-angle lenses, respectively (McClain, 1996). These "perspectives complement each other, and each is needed to see patterns at a given level of specificity versus generality" (Thompson, 2004, p. 73).

The primary problem with higher-order models is interpretation because the first-order factor loadings represent two sources of variance (from both the general factor and the group factor). Thus, the relationship between a second-order factor and a measured variable is fully mediated by the first-order factor. The researcher must, therefore, provide a theoretical justification for the full mediation implied by the higher-order model (Gignac, 2008) and must consider the multiple sources of variance when interpreting the factors and measured variables.

Schmid-Leiman Transformation of Higher-Order Models

"Factors are abstractions of measured variables. Second-order factors, then, are abstractions of abstractions even more removed from the measured variables. Somehow we would like to interpret the second-order factors in terms of the measured variables, rather than as a manifestation of the factors of the measured variables" (Thompson, 2004, p. 74). It is possible to disentangle the variance due to general and group factors and identify the effect of a second-order factor on a measured variable by multiplying the path coefficients (e.g., .61 x .86 = .53; .54 x .81 = .44, etc.). A more elegant solution was provided by Schmid and Leiman (1957) who demonstrated that a higher-order model could be transformed into "orthogonal sources of variance: (1) variance shared between the higher-order general factor and the observed variables; and (2) variance shared between the first-order factors and the respective observed variables specified to load upon them" (Gignac, 2007, p. 40). Orthogonal (uncorrelated) factors are conceptually simpler to interpret because they are independent sources of variance (Carroll, 1983).

Advantages of the Schmid-Leiman transformation (S-L) "rely on two characteristics, the calculation of direct relations between higher-order factors and primary variables, and the provision of information about the independent contribution of factors of different levels to variables" (Wolff & Preising, 2005, p. 48). The S-L was extensively employed by Carroll (1993) and has been recommended by other methodologists (Cattell, 1978; Gignac, 2007; Gorsuch, 1983; Humphreys, 1982; Lubinski & Dawis, 1992; McClain, 1996; Thompson, 2004).

The *psych* package provides a direct computation of the S-L transformation without the necessity of first generating a higher-order model. Salient loadings are subsequently displayed in bold for emphasis.

BOX 17.3 SCHMID-LEIMAN TRANSFORMATION FROM THE *PSYCH* PACKAGE

```
## Schmid Leiman transformation
> sl3=schmid(Holzinger.9,nfactors=3,fm="pa",digits=3,rotate="promax")
> print(sl3,cut=0)
Schmid Leiman Factor loadings greater than  0
                 g    F1*    F2*    F3*    h2    u2    p2
vis perc      0.56   0.04   0.05   0.39  0.47  0.53  0.67
cubes         0.39  -0.02  -0.05   0.34  0.27  0.73  0.56
lozenges      0.55   0.04  -0.06   0.44  0.50  0.50  0.61
par comp      0.53   0.68  -0.04   0.03  0.76  0.24  0.38
sen comp      0.51   0.66   0.08  -0.03  0.70  0.30  0.38
wordmean      0.51   0.65  -0.05   0.04  0.68  0.32  0.38
addition      0.31   0.09   0.68  -0.15  0.59  0.41  0.16
count dot     0.44  -0.13   0.69   0.08  0.69  0.31  0.28
s c caps      0.57   0.03   0.40   0.23  0.54  0.46  0.60

With eigenvalues of:
   g   F1*   F2*   F3*
2.19 1.34 1.12 0.54
general/max  1.63    max/min =    2.47
mean percent general =   0.45    with sd =  0.17 and cv of  0.38
```

In this output, h^2 and u^2 retain their original designations as measures of communality and uniqueness, respectively, whereas p^2 indicates the percent of the common variance of each measured variable that is general factor variance. On average, the general factor accounted for 45% of the common variance in the measured variables. Gorsuch (1983) suggested that a general factor that accounted for ≥ 40% of the variance would be of interest, but "if the highest-order factors only count for 2% or 3% of the variance, then their impact is negligible and they will be of only limited interest" (p. 253). In this case, the extraction of a general factor appears to be justified.

Placing these factor loadings into a path diagram as in Figure 17.3, visually portrays the relationships of group and general factors to the measured variables.

Bifactor Models

Holzinger and Swineford (1937) proposed the bifactor model where each observed variable depends on two factors: a general factor and a smaller factor characterizing a specific subset of the measured variables. The general factor has direct effects on all measured variables but not on the group factors. Thus, it has

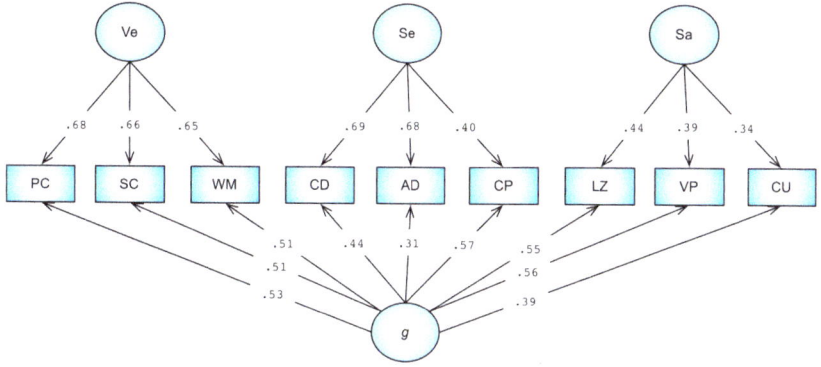

FIGURE 17.3 Schmid-Leiman Transformation of Holzinger Higher-order Model

wide breadth (Humphreys, 1982). The group factors have direct effects on subsets of measured variables and therefore narrower breadth. Both the general and group factors are uncorrelated, allowing for clarity of interpretation. "Bifactor models are potentially applicable when (a) there is a general factor that is hypothesized to account for the commonality of the items; (b) there are multiple domain-specific factors, each of which is hypothesized to account for the unique influence of the specific domain over and above the general factor; and (c) researchers may be interested in the domain specific factors as well as the common factor that is of focal interest" (Chen et al., 2006, p. 190). Reise (2012) argued that a bifactor model, "which views the variance in trait indicators as being influenced by both general and group sources of variance, provides a strong foundation for understanding psychological constructs and their measurement" (p. 692).

Bifactor models appear identical to Schmid-Leiman transformed models when illustrated in a path diagram. However, bifactor models are not mathematically equivalent to the S-L transformation of higher-order models (Chen et al., 2006). Rather, the transformed higher-order model includes mediating variables and proportionality constraints that may bias the estimation of population values (Mansolf & Reise, 2016; Reise et al., 2010). Accordingly, Mansolf and Reise (2016) said to "treat this method as a descriptive technique only, and not as an estimator of a bifactor structure in the population" (p. 714).

Nevertheless, exploratory bifactor models have typically been estimated by S-L transformations because software to compute an exploratory bifactor analysis was not readily available (Reise, 2012). That deficiency was remedied by Jennrich and Bentler (2011) who explicated the mathematics of an exploratory bifactor rotation that was subsequently included in the *psych* package.

BOX 17.4 EXPLORATORY BIFACTOR ANALYSIS FROM THE *PSYCH* PACKAGE

```
## Exploratory bifactor solution
> BF=fa(Holzinger.9,nfactors=4,rotate="bifactor",fm="pa")
> print(BF,cut=0)
Standardized loadings (pattern matrix) based upon correlation matrix
            PA1    PA2    PA3    PA4   h2   u2  com
vis perc  0.71  -0.01  -0.16   0.05 0.54 0.46 1.1
cubes     0.40   0.01  -0.08   0.42 0.34 0.66 2.1
lozenges  0.58   0.07  -0.13   0.41 0.53 0.47 2.0
par comp  0.47   0.73  -0.02   0.04 0.76 0.24 1.7
sen comp  0.48   0.68   0.07  -0.09 0.71 0.29 1.9
wordmean  0.44   0.70  -0.02   0.06 0.68 0.32 1.7
addition  0.32   0.08   0.77  -0.03 0.70 0.30 1.4
count dot 0.55  -0.17   0.55  -0.01 0.63 0.37 2.2
s c caps  0.73  -0.04   0.23  -0.07 0.60 0.40 1.2

                        PA1  PA2  PA3  PA4
SS loadings            2.60 1.53 1.00 0.36
Proportion Var         0.29 0.17 0.11 0.04
Cumulative Var         0.29 0.46 0.57 0.61
Proportion Explained   0.47 0.28 0.18 0.07
Cumulative Proportion  0.47 0.75 0.93 1.00
The root mean square of the residuals (RMSR) is  0.01
```

These results can be placed into a path diagram (Figure 17.4) and compared to the S-L solution pictured in Figure 17.3.

There has been little research on the properties of Jennrich and Bentler's (2011) exploratory bifactor rotation method but Mansolf and Reise (2015, 2016) reported that it produced biased parameter estimates in some conditions and was vulnerable to local minima (i.e., erroneous parameter estimates). More recently, it was found to be sensitive to variables with small factor loadings and relative large cross-loadings (Dombrowski et al., 2019) and less accurate than Schmid-Leiman transformations in recovering population structures (Giordano & Waller, 2020). Given these results, exploratory bifactor analysis should be employed with care. More research is needed to clarify the strengths and weaknesses of exploratory bifactor analysis rotations (Lorenzo-Seva & Ferrando, 2019). Before employing higher-order or bifactor models, the user should consult Brunner et al. (2012), Chen et al. (2006), Mansolf and Reise (2016), and Reise (2012).

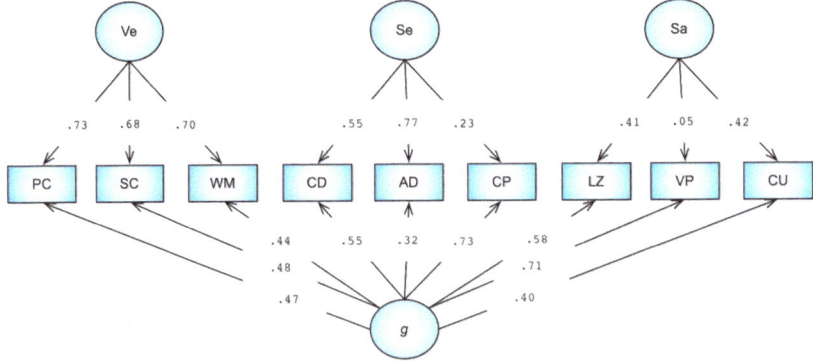

FIGURE 17.4 Exploratory Bifactor Solution from Holzinger Data

Alternative Measures of Reliability

To this point, reliability estimation has consisted of coefficient alpha (Cronbach, 1951). Although popular, most applications of coefficient alpha have ignored its statistical assumptions, resulting in biased estimates of reliability (Watkins, 2017). Model-based reliability estimates have been proposed as alternatives to alpha that make fewer and more realistic assumptions (Reise, 2012). Especially useful are the omega (ω) family of coefficients described by McDonald (1999). Based on an orthogonal factor model, these indices allow a judgment of the relative strength of the general factor and its influence on derived scale scores as well as the viability of global and subscale domains (Rodriguez et al., 2016; Zinbarg et al., 2005). A tutorial on model-based estimates of reliability was provided by Watkins (2017).

The *psych* package contains routines for computing omega reliability estimates. It conducts an internal series of analyses to arrive at omega estimates: (a) factor analyze the original data set; (b) rotate the factors obliquely; (c) factor that correlation matrix; (d) perform a Schmid-Leiman transformation to find general factor loadings; and (e) then find omega estimates.

BOX 17.5 OMEGA RELIABILITY ESTIMATES FROM THE *PSYCH* PACKAGE

```
## Estimate reliability of factors within an orthogonal model
> Ro=omega(Holzinger.9,nfactors=3,rotate="oblimin",fm="minres",
  n.obs=145,n.iter=25)
> print(Ro,cut=0,digits=3)
Alpha:                      0.807
G.6:                        0.846
Omega Hierarchical:         0.528
Omega H asymptotic:         0.600
Omega Total                 0.881
::::::::::::::::::::::::::::::::::::::::::::::::::::::::::::::::::::::::
 Total, General and Subset omega for each subset
                                              g    F1*   F2*   F3*
Omega total for total scores and subscales   0.881 0.881 0.795 0.671
Omega general for total scores and subscales 0.528 0.321 0.231 0.361
Omega group for total scores and subscales   0.287 0.560 0.564 0.310

 Estimates and bootstrapped confidence intervals
          lower estimate upper
omega h    0.367    0.528 0.842
alpha      0.796    0.807 0.947
omega tot  0.880    0.881 0.976
G6         0.848    0.846 0.984
omega_lim  0.468    0.600 0.912
```

Several omega variants can be computed to describe how precisely "total and subscale scores reflect their intended constructs" and determine "whether subscale scores provide unique information above and beyond the total score" (Rodriguez et al., 2016, p. 223). The most general omega coefficient is omega total (ω), "an estimate of the proportion of variance in the unit-weighted total score attributable to all sources of common variance" (Rodriguez et al., 2016, p. 224). Omega total is essentially a model-based substitute for alpha. In this case (Box 17.5), the omega total estimates for the general and group factor scores were .881, .881, .795, and .671, respectively. These values are acceptable given the group nature of this research but might be too unstable for making important decisions about individuals (DeVellis, 2017). However, the amalgam of general and group factor variance reflected by ω total does not allow the contributions of general and group factor variance to be disentangled.

A second omega variant, called "omega general" in the *psych* output, is the amount of variance in that unit-weighted score that is accounted for by the general factor alone. These omega values were .321 for F1, .231 for F2, and .361 for F3. Thus, each unit-weighted factor score reflects considerable general factor variance (23% to 36%) and interpretation of them as pure measures of spatial, verbal, or mental speed would be mistaken.

A third omega variant is called "omega group for total scores and subscales" in the *psych* output and omega hierarchical subscale by other authors. When applied to group factors, omega hierarchical subscale indicates the proportion of variance in the subscale score that is accounted for by its intended group factor to the total variance of that subscale score and indexes the reliable variance associated with that subscale after controlling for the effects of the general factor. Given the substantial influence of the general factor on group factor scores (i.e., omega general values), hierarchical subscale values were considerably reduced from their omega total values. There is no universally accepted guideline for acceptable or adequate levels of omega reliability for clinical decisions, but it has been recommended that omega hierarchical coefficients should exceed .50 at a minimum with .75 preferable (Reise, 2012). Additional details about the use and interpretation of omega coefficients are provided by Rodriguez et al. (2016), Watkins (2017), and Zinbarg et al. (2005).

As is often the case, other **R** packages can also compute omega reliability. The *MBESS* package is especially flexible, able to compute alpha and omega reliability coefficients as well as confidence intervals via a bootstrap approach (Kelley & Pornprasertmanit, 2016). However, *MBESS* requires raw data for computation of omega coefficients.

BOX 17.6 OMEGA RELIABILITY ESTIMATES FROM THE *MBESS* PACKAGE

```
## Estimate omega reliability with MBESS package
> library(MBESS)
> ci.reliability(sdq,N=425,type="omega",B=1000,conf.level = 0.95)
$est
[1] 0.8182749

$se
[1] 0.02495843

$ci.lower
[1] 0.7693573

$ci.upper
[1] 0.8671925

$conf.level
[1] 0.95
```

18

EXPLORATORY VERSUS CONFIRMATORY FACTOR ANALYSIS

Exploratory and confirmatory factor analysis (CFA) are both based on the common factor model: both attempt to reproduce the correlations among a set of measured variables with a smaller set of latent variables (Brown, 2015). However, the two methods differ in the measurement model: EFA allows all factors to relate to all measured variables whereas CFA restricts relationships between factors and measured variables to those specified beforehand by the analyst. Thus, EFA is sometimes called unrestricted factor analysis and CFA is called restricted factor analysis (Widaman, 2012). This pattern is shown by the measurement models in Figure 18.1.

In the EFA model, every variable loads onto every factor. As described previously, the researcher applies the principle of simple structure and specifies the magnitude of factor loadings required for salience to remove the presumably trivial variable-factor relationships from consideration. In CFA, the researcher must specify beforehand the number of factors, how the factors relate to each other, and which variables load onto each factor. In a typical CFA (as in Figure 18.1), the loadings of variables V1–V3 onto Factor 2 and those of variable

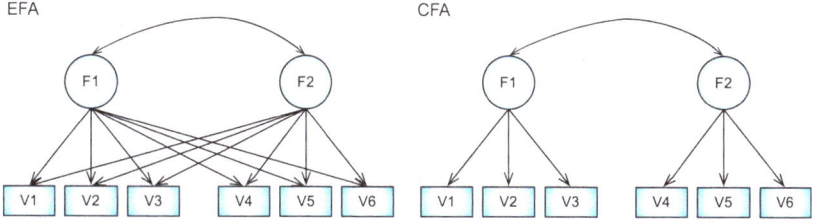

FIGURE 18.1 Simplified Exploratory and Confirmatory Factor Analysis Models

V4–V6 onto Factor 1 are prespecified to be zero and therefore omitted from the path diagram. Although other patterns are possible, this independent clusters model (ICM) is most common (each variable is allowed to load on one factor and its loadings on all other factors constrained to zero). This a priori specification of simple structure removes the need for factor rotation in CFA.

Many methodologists believe that "the purpose of EFA is typically to identify the latent constructs or to generate hypotheses about their possible structures, whereas the purpose of CFA is to evaluate hypothesized structures of the latent constructs and/or to develop a better understanding of such structures" (Bandalos & Finney, 2019, p. 98). That is, EFA generates models whereas CFA tests models (Matsunaga, 2010; Norman & Streiner, 2014). Obviously, any CFA model's veracity depends on the accuracy and thoroughness of its prespecified parameters. As judged by Carroll (1993), "it is highly desirable, or perhaps mandatory, that the hypotheses to be tested have excellent logical or psychological support in some theory of individual differences and their measurements, or in prior analyses of datasets other than the one on which the hypotheses are to be tested" (p. 82).

Some methodologists consider EFA to be inferior to CFA because EFA "tends to be guided by ad hoc rules and intuition, whereas confirmatory factor analysis is imbued with robust dual tests for both parameters (factor loadings) and the quality of the factor" (Ramlall, 2017, p. 5). Likewise, Little et al. (2017) disparaged EFA, asserting that "EFA is a data-driven enterprise that presents too many misguiding temptations for misunderstanding the nature of the construct of interest. Using CFA with careful and skillful scrutiny of all indicated modifications will reveal the structure of a scale that will retain optimal validity" (p. 127).

CFA Model Fit

Thus, it is often claimed that CFA provides an objective test of factor models (Hoyle, 2000; Ramlall, 2017). Maximum likelihood estimation is typically employed in CFA (Russell, 2002) and CFA models are commonly assessed with a statistical test of overall model fit, the chi-square goodness-of-fit, that assesses the discrepancy between the observed relationship between the measured variables versus the relationship implied by the prespecified model. The chi-square value will be statistically non-significant if the two are identical but statistically significant if the model and actual data relationships differ (Barrett, 2007). Unfortunately, the chi-square test is sensitive to sample size: large samples may produce statistically significant chi-square values even when the difference between actual and model implied relationships is trivial and small sample sizes may fail to distinguish between quite discrepant models (Kline, 1994).

In reality, most CFA models produce statistically significant chi-square values so common practice is to ignore that result and rely on approximate fit indices that measure some aspect of closeness of fit of the actual and implied models (Brown, 2015; Browne, 2001; Hancock & Schoonen, 2015; Hoyle, 2000;

Hurley et al., 1997; Maydeu-Olivares, 2017; Ropovik, 2015; Saris et al., 2009). Essentially, this practice acknowledges that the model is not an exact representation of reality but that it might be useful if it sufficiently corresponds to the real world and is not entirely incorrect (MacCallum, 2003). Thus, the idea that CFA provides an objective test of models is both true and false: true that the chi-square test of exact fit is conducted but false that the model is disconfirmed by that test in typical practice (Hurley et al., 1997; Ropovik, 2015). Rather, approximate fit indices are used to subjectively judge that a model is close enough to reality to be useful.

Unfortunately, there is no clear empirical demarcation to the quantification of "close enough" (Berk, 2011). Dozens of approximate fit indices have been developed to measure a model's "closeness to reality" but many "are subjective in nature or do not follow known statistical distributions" (DiStefano, 2016, p. 167). In practice, fit indices may conflict (i.e., one signaling close fit and another poor fit); thus, "researchers are likely to be confused and potentially make incorrect research conclusions" (Lai & Green, 2016, p. 220). Statistical simulations have been conducted to develop "rules of thumb" for optimal cut-points of approximate fit indices (e.g., Hu & Bentler, 1999) but each fit index is differentially sensitive to estimation method, sample size, distributional characteristics, model size, and model misspecification (Clark & Bowles, 2018; Preacher & Merkle, 2012; Saris et al., 2009; Savalei, 2012; Shi & Maydeu-Olivares, 2020; Tomarken & Waller, 2003) with the result that "cutoff values for fit indices, confidence intervals for model fit/misfit, and power analysis based on fit indices are open to question" (Yuan, 2005, p. 142). As summarized by Greiff and Heene (2017), "there are no golden rules for cutoff values, there are only misleading ones" (p. 315).

Approximate fit indices are not sensitive in detecting the correct number of factors (Heene et al., 2011), especially with ordinal data (Garrido et al., 2016; Themessl-Huber, 2014). Nor do they uniquely identify correctly specified models. This was vividly illustrated by Orcan (2018), who simulated a simple model with two correlated factors, each with four measured variables. CFA fit indices indicated good fit for the correct model as well as for two purposively misspecified models. In common practice, "if a goodness-of-fit index meets the recommended cutoff values, the model is retained and used as if it were correctly specified … [and] inferences on the model parameters are made as if the model were correct, when in fact, it is mis-specified" (Maydeu-Olivares, 2017, pp. 538–539). By relying on goodness-of-fit, "essentially unidimensional measures might require multidimensional specifications for the degree of fit to be acceptable. And the resulting solution generally consists of minor, ill-defined factors that yield poor factor score estimates" (Ferrando et al., 2019, p. 124).

Browne and Cudeck (1993) reminded researchers that "fit indices should not be regarded as measures of usefulness of a model. They contain some information about the lack of fit of a model, but none about plausibility" (p. 157). Even worse, subjectivity in model selection is enhanced by the availability of numerous fit indices, each with different cut-points (Hayduk, 2014; Heene et al., 2011;

McCoach et al., 2013; McDonald, 2010). The probability that "close enough" models are scientifically useful is usually neglected, but is unlikely according to basic principles of logic and science (Meehl, 2006; Platt, 1964; Popper, 2002; Roberts & Pashler, 2000; Ropovik, 2015; Wasserstein & Lazar, 2016).

CFA Model Respecification

If a model with acceptable fit cannot be found among the candidate models, model modifications or respecifications are often guided by "modification indices" produced by the CFA software (MacCallum, 2003; Marsh et al., 2009; Maydeu-Olivares, 2017; McCoach et al., 2013; Tarka, 2017). Modification indices statistically approximate how much the chi-square goodness of fit test and accompanying approximate fit indices might improve if a particular prespecified fixed parameter (i.e., factor loading, interfactor correlation, etc.) were allowed to be estimated rather than fixed (Brown, 2015). According to Brown (2015), model modifications "should only be pursued if they can be justified on empirical or conceptual grounds" (Brown, 2013, p. 265). However, "if a model modification is highly interpretable, then why was it not represented in the initial model" (MacCallum et al., 1992, p. 492)? In fact, it does not seem difficult for researchers to find theoretical justifications for most respecifications (Armstrong & Soelberg, 1968; Steiger, 1990). Additionally, respecifications tend not to generalize to new samples nor to the population (Bandalos & Finney, 2019; Kline, 2012, 2013; MacCallum et al., 1992), especially when there are fewer than 1,200 participants in the sample (Hutchinson, 1998). This respecification procedure has been called "a dangerous practice because it capitalizes on chance …. none of the significance tests nor the goodness-of-fit measures take this capitalization into account" (Gorsuch, 2003, p. 151). Almost identical warnings have been sounded by other methodologists (Cliff, 1983; Cribbie, 2000; Jebb et al., 2017; McArdle, 2011; Sass & Schmitt, 2010; Tomarken & Waller, 2003). If not disclosed, respecification based on examination of the data is unethical and can impede scientific progress (Breckler, 1990; Murphy & Aguinis, 2019; Rubin, 2017; Simmons et al., 2011).

   Box (1976) provided cogent scientific guidance more than 40 years ago. "Since all models are wrong the scientist cannot obtain a 'correct' one by excessive elaboration. On the contrary following William of Occam he should seek an economical description of natural phenomena … overelaboration and over-parameterization is often the mark of mediocrity" (p. 792). Therefore, even if justified by theory, respecification means that the analysis has become exploratory rather than confirmatory (Brown, 2015; Browne, 2001; Gorsuch, 1997; Hancock & Schoonen, 2015; Ropovik, 2015; Schmitt, 2011; Tarka, 2018) and "has the worst of both exploratory and confirmatory factor analysis and cannot be recommended" (Gorsuch, 1988, p. 235). Accordingly, "it is better to identify potential problems [via EFA] prior to fitting a confirmatory model than it is to fit a confirmatory model, find problems in fit, and try to diagnose (and 'fix') them" (Reise et al., 2018, p. 699).

CFA Model Assumptions

These complexities are often overlooked by researchers (Hayduk, 2014; Hoyle, 2000; Ramlall, 2017; Schmitt et al., 2018). Additionally, researchers tend to ignore the statistical assumptions necessary for unbiased CFA results (Kline, 2012) and "the sheer technical complexity of the [CFA] method tends to overwhelm critical judgement" (Freedman, 1987, p. 102). Kline (2012) reported that several assumptions must be considered in CFA. These include attentiveness to the direction of causal influence from factor to measured variables and the absence of other plausible explanations. At the most basic level, it is assumed that the model is correctly specified (DiStefano, 2016; Kline, 2012). Three primary model specifications are assumed: (a) the correct number of factors, (b) the correct pattern of factor loadings, and (c) the absence of unmodeled subfactors (Hoyle, 2000). Assumptions about the data in CFA include those assumptions that underlie use of maximum likelihood estimation applied to the covariance, rather than the correlation, matrix (Brown, 2013; Kline, 2012). Specifically, "linearity, independent observations, sufficiently large sample size, multivariate normality of indicators, and a correctly specified model" (DiStefano, 2016, p. 167). Thus, CFA results will be unbiased if the measured variables are multivariate normally distributed, the number of participants is sufficiently large, and the model is correctly specified (DiStefano, 2016). However, correct model specification is unlikely in many practical situations (Bandalos, 2018; DiStefano, 2016; Hurley et al., 1997; Kline, 2012; Orcan, 2018; Tomarken & Waller, 2003, 2005). In fact, CFA has been found to be especially prone to overfactoring with ordinal data (Garrido et al., 2016; van der Eijk & Rose, 2015; Xia & Yang, 2019). Additionally, data in the social sciences are rarely multivariate normally distributed (Cain et al., 2017) and all inferences based on [misspecified models] are suspect (Maydeu-Olivares, 2017, p. 533), consequently "the interpretation of results in the typical [CFA] may be unwarranted" (Kline, 2012, p. 111).

The limitations of CFA have become especially apparent to researchers who investigate the structure of psychological instruments (Hoelzle & Meyer, 2013; Hopwood & Donnellan, 2010; Marsh et al., 2009). The typical independent clusters model (ICM) approach appears to be too restrictive because test items are often ordinal and exhibit small cross-loadings on several factors (Hurley et al., 1997; Schmitt, 2011). In an EFA, these small cross-loadings are assumed to be indicators of ill-defined factors of no substantive interest and are therefore ignored. However, constraining these minor loadings to zero in CFA causes a degradation of model fit and systematic inflation of the interfactor correlations. For example, Marsh et al. (2009) found a median correlation of .34 among factors in an exploratory analysis that increased to .72 in a CFA. As summarized by Schmitt et al. (2018), violation of the ICM assumption can lead to "rather arbitrary modifications, unrealistic factor loadings, and elevated interfactor correlations" (p. 349). However, an EFA model will be unaffected by these conditions. See Morin et al. (2020) for an in-depth discussion of this issue.

Exploratory Use of CFA

Reliance on approximate fit indices, post hoc modification of models based on data characteristics, and violation of statistical assumptions have created a situation where CFA is often used in an exploratory manner (Bandalos & Finney, 2019; Browne, 2001; Cliff, 1983; DiStefano, 2016; Gerbing & Hamilton, 1996; Gorsuch, 1988; Hancock & Schoonen, 2015; Heene et al., 2011; Kline, 2012; MacCallum et al., 1992; Maydeu-Olivares, 2017; Tomarken & Waller, 2003, 2005). Some methodologists have suggested that CFA is superior to EFA because it provides a statistical test of models and its decisions are more objective (Little et al., 2017; Ramlall, 2017). However, exploratory use of CFA leaves researchers vulnerable to confirmatory bias (MacCallum & Austin, 2000; Roberts & Pashler, 2000). That is, they may "persevere by revising procedures until obtaining a theory-predicted result" (Greenwald et al., 1986). As previously described, statistical tests in CFA are conducted but often ignored (Hayduk, 2014). Likewise, the decision steps in CFA are not nearly as objective as claimed: "with all its breadth and versatility come many opportunities for misuse" (Hancock & Schoonen, 2015, p. 175). For example, DiStefano and Hess (2005) reviewed published CFA studies and found that more than 50% provided inadequate theoretical support for the tested models, failed to consider statistical assumptions of CFA, and appeared to select approximate fix indices and their thresholds opportunistically. Literature reviews have also found that published CFA studies often fail to report critical information such as method of estimation, type of matrix analyzed, justification of sample size, and distributional characteristics of the data (MacCallum & Austin, 2000; Ropovik, 2015; Russell, 2002).

EFA versus CFA

Given the increased popularity of CFA methods and the widespread belief that EFA is not acceptable, researchers may be criticized by journal editors for choosing EFA over CFA (Haig, 2018; Hayduk, 2014; Hurley et al., 1997; Marsh et al., 2009). However, the differences between EFA and CFA are not as distinct as sometimes claimed (Child, 2006; Fabrigar & Wegener, 2012; Hoelzle & Meyer, 2013; Hoyle, 2000). EFA and CFA are both valuable statistical tools for scientific inquiry (Gorsuch, 1988). Haig (2018) discussed the role of factor analysis in scientific method and argued that "science is as much concerned with theory generation as it is with theory testing" (p. 84) and that "EFA has a legitimate, and important, role as a method of theory generation, and that EFA and CFA should be viewed as complementary, not competing, methods of common factor analysis" (p. 83). Clark and Bowles (2018) noted that to the extent that EFA and CFA "methods converge on a conceptually coherent solution, it is possible to have greater confidence in that solution, even if there are documented flaws with any one method" (p. 555). Other methodologists have also suggested that EFA can be productively used in conjunction with CFA (Bandalos & Finney, 2010; Carroll, 1995a; DeVellis, 2017; Fabrigar et al., 1999; Gerbing & Hamilton, 1996; Goldberg & Velicer, 2006; Gorsuch, 2003; Hurley et al., 1997; Jebb et al., 2017; Morin et al., 2016; Nesselroade, 1994; Schmitt, 2011; Schmitt et al., 2018; Selbom & Tellegen, 2019; Wegener & Fabrigar, 2004).

In summary, both EFA and CFA require thoughtful and evidence-based methodological decisions that offer many opportunities for error (Bandalos & Boehm-Kaufman, 2009; Fabrigar et al., 1999; Hancock & Schoonen, 2015; Hurley et al., 1997; McCoach et al., 2013; Steiger, 2001; Stewart, 2001; Tarka, 2018; Widaman, 2012). The users of CFA, in particular, are often unaware of the limitations of that methodology (Brannick, 1995; DiStefano & Hess, 2005; Hayduk, 2014; Kline, 2000, 2012; Ropovik, 2015; Schmitt et al., 2018), possess misconceptions about its application (MacCallum & Austin, 2000), and "tend to overstate both the strength and certainty of [its] conclusions" (Tomarken & Waller, 2005, p. 48). It appears that many users of CFA are unaware that the many possible choices for each decision lead to a "garden of forking paths" (Gelman & Loken, 2014, p. 460), resulting in findings that do not replicate. Hussey and Hughes (2020) referred to this practice as v-hacking: "selectively choosing and reporting a combination of metrics, including their implementations and cutoffs, and taking advantage of other degrees of experimenter freedom so as to improve the apparent validity of measures" (p. 180).

Accordingly, the use of EFA may be preferable when: (a) "a strong empirical or conceptual foundation to guide the specification and evaluation of factor model" is missing (Brown, 2013, p. 258); (b) the measured variables are not multivariate normally distributed (Lei & Wu, 2012); (c) or the model is incorrectly specified (Browne, 2001). Categorical measured variables, especially test items, may be more productively analyzed with EFA (Schumacker & Lomax, 2004), especially when the number of factors is in doubt because Garrido et al. (2016) demonstrated that parallel analysis was more accurate than fit indices in determining the number of factors. Likewise, EFA may be more appropriate when items fail to meet the assumption of the independent clusters model (Marsh et al., 2009). EFA may also be superior to the post hoc model respecification of poor-fitting CFA models (Bandalos & Finney, 2019; Browne, 2001; Flora & Flake, 2017; Gorsuch, 1997; Schmitt, 2011; Schmitt et al., 2018; Warne & Burningham, 2019; Wegener & Fabrigar, 2000). In contrast, CFA may be a more appropriate choice when: (a) strong conceptual and empirical foundations are available for specification of a model (Orcan, 2018; Thompson, 2004); (b) the purpose is to test the invariance of a factor model across multiple groups (Osborne et al., 2007); or (c) direct estimation of a bifactor model is desired (Mansolf & Reise, 2015, 2016). Therefore, researchers should "not abandon EFA for the more recently developed confirmatory methods, but develop a heuristic strategy that builds on the comparative strengths of the two techniques" (Gerbing & Hamilton, 1996, p. 63).

Interestingly, similar issues have been explored in the past but within different contexts. Tukey (1980) asserted that "neither exploratory nor confirmatory is sufficient alone" (p. 23) and Box (1976) noted that science can only progress via "a motivated *iteration* between theory and practice" (p. 791). Thus, some facts lead to a tentative theory and then deductions from that tentative theory are found to be discrepant with other facts which, in turn, generates a modified theory. This abductive, deductive, and inductive cycle continues almost indefinitely as science progresses (Haig, 2018; Mulaik, 2018; Rummel, 1967). However, there are two impediments to this progress described by Box (1976) as *cookbookery* and *mathematistry*. "The symptoms of the former are a tendency to force all problems into the molds of one or two routine techniques" whereas mathematistry "is characterized by development of theory for theory's sake" (p. 797). Cookbookery can be recognized by routine use of a statistical method without consideration of its assumptions whereas mathematistry can be seen when researchers adopt inappropriate statistical procedures they do not understand. Consequently, the choice of factor analysis method must not degenerate into cookbookery and should not be determined solely by statistical complexity.

PRACTICE EXERCISES

Exercise 1

To this point, readers have had an opportunity to conduct best-practice, evidence-based exploratory factor analysis (EFA) with both continuous and categorical data sets. Each EFA has followed a step-by-step process and each EFA has included **R** code, **R** output, and a discussion of the relevant principles. This third dataset is provided as an independent exercise. Readers are encouraged to analyze this dataset and check their results with the sample report provided at the end of this chapter.

Data

The Rmotivate.xls dataset can be downloaded as per the Data chapter and imported into the RStudio environment as per the Importing and Saving Data and Results chapter. Remember, the data will initially be a matrix object and may have to be converted to a data frame object for analysis in **R**.

Variables Included

The 20 reading motivation items in this dataset are hypothesized to reflect two aspects of reading motivation: reading self-concept (odd items) and value of reading (even items). Each item offered four ordered response options.

Participants

The 20 reading motivation items were answered by 500 elementary school students equally distributed across grades 2 through 6.

Is the Data Appropriate?

Are data values accurate and plausible? Is there missing data and if so, how much and how was it handled? Are there outliers that bias the results? Are these data normally distributed? If not, how nonnormal are they? Consequently, what correlation matrix should be employed for the EFA and why?

Is EFA Appropriate?

Why or why not? Be sure to report quantitative evidence to support that decision.

What Model of Factor Analysis Was Employed?

Choice between principal components analysis and common factor analysis. Rationale for that choice.

What Factor Extraction Method Was Used?

Specify and provide a rationale for that choice.

How Many Factors Were Retained?

What methods were selected to guide this decision? Rationale for choice of methods.

What Factor Rotation Was Applied?

Rationale for choice of orthogonal or oblique rotation and specific type of orthogonal or oblique rotation.

Interpretation of Results

Employ a model selection approach with a priori guidelines for interpretation.

Report Results

Sufficient detail to demonstrate that evidence-based decisions were made and results are professionally competent and reasonable. Follow the step-by-step checklist.

Compare your report to the sample report that follows.

Exercise 1 Report

Method

Participants were 500 elementary school students equally distributed across grades 2 through 6. Rouquette and Falissard (2011) simulated ordinal scale data and reported that scales with 10 items and two factors required at least 350 participants to obtain stable and accurate factor analysis results. Consequently, the current sample size of 500 participants was judged to be adequate.

Given the uncertainty surrounding the structure of this reading motivation scale, exploratory rather than confirmatory factor analysis was employed (Flora, 2018). Common factor analysis was selected over principal components analysis because the goal of this study was to identify the scale's latent structure (Widaman, 2018). Additionally, common factor analysis may produce more accurate estimates of population parameters than does principal components analysis (Widaman, 1993). Principal axis extraction was applied due to its relative tolerance of multivariate nonnormality and its superior recovery of weak factors (Briggs & MacCallum, 2003). Communalities were initially estimated by squared multiple correlations (Flora, 2018). Given non-normal categorical data with only four response options, a polychoric correlation matrix was submitted for analysis (Flora & Flake, 2017; Mueller & Hancock, 2019).

Following the advice of Velicer et al. (2000), minimum average partials (MAP; Velicer, 1976) and parallel analysis (Horn, 1965), supplemented by a visual scree test (Cattell, 1966), were used to determine the number of factors to retain for rotation. For both theoretical and empirical reasons, it was assumed that factors would be correlated (Gorsuch, 1997; Meehl, 1990). Thus, a Promax rotation with a k value of 4 was selected (Tataryn et al., 1999). To ensure both practical (10% variance explained) and statistical significance ($p < .01$), the threshold for salience was set at .32 (Norman & Streiner, 2014).

Some evidence favors overestimating rather than underestimating the number of factors (Wood et al., 1996); therefore, experts suggest that the highest to lowest number of factors be examined until the most interpretable solution is found (Fabrigar et al., 1999; Flora, 2018). Guidelines for model acceptability include: (a) root mean squared residual (RMSR) values ≤ .08 (Brown, 2015); (b) three salient item loadings (pattern coefficients) are necessary to form a factor with the exclusion of complex loadings (Gorsuch, 1997); (c) an internal consistency reliability coefficient (alpha) of at least .80 for each factor because the intended use of this scale is for non-critical decisions about individual students (DeVellis, 2017); and (d) robustness of results across alternative extraction and rotation methods.

Results

There were no obvious illegal values or outliers and there was no missing data. Although univariate skew and kurtosis values were not extreme (2.06 and 3.72, respectively), Mardia's multivariate kurtosis was large and statistically significant

(535.9, $p < .001$) thereby justifying the use of polychoric correlations (Mueller & Hancock, 2019).

The Kaiser-Meyer-Olkin (KMO) measure of sampling adequacy (Kaiser, 1974) was acceptable (.92 for the total group of variables and .90 to .94 for each of the measured variables). Bartlett's test of sphericity (1950) statistically rejected the hypothesis that the correlation matrix was an identity matrix (chi-square of 4467.6 with 190 degrees of freedom) at $p < .001$). A visual scan of the polychoric matrix revealed numerous coefficients $\geq .30$ (Tabachnick & Fidell, 2019). Altogether, these measures indicate that factor analysis is appropriate.

Parallel analysis, MAP, and scree criteria were in agreement that two factors should be extracted for rotation and subsequent interpretation. However, models with three, two, and one factor(s) were sequentially evaluated for acceptability with the aforementioned guidelines. The three-factor model explained 51% of the total variance, but the third factor accounted for only 2.4% of the total variance and 5% of the common variance prior to rotation. The third factor was saliently loaded by only two items, and both were complex. This is an indicator of overextraction, and suggests that one less factor might be more appropriate.

The two-factor model explained 49% of the total variance. Prior to rotation, the first factor accounted for 38% of the total variance and 78% of the common variance while the second factor accounted for 11% of the total variance and 22% of the common variance. This model was consistent with the theoretical underpinning of the scale with 10 items loading saliently on a reading self-concept factor (.51 to .83) and 10 items on a reading value factor (.46 to .89) in a simple structure configuration. The interfactor correlation of .55. was low enough to pose no threat to discriminant validity (Brown, 2015) and the factors exhibited alpha reliability coefficients of .86, 95% CI [.85, .88] for the reading self-concept factor and .87, 95% CI [.85, .88] for the reading value factor. The two-factor RMSR value of .039 was below the guideline of .08 (Brown, 2015), suggesting that little residual variance remained after extracting two factors.

The one-factor model accounted for 37% of the total variance. All 20 items loaded saliently in the one-factor model but its RMSR value of .114 is an indicator of underextraction and suggests that one more factor might be extracted.

Similar results were obtained when the extraction method was changed to ordinary least squares and the rotation method to oblimin. Likewise, there were no substantive changes when maximum likelihood extraction and oblimin rotation were applied to the original Pearson correlation matrix. Thus, these results were robust in demonstrating that this reading motivation scale is best described by two factors, reading self-concept and reading value.

Exercise 2

This fourth dataset (second practice exercise) is also provided for independent practice. Readers are encouraged to analyze this dataset and compare their choices and **R** code provided at the end of this chapter. No report is provided with this practice exercise.

Data

This dataset is also in spreadsheet format and contains 10 variables. Each variable is one item from a rating scale designed to tap the symptoms of attention-deficit hyperactivity disorder (ADHD) that was completed by 500 respondents. This data file labeled "adhd.xls" can be imported via RStudio as was previously described in the Importing Raw Data section using the menu commands select *File > Import Dataset > From Excel*. Respondents reported the frequency of each item on a four-point scale: 0 (*Never or Rarely*), 1 (*Sometimes*), 2 (*Often*), and 3 (*Very Often*). Thus, the data are ordered and not continuous.

These 10 items are hypothesized to reflect two behavioral aspects of ADHD: attention problems and over-activity/impulsivity problems. It was assumed that the first five items would tap the attention problems dimension while the final five items would tap the over-activity/impulsivity dimension of ADHD. Scales with more items have typically found internal consistency reliability coefficients of around .85 to .90 for these factors (Nichols et al., 2017).

Are the Data Appropriate for EFA?

BOX 19.1   EXPLORE DATA WITH THE *PSYCH* PACKAGE

```
## Convert table object to data frame object
> adhd = as.data.frame(adhd)
> attach(adhd)
## Activate psych package
> library(psych)
## Descriptive Statistics
> describe(adhd)
          vars   n mean   sd median trimmed  mad min max range skew kurtosis   se
instruct     1 500 0.47 0.73      0    0.34 0.00   0   3     3 1.74     3.04 0.03
effort       2 500 0.73 0.86      1    0.60 1.48   0   3     3 1.04     0.36 0.04
organize     3 500 0.54 0.77      0    0.38 0.00   0   3     3 1.44     1.64 0.03
forget       4 500 0.83 0.86      1    0.72 1.48   0   3     3 0.86     0.08 0.04
attention    5 500 0.65 0.83      0    0.50 0.00   0   3     3 1.22     0.83 0.04
go           6 500 0.83 0.99      1    0.66 1.48   0   3     3 0.97    -0.20 0.04
talks        7 500 1.00 0.92      1    0.88 1.48   0   3     3 0.70    -0.30 0.04
fidgets      8 500 0.87 0.98      1    0.74 1.48   0   3     3 0.80    -0.51 0.04
turns        9 500 0.43 0.73      0    0.28 0.00   0   3     3 1.86     3.19 0.03
runs        10 500 0.42 0.69      0    0.29 0.00   0   3     3 1.77     3.11 0.03
## Scatterplot matrix for all variables from psych package
> pairs.panels(adhd,pch='.',lm=T,ellipses=F,scale=F,
  method="pearson",main="Scatterplot Matrix")
## Mardia multivariate normality
> mardia(adhd)
n.obs = 500   num.vars =  10
b1p =  19.19   skew =  1598.76  with probability =  0
b2p =  166.87  kurtosis =  33.82  with probability =  0
## Boxplot
> boxplot(adhd,notch=FALSE,boxfill="blue",whiskcol="blue",
  pch=16,outcol="red")
## Identification of outliers
> out=outlier(adhd,bad=5,plot=T,na.rm=T,bg=c("red"),
  pch=21,ylab="D2",cex=.75,ylim=c(0,25))
```

Is EFA Appropriate?

BOX 19.2 CORRELATION GRAPHS, KMO, AND BARTLETT'S TESTS

```
## graph Pearson correlation matrix to visualize those > .30.
> library(qgraph)
> qgraph(cor(adhd),cut=.30,details=TRUE,posCol="green3",
  negCol="red",labels=names(adhd))
## KMO Test
> KMO(adhd)
Kaiser-Meyer-Olkin factor adequacy
Overall MSA =  0.91
MSA for each item =
  instruct    effort organize   forget attention     go   talks  fidgets   turns   runs
    0.91      0.91     0.91     0.94     0.93      0.85   0.90     0.88    0.95   0.95
## Bartlett test
> cortest.bartlett(adhd,n=500)
$chisq                    $p.value                        $df
[1] 2274.726              [1] 0                           [1] 45
## Polychoric correlation
> out=polychoric(adhd)
> adhdP=out$rho
## graph polychoric correlation matrix to visualize those > .30.
> qgraph(adhdP,cut=.30,details=TRUE,posCol="blue3",
  negCol="red",labels=names(adhd))
## KMO Test
> KMO(adhdP)
Kaiser-Meyer-Olkin factor adequacy
Overall MSA =  0.91
MSA for each item =
  instruct    effort organize   forget attention     go   talks  fidgets   turns   runs
    0.90      0.91     0.91     0.94     0.93      0.86   0.89     0.89    0.95   0.96
## Bartlett test
> cortest.bartlett(adhdP,n=500)
$chisq                    $p.value                        $df
[1] 3231.54               [1] 0                           [1] 45
```

How Many Factor to Retain?

BOX 19.3 PARALLEL ANALYSIS AND MAP WITH *PSYCH* PACKAGE

```
## Parallel analysis with 500 repetitions using Pearson corr
> fa.parallel(adhd,fa="pc",n.iter=500,ylab="Eigenvalues",
  quant=.50,n.obs=500)
Parallel analysis suggests that the number of factors =  NA  and the
number of components =  2
## MAP Pearson corr
> VSS(adhd,rotate="promax",fm="pc",plot=FALSE,n.obs=500)
The Velicer MAP achieves a minimum of 0.03 with 2 factors
## Standard scree plot
> scree(adhd,pc=TRUE,factors=TRUE,hline="-1",main="Scree Plot")

## Parallel analysis with 500 repetitions using polychoric corr
> fa.parallel(adhdP,fa="pc",n.iter=500,ylab="Eigenvalues",
  quant=.50,n.obs=500)
Parallel analysis suggests that the number of factors =  NA  and the
number of components =  2
## MAP polychoric corr
> VSS(adhdP,rotate="promax",fm="pc",plot=FALSE,n.obs=500)
The Velicer MAP achieves a minimum of 0.03 with 2 factors
```

Factor Models: Three Factors

BOX 19.4   EFA WITH THREE FACTORS AND ALPHA RELIABILITY ESTIMATES

```
## Three-factor model from polychoric matrix
> f3=fa(adhdP,nfactors=3,rotate="promax",residuals=TRUE,
  SMC=TRUE,fm="pa",max.iter=200,n.obs=500)
> print(f3,cut=0,digits=3)
Standardized loadings (pattern matrix) based upon correlation matrix
             PA1    PA2    PA3    h2    u2   com
instruct    0.910 -0.074 -0.001 0.744 0.256 1.01
effort      0.863  0.003 -0.082 0.666 0.334 1.02
organize    0.845 -0.209  0.176 0.688 0.312 1.21
forget      0.632  0.124 -0.032 0.487 0.513 1.08
attention   0.618  0.368 -0.094 0.701 0.299 1.69
go         -0.131  0.745  0.302 0.823 0.177 1.39
talks      -0.068  0.067  0.841 0.724 0.276 1.03
fidgets    -0.040  0.932 -0.078 0.721 0.279 1.02
turns       0.219  0.148  0.481 0.586 0.414 1.61
runs        0.180  0.435  0.234 0.586 0.414 1.91

                          PA1   PA2   PA3
SS loadings             3.229 2.094 1.402
Proportion Var          0.323 0.209 0.140
Cumulative Var          0.323 0.532 0.673
Proportion Explained    0.480 0.311 0.209
Cumulative Proportion   0.480 0.791 1.000


 With factor correlations of
       PA1   PA2   PA3
PA1 1.000 0.661 0.633
PA2 0.661 1.000 0.753
PA3 0.633 0.753 1.000


The root mean square of the residuals (RMSR) is  0.017
The df corrected root mean square of the residuals is  0.027
::::::::::::::::::::::::::::::::::::::::::::::::::::::::::::::::::::
Measures of factor score adequacy
                                             PA1   PA2   PA3
Correlation of (regression) scores with factors  0.957 0.949 0.918
Multiple R square of scores with factors        0.915 0.900 0.843
Minimum correlation of possible factor scores   0.831 0.800 0.686
## Residuals
> resd3=residuals(f3,diag=FALSE,na.rm=TRUE)
> hist(resd3,col="pink2",main="",xlab="Residuals")
> max(abs(resd3),na.rm=TRUE)
[1] 0.04762781
## Reliability of factors
## 1st factor
> final1 = data.frame(instruct,effort,organize,forget,attention)
> alpha(final1)
  lower alpha upper     95% confidence boundaries
   0.84 0.86  0.88
## 2nd factor
> final2 = data.frame(attention,go,fidgets,turns,runs)
> alpha(final2)
 lower alpha upper     95% confidence boundaries
  0.81 0.83  0.85
## 3rd factor -- only 1 item. alpha not possible.
```

Factor Models: Two Factors

BOX 19.5   EFA WITH TWO FACTORS AND ALPHA RELIABILITY ESTIMATES

```
## Two-factor model from polychoric matrix
> f2=fa(adhdP,nfactors=2,rotate="promax",residuals=TRUE,
  SMC=TRUE,missing=FALSE,fm="pa",n.obs=500)
> print(f2,cut=0,digits=3)
Standardized loadings (pattern matrix) based upon correlation matrix
             PA1    PA2     h2    u2   com
instruct   0.915 -0.074 0.750 0.250 1.01
effort     0.857 -0.063 0.664 0.336 1.01
organize   0.838 -0.035 0.664 0.336 1.00
forget     0.624  0.099 0.485 0.515 1.05
attention  0.595  0.288 0.675 0.325 1.44
go        -0.167  1.032 0.854 0.146 1.05
fidgets   -0.029  0.797 0.603 0.397 1.00
turns      0.225  0.572 0.556 0.444 1.30
runs       0.165  0.648 0.595 0.405 1.13

                          PA1   PA2
SS loadings             3.211 3.182 ← eigenvalues after rotation
Proportion Var          0.321 0.318 ← % total variance for each factor after rotation
Cumulative Var          0.321 0.639 ← cumulative % total variance after rotation
Proportion Explained    0.502 0.498 ← % common variance after rotation
Cumulative Proportion   0.502 1.000 ← cumulative % common variance after rotation


With factor correlations of
      PA1   PA2
PA1 1.000 0.691
PA2 0.691 1.000


The root mean square of the residuals (RMSR) is  0.028
The df corrected root mean square of the residuals is  0.037
:::::::::::::::::::::::::::::::::::::::::::::::::::::::::::::::::
                                                     PA1   PA2
Correlation of (regression) scores with factors    0.956 0.964
Multiple R square of scores with factors           0.913 0.929
Minimum correlation of possible factor scores      0.826 0.857
## Residuals
> resd2=residuals(f2,diag=FALSE,na.rm=TRUE)
> hist(resd2,col="purple",main="",xlab="Residuals")
> max(abs(resd2),na.rm=TRUE)
[1]  0.07909942
## Reliability of 1st factor
> final1 = data.frame(instruct,effort,organize,forget,attention)
> alpha(final1)
lower alpha upper      95% confidence boundaries
0.84  0.86  0.88
## Reliability of 2nd factor
> final2 = data.frame(go,talks,fidgets,turns,runs)
> alpha(final2)
lower alpha upper      95% confidence boundaries
0.81  0.83  0.85
## Unrotated solution for variance allocation to factors
> f2u=fa(adhdP,nfactors=2,rotate="none",missing=FALSE,fm="pa",n.obs=500)
> print(f2u,cut=0,digits=3)
                          PA1   PA2
SS loadings             5.471 0.922 ← eigenvalues before rotation
Proportion Var          0.547 0.092 ← % total variance for each factor before rotation
Cumulative Var          0.547 0.639 ← cumulative % total variance before rotation
Proportion Explained    0.856 0.144 ← % common variance after rotation
Cumulative Proportion   0.856 1.000 ← cumulative % common variance before rotation
```

Factor Models: One Factor

BOX 19.6   EFA WITH ONE FACTOR AND ALPHA RELIABILITY ESTIMATE

```
## One-factor model from polychoric matrix
> f1=fa(adhdP,nfactors=1,residuals=TRUE,SMC=TRUE,missing=FALSE,
  fm="pa",n.obs=500)
> print(f1,cut=0,digits=3)
Standardized loadings (pattern matrix) based upon correlation matrix
            PA1     h2     u2 com
instruct  0.758 0.574 0.426    1
effort    0.719 0.516 0.484    1
organize  0.729 0.532 0.468    1
forget    0.667 0.444 0.556    1
attention 0.820 0.672 0.328    1
go        0.763 0.582 0.418    1
talks     0.675 0.456 0.544    1
fidgets   0.696 0.484 0.516    1
turns     0.738 0.545 0.455    1
runs      0.750 0.562 0.438    1

                 PA1
SS loadings    5.367
Proportion Var 0.537

The root mean square of the residuals (RMSR) is  0.093
The df corrected root mean square of the residuals is  0.105
:::::::::::::::::::::::::::::::::::::::::::::::::::::::::::::::::::
Measures of factor score adequacy
                                                   PA1
Correlation of (regression) scores with factors  0.961
Multiple R square of scores with factors          0.924
Minimum correlation of possible factor scores     0.848
## Residuals
> resd1=residuals(f1,diag=FALSE,na.rm=TRUE)
> hist(resd1,col="orange",main="",xlab="Residuals")
> max(abs(resd1),na.rm=TRUE)
[1] 0.2083874
## alpha reliability
> final1 = data.frame(instruct,effort,organize,forget,attention,go,
  talks,fidgets,turns,runs)
> alpha(final1)
lower alpha upper     95% confidence boundaries
0.87  0.89  0.90
```

Factor Models: Robustness Evaluation of Two-Factor Model

BOX 19.7   EFA WITH TWO FACTORS BASED ON PEARSON CORRELATION MATRIX

```
## Two-factor model from Pearson matrix
> f2p=fa(adhd,nfactors=2,rotate="oblimin",residuals=TRUE,
  SMC=TRUE,fm="minres",n.obs=500)
> print(f2p,cut=0,digits=3)
Standardized loadings (pattern matrix) based upon correlation matrix
             MR1     MR2    h2    u2    com
instruct    0.817 -0.055 0.617 0.383 1.01
effort      0.771 -0.024 0.573 0.427 1.00
organize    0.781 -0.021 0.592 0.408 1.00
forget      0.577  0.117 0.427 0.573 1.08
attention   0.581  0.261 0.588 0.412 1.39
go         -0.069  0.930 0.793 0.207 1.01
talks       0.114  0.591 0.443 0.557 1.07
fidgets     0.026  0.714 0.533 0.467 1.00
turns       0.306  0.428 0.433 0.567 1.81
runs        0.225  0.508 0.445 0.555 1.38

                          MR1   MR2
SS loadings             2.950 2.495
Proportion Var          0.295 0.249
Cumulative Var          0.295 0.544
Proportion Explained    0.542 0.458
Cumulative Proportion   0.542 1.000


 With factor correlations of
      MR1   MR2
MR1 1.000 0.599
MR2 0.599 1.000

The root mean square of the residuals (RMSR) is  0.025
The df corrected root mean square of the residuals is  0.032
::::::::::::::::::::::::::::::::::::::::::::::::::::::::::::::::::::
Measures of factor score adequacy
                                                   MR1   MR2
Correlation of (regression) scores with factors  0.934 0.939
Multiple R square of scores with factors         0.873 0.882
Minimum correlation of possible factor scores    0.746 0.763
## Residuals
> resd2=residuals(f2p,diag=FALSE,na.rm=TRUE)
> hist(resd2,col="yellow",main="",xlab="Residuals")
> max(abs(resd2),na.rm=TRUE)
[1] 0.07927109
```

REFERENCES AND RESOURCES

Aiken, L. S., West, S. G., & Millsap, R. E. (2008). Doctoral training in statistics, measurement, and methodology in psychology. *American Psychologist, 63*(1), 32–50. https://doi.org/10.1037/0003-066X.63.1.32.

Anscombe, F. J. (1973). Graphs in statistical analysis. *The American Statistician, 27*(1), 17–21. https://doi.org/10.2307/2682899.

Armstrong, J. S., & Soelberg, P. (1968). On the interpretation of factor analysis. *Psychological Bulletin, 70*(5), 361–364. https://doi.org/10.1037/h0026434.

Auerswald, M., & Moshagen, M. (2019). How to determine the number of factors to retain in exploratory factor analysis: A comparison of extraction methods under realistic conditions. *Psychological Methods, 24*(4), 468–491. http://dx.doi.org/10.1037/met0000200.

Bandalos, D. L. (2018). *Measurement theory and applications in the social sciences.* Guilford.

Bandalos, D. L., & Boehm-Kaufman, M. R. (2009). Four common misconceptions in exploratory factor analysis. In C. E. Lance & R. J. Vandenberg (Eds.), *Statistical and methodological myths and urban legends: Doctrine, verity and fable in the organizational and social sciences* (pp. 61–87). Routledge.

Bandalos, D. L., & Finney, S. J. (2019). Factor analysis: Exploratory and confirmatory. In G. R. Hancock, L. M. Stapleton, & R. O. Mueller (Eds.), *The reviewer's guide to quantitative methods in the social sciences* (2nd ed., pp. 98–122). Routledge.

Bandalos, D. L., & Gerstner, J. J. (2016), Using factor analysis in test construction. In K. Schweizer & C. DiStefano (Eds.), *Principles and methods of test construction: Standards and recent advances* (pp. 26–51). Hogrefe.

Baraldi, A. N., & Enders, C. K. (2013). Missing data methods. In T. D. Little (Ed.), *Oxford handbook of quantitative methods: Statistical analyses* (Vol. 2, pp. 635–664). Oxford University Press.

Barendse, M. T., Oort, F. J., & Timmerman, M. E. (2015). Using exploratory factor analysis to determine the dimensionality of discrete responses. *Structural Equation Modeling, 22*(1), 87–101. https://doi.org/10.1080/10705511.2014.934850.

Barrett, P. (2007). Structural equation modelling: Adjudging model fit. *Personality and Individual Differences*, *42*(5), 815–824. https://doi.org/10.1016/j.paid.2006.09.018.

Barrett, P. T., & Kline, P. (1982). Factor extraction: An examination of three methods. *Personality Study and Group Behaviour*, *3*(1), 84–98.

Bartholomew, D. J. (1995). Spearman and the origin and development of factor analysis. *British Journal of Mathematical and Statistical Psychology*, *48*(2), 211–220. https://doi.org/10.1111/j.2044-8317.1995.tb01060.x.

Bartlett, M. S. (1950). Tests of significance in factor analysis. *British Journal of Psychology*, *3*(2), 77–85. https://doi.org/10.1111/j.2044-8317.1950.tb00285.x.

Basto, M., & Pereira, J. M. (2012). An SPSS R-menu for ordinal factor analysis. *Journal of Statistical Software*, *46*(4), 1–29. https://doi.org/10.18637/jss.v046.i04.

Beaujean, A. A. (2013). Factor analysis using R. *Practical Assessment, Research & Evaluation*, *18*(4), 1–11. https://doi.org/10.7275/z8wr-4j42.

Beavers, A. S., Lounsbury, J. W., Richards, J. K., Huck, S. W., Skolits, G. J., & Esquivel, S. L. (2012). Practical considerations for using exploratory factor analysis in educational research. *Practical Assessment, Research & Evaluation*, *18*(6), 1–13. https://doi.org/10.7275/qv2q-rk76.

Benson, J. (1998). Developing a strong program of construct validation: A test anxiety example. *Educational Measurement: Issues and Practice*, *17*(1), 10–22. https://doi.org/10.1111/j.1745-3992.1998.tb00616.x.

Benson, J., & Nasser, F. (1998). On the use of factor analysis as a research tool. *Journal of Vocational Education Research*, *23*(1), 13–33.

Bentler, P. M. (2005). *EQS 6 structural equations program manual*. Multivariate Software.

Berk, R. (2011). Evidence-based versus junk-based evaluation research: Some lessons from 35 years of the Evaluation Review. *Evaluation Review*, *35*(3), 191–203. https://doi.org/10.1177/0193841×11419281.

Bernstein, I. H., & Teng, G. (1989). Factoring items and factoring scales are different: Spurious evidence for multidimensionality due to item categorization. *Psychological Bulletin*, *105*(3), 467–477. https://doi.org/10.1037/0033-2909.105.3.467.

Bishara, A. J., & Hittner, J. B. (2015). Reducing bias and error in the correlation coefficient due to nonnormality. *Educational and Psychological Measurement*, *75*(5), 785–804. https://doi.org/10.1177/0013164414557639.

Bollen, K. A. (2002). Latent variables in psychology and the social sciences. *Annual Review of Psychology*, *53*(1), 605–634. https://doi.org/10.1146/annurev.psych.53.100901.135239.

Bollen, K. A., & Barb, K. H. (1981). Pearson's R and coarsely categorized measures. *American Sociological Review*, *46*(2), 232–239. https://doi.org/10.2307/2094981.

Box, G. E. P. (1976). Science and statistics. *Journal of the American Statistical Association*, *71*(356), 791–799. http://doi.org/10.1080/01621459.1976.10480949.

Brannick, M. T. (1995). Critical comments on applying covariance structure modeling. *Journal of Organizational Behavior*, *16*(3), 201–213. https://doi.org/10.1002/job.4030160303.

Breckler, S. J. (1990). Applications of covariance structure modeling in psychology: Cause for concern? *Psychological Bulletin*, *107*(2), 260–273. https://doi.org/10.1037/0033-2909.107.2.260.

Briggs, S. R., & Cheek, J. M. (1986). The role of factor analysis in the development and evaluation of personality scales. *Journal of Personality*, *54*(1), 106–148. https://doi.org/10.1111/j.1467-6494.1986.tb00391.x.

Briggs, N. E., & MacCallum, R. C. (2003). Recovery of weak common factors by maximum likelihood and ordinary least squares estimation. *Multivariate Behavioral Research*, *38*(1), 25–56. https://doi.org/10.1207/S15327906MBR3801_2.

Brown, T. A. (2013). Latent variable measurement models. In T. D. Little (Ed.), *Oxford handbook of quantitative methods: Statistical analysis* (Vol. 2, pp. 257–280). Oxford University Press.

Brown, T. A. (2015). *Confirmatory factor analysis for applied research* (2nd ed.). Guilford.

Browne, M. W. (2001). An overview of analytic rotation in exploratory factor analysis. *Multivariate Behavioral Research*, *36*(1), 111–150. https://doi.org/10.1207/S15327906MBR3601_05.

Browne, M. W., & Cudeck, R. (1993). Alternative ways of assessing model fit. In K. A. Bollen & J. S. Long (Eds.), *Testing structural equation models* (pp. 136–162). Sage.

Brunner, M., Nagy, G., & Wilhelm, O. (2012). A tutorial on hierarchically structured constructs. *Journal of Personality*, *80*(4), 796–846. https://doi.org/10.1111/j.1467-6494.2011.00749.x.

Budaev, S. V. (2010). Using principal components and factor analysis in animal behaviour research: Caveats and guidelines. *Ethology*, *116*(5), 472–480. https://doi.org/10.1111/j.1439-0310.2010.01758.x.

Buja, A., & Eyuboglu, N. (1992). Remarks on parallel analysis. *Multivariate Behavioral Research*, *27*(4), 509–540. https://doi.org/10.1207/s15327906mbr2704_2.

Burnham, K. P., & Anderson, D. R. (2004). Multimodel inference: Understanding AIC and BIC in model selection. *Sociological Methods & Research*, *33*(2), 261–304. https://doi.org/10.1177/0049124104268644.

Burt, C. (1940). *The factors of the mind: An introduction to factor-analysis in psychology.* University of London Press.

Cain, M. K., Zhang, Z., & Yuan, K.-H. (2017). Univariate and multivariate skewness and kurtosis for measuring nonnormality: Prevalence, influence, and estimation. *Behavior Research Methods*, *49*(5), 1716–1735. https://doi.org/10.3758/s13428-016-0814-1.

Canivez, G. L., & Watkins, M. W. (2010). Exploratory and higher-order factor analyses of the Wechsler Adult Intelligence Scale-Fourth Edition (WAIS-IV) adolescent sub-sample. *School Psychology Quarterly*, *25*(4), 223–235. https://doi.org/10.1037/a0022046.

Canivez, G. L., Watkins, M. W., & Dombrowski, S. C. (2016). Factor structure of the Wechsler Intelligence Scale for Children-Fifth Edition: Exploratory factor analysis with the 16 primary and secondary subtests. *Psychological Assessment*, *28*(8), 975–986. https://doi.org/10.1037/pas0000238.

Caron, P.-O. (2019). Minimum average partial correlation and parallel analysis: The influence of oblique structures. *Communications in Statistics: Simulation and Computation*, *48*(7), 2110–2117. https://doi.org/10.1080/03610918.2018.1433843.

Carretta, T. R., & Ree, J. J. (2001). Pitfalls of ability research. *International Journal of Selection and Assessment*, *9*(4), 325–335. https://doi.org/10.1111/1468-2389.00184.

Carroll, J. B. (1961). The nature of the data, or how to choose a correlation coefficient. *Psychometrika*, *26*(4), 347–372. https://doi.org/10.1007/BF02289768.

Carroll, J. B. (1978). How shall we study individual differences in cognitive abilities?–Methodological and theoretical perspectives. *Intelligence*, *2*(2), 87–115. https://doi.org/10.1016/0160-2896(78)90002-8.

Carroll, J. B. (1983). Studying individual differences in cognitive abilities: Through and beyond factor analysis. In R. F. Dillon & R. R. Schmeck (Eds.), *Individual differences in cognition* (pp. 1–33). Academic Press.

Carroll, J. B. (1985). Exploratory factor analysis: A tutorial. In D. K. Detterman (Ed.), *Current topics in human intelligence* (pp. 25–58). Ablex Publishing Company.

Carroll, J. B. (1993). *Human cognitive abilities: A survey of factor-analytic studies*. Cambridge University Press.

Carroll, J. B. (1995a). On methodology in the study of cognitive abilities. *Multivariate Behavioral Research, 30*(3), 429–452. https://doi.org/10.1207/s15327906mbr3003_6.

Carroll, J. B. (1995b). Reflections on Stephen Jay Gould's *the Mismeasure of Man* (1981): A retrospective review. *Intelligence, 21*(2), 121–134. https://doi.org/10.1016/0160-2896(95)90022-5.

Cattell, R. B. (1946). *The description and measurement of personality*. World Book.

Cattell, R. B. (1952). *Factor analysis: An introduction and manual for the psychologist and social scientist*. Greenwood Press.

Cattell, R. B. (1966). The scree test for the number of factors. *Multivariate Behavioral Research, 1*(2), 245–276. https://doi.org/10.1207/s15327906mbr0102_10.

Cattell, R. B. (1978). *The scientific use of factor analysis in behavioral and life sciences*. Plenum Press.

Chen, F. F., West, S. G., & Sousa, K. H. (2006). A comparison of bifactor and second-order models of quality of life. *Multivariate Behavioral Research, 41*(2), 189–225.

Chen, S.-F., Wang, S., & Chen, C.-Y. (2012). A simulation study using EFA and CFA programs based on the impact of missing data on test dimensionality. *Expert Systems with Applications, 39*(4), 4026–4031. https://doi.org/10.1016/j.eswa.2011.09.085.

Child, D. (2006). *The essentials of factor analysis* (3rd ed.). Continuum.

Cho, S.-J., Li, F., & Bandalos, D. (2009). Accuracy of the parallel analysis procedure with polychoric correlations. *Educational and Psychological Measurement, 69*(5), 748–759. https://doi.org/10.1177/0013164409332229.

Choi, J., Peters, M., & Mueller, R. O. (2010). Correlational analysis of ordinal data: From Pearson's r to Bayesian polychoric correlation. *Asia Pacific Education Review, 11*(4), 459–466. https://doi.org/10.1007/s12564-010-9096-y.

Clark, D. A., & Bowles, R. P. (2018). Model fit and item factor analysis: Overfactoring, underfactoring, and a program to guide interpretation. *Multivariate Behavioral Research, 53*(4), 544–558. https://doi.org/10.1080/00273171.2018.1461058.

Cliff, N. (1983). Some cautions concerning the application of causal modeling methods. *Multivariate Behavioral Research, 18*(1), 115–126. https://doi.org/10.1207/s15327906mbr1801_7.

Clifton, J. D. W. (2020). Managing validity versus reliability trade-offs in scale-building decisions. *Psychological Methods, 25*(3), 259–270. https://doi.org/10.1037/met0000236.

Comrey, A. L. (1988). Factor-analytic methods of scale development in personality and clinical psychology. *Journal of Consulting and Clinical Psychology, 56*(5), 754–761. https://doi.org/10.1037//0022-006x.56.5.754.

Comrey, A. L., & Lee, H. B. (1992). *A first course in factor analysis* (2nd ed.). Erlbaum.

Conway, J. M., & Huffcutt, A. I. (2003). A review and evaluation of exploratory factor analysis practices in organizational research. *Organizational Research Methods, 6*(2), 147–168. https://doi.org/10.1177/1094428103251541.

Cooper, C. (2019). *Psychological testing: Theory and practice*. Routledge.

Costello, A. B., & Osborne, J. W. (2005). Best practices in exploratory factor analysis: Four recommendations for getting the most from your analysis. *Practical Assessment, Research & Evaluation, 10*(7), 1–9. https://doi.org/10.7275/jyj1-4868.

Crawford, A. V., Green, S. B., Levy, R., Lo, W.-J., Scott, L., Svetina, D., & Thompson, M. S. (2010). Evaluation of parallel analysis methods for determining the number of factors. *Educational and Psychological Measurement, 70*(6), 885–901. https://doi.org/10.1177/0013164410379332.

Crawley, M. J. (2012). *The R book* (2nd ed.). Wiley.

Cribbie, R. A. (2000). Evaluating the importance of individual parameters in structural equation modeling: The need for type I error control. *Personality and Individual Differences, 29*(3), 567–577. https://doi.org/10.1016/S0191-8869(99)00219-6.

Cronbach, L. J. (1951). Coefficient alpha and the internal structure of tests. *Psychometrika, 16*(3), 297–334. https://doi.org/10.1007/BF02310555.

Cudeck, R. (2000). Exploratory factor analysis. In H. E. A. Tinsley & S. D. Brown (Eds.), *Handbook of applied multivariate statistics and mathematical modeling* (pp. 265–296). Academic Press.

Curran, P. J. (2016). Methods for the detection of carelessly invalid responses in survey data. *Journal of Experimental Social Psychology, 66,* 4–19. https://doi.org/10.1016/j.jesp.2015.07.006.

Curran, P. J., West, S. G., & Finch, J. F. (1996). The robustness of test statistics to nonnormality and specification error in confirmatory factor analysis. *Psychological Methods, 1*(1), 16–29. https://doi.org/10.1037/1082-989X.1.1.16.

DeCarlo, L. T. (1997). On the meaning and use of kurtosis. *Psychological Methods, 2*(3), 292–307. https://doi.org/10.1037/1082-989X.2.3.292.

DeSimone, J. A., Harms, P. D., & DeSimone, A. J. (2015). Best practice recommendations for data screening. *Journal of Organizational Behavior, 36*(2), 171–181. https://doi.org/10.1002/job.1962.

DeVellis, R. F. (2017). *Scale development: Theory and applications* (4th ed.). Sage.

de Winter, J. C. F., & Dodou, D. (2012). Factor recovery by principal axis factoring and maximum likelihood factor analysis as a function of factor pattern and sample size. *Journal of Applied Statistics, 39*(4), 695–710. https://doi.org/10.1080/02664763.2011.610445.

de Winter, J. C. F., Dodou, D., & Wieringa, P. A. (2009). Exploratory factor analysis with small sample sizes. *Multivariate Behavioral Research, 44*(2), 147–181. https://doi.org/10.1080/00273170902794206.

de Winter, J. C. F., Gosling, S. D., & Potter, J. (2016). Comparing the Pearson and Spearman correlation coefficients across distributions and sample sizes: A tutorial using simulations and empirical data. *Psychological Methods, 21*(3), 273–290. https://doi.org/10.1037/met0000079.

Diaconis, P., & Efron, B. (1983). Computer-intensive methods in statistics. *Scientific American, 248*(5), 116–130.

Digman, J. M. (1990). Personality structure: Emergence of the five-factor model. *Annual Review of Psychology, 41,* 417–440. https://doi.org/10.1146/annurev.ps.41.020190.002221.

Dinno, A. (2009). Exploring the sensitivity of Horn's parallel analysis to the distributional form of random data. *Multivariate Behavioral Research, 44*(3), 362–388. https://doi.org/10.1080/00273170902938969.

DiStefano, C. (2002). The impact of categorization with confirmatory factor analysis. *Structural Equation Modeling, 9*(3), 327–346. https://doi.org/10.1207/S15328007SEM0903_2.

DiStefano, C. (2016). Examining fit with structural equation models. In K. Schweizer & C. DiStefano (Eds.), *Principles and methods of test construction: Standards and recent advances* (pp. 166–193). Hogrefe.

DiStefano, C., & Hess, B. (2005). Using confirmatory factor analysis for construct validation: An empirical review. *Journal of Psychoeducational Assessment, 23*(3), 225–241. https://doi.org/10.1177/073428290502300303.

DiStefano, C., Zhu, M., & Mindrila, D. (2009). Understanding and using factor scores: Considerations for the applied researcher. *Practical Assessment, Research & Evaluation, 14*(20), 1–11. https://doi.org/10.7275/da8t-4g52.

Dombrowski, S. C., Beaujean, A. A., McGill, R. J., Benson, N. F., & Schneider, W. J. (2019). Using exploratory bifactor analysis to understand the latent structure of multidimensional psychological measures: An example featuring the WISC-V. *Structural Equation Modeling, 26*(6), 847–860. https://doi.org/10.1080/10705511.2019.1622421.

Dombrowski, S. C., Canivez, G. L., & Watkins, M. W. (2018). Factor structure of the 10 WISC-V primary subtests across four standardization age groups. *Contemporary School Psychology, 22*(1), 90–104. https://doi.org/10.1007/s40688-017-0125-2.

Dunn, A. M., Heggestad, E. D., Shanock, L. R., & Theilgard, N. (2018). Intra-individual response variability as an indicator of insufficient effort responding: Comparison to other indicators and relationships with individual differences. *Journal of Business and Psychology, 33*(1), 105–121. https://doi.org/10.1007/s10869-016-9479-0.

Dziuban, C. D., & Shirkey, E. S. (1974). When is a correlation matrix appropriate for factor analysis? Some decision rules. *Psychological Bulletin, 81*(6), 358–361. https://doi.org/10.1037/h0036316.

Edwards, J. R., & Bagozzi, R. P. (2000). On the nature and direction of relationships between constructs and measures. *Psychological Methods, 5*(2), 155–174. https://doi.org/10.1037/1082-989x.5.2.155.

Efron, B. (1987). Better bootstrap confidence intervals. *Journal of the American Statistical Association, 82*(397), 171–185. https://doi.org/10.1080/01621459.1987.10478410.

Enders, C. K. (2017). Multiple imputation as a flexible tool for missing data handling in clinical research. *Behaviour Research and Therapy, 98*, 4–18. https://doi.org/10.1016/j.brat.2016.11.008.

Epskamp, S., Maris, G., Waldorp, L. J., & Borsboom, D. (2018). In P. Iwing, T. Booth, & D. J. Hughes (Eds.), *The Wiley handbook of psychometric testing: A multidisciplinary reference on survey, scale and test development* (pp. 953–986). Wiley.

Fabrigar, L. R., & Wegener, D. T. (2012). *Exploratory factor analysis.* Oxford University Press.

Fabrigar, L. R., Wegener, D. T., MacCallum, R. C., & Strahan, E. J. (1999). Evaluating the use of exploratory factor analysis in psychological research. *Psychological Methods, 4*(3), 272–299. https://doi.org/10.1037/1082-989X.4.3.272.

Fava, J. L., & Velicer, W. F. (1992). The effects of overextraction on factor and component analysis. *Multivariate Behavioral Research, 27*(3), 387–415. https://doi.org/10.1207/s15327906mbr2703_5.

Fava, J. L., & Velicer, W. F. (1996). The effects of underextraction in factor and component analysis. *Educational and Psychological Measurement, 56*(6), 907–929. https://doi.org/10.1177/0013164496056006001.

Feldt, L. S., & Brennan, R. L. (1993). Reliability. In R. L. Linn (Ed.), *Educational measurement* (3rd ed., pp. 105–146). Oryx Press.

Fernstad, S. J. (2019). To identify what is not there: A definition of missingness patterns and evaluation of missing value visualization. *Information Visualization, 18*(2), 230–250. https://doi.org/10.1177/1473871618785387.

Ferrando, P. J., & Lorenzo-Seva, U. (2018). Assessing the quality and appropriateness of factor solutions and factor score estimates in exploratory item factor analysis. *Educational and Psychological Measurement, 78*(5), 762–780. https://doi.org/10.1177/0013164417719308.

Ferrando, P. J., Navarro-González, D., & Lorenzo-Seva, U. (2019). Assessing the quality and effectiveness of the factor score estimates in psychometric factor-analytic applications. *Methodology*, *15*(3), 119–127. https://doi.org/10.1027/1614-2241/a000170.

Field, A., Miles, J., & Field, Z. (2012). *Discovering statistics using R*. Sage.

Finch, H. (2006). Comparison of the performance of varimax and promax rotations: Factor structure recovery for dichotomous items. *Journal of Educational Measurement*, *43*(1), 39–52. https://doi.org/10.1111/j.1745-3984.2006.00003.x.

Finch, W. H. (2013). Exploratory factor analysis. In T. Teo (Ed.), *Handbook of quantitative methods for educational research* (pp. 167–186). Sense Publishers.

Finch, W. H. (2020a). *Exploratory factor analysis*. Sage.

Finch, W. H. (2020b). Using fit statistic differences to determine the optimal number of factors to retain in an exploratory factor analysis. *Educational and Psychological Measurement*, *80*(2), 217–241. https://doi.org/10.1177/0013164419865769.

Finney, S. J., & DiStefano, C. (2013). Nonnormal and categorical data in structural equation modeling. In G. R. Hancock & R. O. Mueller (Eds.), *Structural equation modeling: A second course* (2nd ed., pp. 439–492). Information Age Publishing.

Flake, J. K., & Fried, E. I. (2020). Measurement schmeasurement: Questionable measurement practices and how to avoid them. *PsyArXiv*. https://doi.org/10.31234/osf.io/hs7wm.

Flora, D. B. (2018). *Statistical methods for the social and behavioural sciences: A model-based approach*. Sage.

Flora, D. B., & Curran, P. J. (2004). An empirical evaluation of alternative methods of estimation for confirmatory factor analysis with ordinal data. *Psychological Methods*, *9*(4), 466–491. https://doi.org/10.1037/1082-989X.9.4.466.

Flora, D. B., & Flake, J. K. (2017). The purpose and practice of exploratory and confirmatory factor analysis in psychological research: Decisions for scale development and validation. *Canadian Journal of Behavioural Science*, *49*(2), 78–88. https://doi.org/10.1037/cbs0000069.

Flora, D. B., LaBrish, C., & Chalmers, R. P. (2012). Old and new ideas for data screening and assumption testing for exploratory and confirmatory factor analysis. *Frontiers in Psychology*, *3*(55), 1–21. https://doi.org/10.3389/fpsyg.2012.00055.

Floyd, F. J., & Widaman, K. F. (1995). Factor analysis in the development and refinement of clinical assessment instruments. *Psychological Assessment*, *7*(3), 286–299. https://doi.org/10.1037/1040-3590.7.3.286.

Ford, J. K., MacCallum, R. C., & Tait, M. (1986). The application of exploratory factor analysis in applied psychology: A critical review and analysis. *Personnel Psychology*, *39*(2), 291–314. https://doi.org/10.1111/j.1744-6570.1986.tb00583.x.

Freedman, D. A. (1987). A rejoinder on models, metaphors, and fables. *Journal of Educational Statistics*, *12*(2), 206–223. https://doi.org/10.3102/10769986012002206.

French, J. W., Tucker, L. R., Newman, S. H., & Bobbitt, J. M. (1952). A factor analysis of aptitude and achievement entrance tests and course grades at the United States Coast Guard Academy. *Journal of Educational Psychology*, *43*(2), 65–80. https://doi.org/10.1037/h0054549.

Garrido, L. E., Abad, F. J., & Ponsoda, V. (2011). Performance of Velicer's minimum average partial factor retention method with categorical variables. *Educational and Psychological Measurement*, *71*(3), 551–570. https://doi.org/10.1177/0013164410389489.

Garrido, L. E., Abad, F. J., & Ponsoda, V. (2013). A new look at Horn's parallel analysis with ordinal variables. *Psychological Methods*, *18*(4), 454–474. https://doi.org/10.1037/a0030005.

Garrido, L. E., Abad, F. J., & Ponsoda, V. (2016). Are fit indices really fit to estimate the number of factors with categorical variables? Some cautionary findings via Monte Carlo simulation. *Psychological Methods*, *21*(1), 93–111. http://dx.doi.org/10.1037/met0000064.

Garson, G. D. (2013). *Factor analysis*. Statistical Publishing Associates.

Gaskin, C. J., & Happell, B. (2014). Exploratory factor analysis: A review of recent evidence, an assessment of current practice, and recommendations for future use. *International Journal of Nursing Studies*, *51*(3), 511–521. https://doi.org/10.1016/j.ijnurstu.2013.10.005.

Giordano, C., & Waller, N. G. (2020). Recovering bifactor models: A comparison of seven methods. *Psychological Methods*, *25*(2), 143–156. https://doi.org/10.1037/met0000227.

Gelman, A., & Loken, E. (2014). The statistical crisis in science. *American Scientist*, *102*(6), 460–465. https://doi.org/10.1511/2014.111.460.

Gerbing, D. W., & Hamilton, J. G. (1996). Viability of exploratory factor analysis as a precursor to confirmatory factor analysis. *Structural Equation Modeling*, *3*(1), 62–72. https://doi.org/10.1080/10705519609540030.

Gignac, G. E. (2007). Multi-factor modeling in individual differences research: Some recommendations and suggestions. *Personality and Individual Differences*, *42*(1), 37–48. https://doi.org/10.1016/j.paid.2006.06.019.

Gignac, G. E. (2008). Higher-order models versus direct hierarchical models: g as superordinate or breadth factor? *Psychology Science Quarterly*, *50*(1), 21–43.

Gilman, R., Laughlin, J. E., & Huebner, E. S. (1999). Validation of the Self-Description Questionnaire-II with an American sample. *School Psychology International*, *20*(3), 300–307. https://doi.org/10.1177/0143034399203005.

Glorfeld, L. W. (1995). An improvement on Horn's parallel analysis methodology for selecting the correct number of factors to retain. *Educational and Psychological Measurement*, *55*(3), 377–393. https://doi.org/10.1177/0013164495055003002.

Goldberg, L. R., & Velicer, W. F. (2006). Principles of exploratory factor analysis. In S. Strack (Ed.), *Differentiating normal and abnormal personality* (2nd ed., pp. 209–237). Springer.

Golino, H. F., & Epskamp, S. (2017). Exploratory graph analysis: A new approach for estimating the number of dimensions in psychological research. *PlosOne*, *12*(6), 1–26. https://doi.org/10.1371/journal.pone.0174035.

Golino, H., Shi, D., Christensen, A. P., Garrido, L. E., Nieto, M. D., Sadana, R., & Martinez-Molina, A. (2020). Investigating the performance of exploratory graph analysis and traditional techniques to identify the number of latent factors: A simulation and tutorial. *Psychological Methods*, *25*(3), 292–320. https://doi.org/10.1037/met0000255.

Goodwin, L. D. (1999). The role of factor analysis in the estimation of construct validity. *Measurement in Physical Education and Exercise Science*, *3*(2), 85–100. https://doi.org/10.1207/s15327841mpee0302_2.

Goodwin, L. D., & Leech, N. L. (2006). Understanding correlation: Factors that affect the size of r. *Journal of Experimental Education*, *74*(3), 251–266. https://doi.org/10.3200/JEXE.74.3.249-266.

Gorsuch, R. L. (1983). *Factor analysis* (2nd ed.). Erlbaum.

Gorsuch, R. L. (1988). Exploratory factor analysis. In J. R. Nesselrode & R. B. Cattell (Eds.), *Handbook of multivariate experimental psychology* (2nd ed.). Plenum Press.

Gorsuch, R. L. (1990). Common factor analysis versus component analysis: Some well and little known facts. *Multivariate Behavioral Research*, *25*(1), 33–39. https://doi.org/10.1207/s15327906mbr2501_3.

Gorsuch, R. L. (1997). Exploratory factor analysis: Its role in item analysis. *Journal of Personality Assessment*, *68*(3), 532–560. https://doi.org/10.1207/s15327752jpa6803_5.

Gorsuch, R. L. (2003). Factor analysis. In J. A. Schinka & W. F. Velicer (Eds.), *Handbook of psychology: Research methods in psychology* (Vol. 2, pp. 143–164). Wiley.

Graham, J. M., Guthrie, A. C., & Thompson, B. (2003). Consequences of not interpreting structure coefficients in published CFA research: A reminder. *Structural Equation Modeling*, *10*(1), 142–153. https://doi.org/10.1207/S15328007SEM1001_7.

Greenwald, A. G., Pratkanis, A. R., Leippe, M. R., & Baumgardner, M. H. (1986). Under what conditions does theory obstruct research progress? *Psychological Review*, *93*(2), 216–229. https://doi.org/10.1037/0033-295X.93.2.216.

Greer, T., Dunlap, W. P., Hunter, S. T., & Berman, M. E. (2006). Skew and internal consistency. *Journal of Applied Psychology*, *91*(6), 1351–1358. https://doi.org/10.1037/0021-9010.91.6.1351.

Greiff, S., & Heene, M. (2017). Why psychological assessment needs to start worrying about model fit. *European Journal of Psychological Assessment*, *33*(5), 313–317. https://doi.org/10.1027/1015-5759/a000450.

Grice, J. W. (2001). Computing and evaluating factor scores. *Psychological Methods*, *6*(4), 430–450. https://doi.org/10.1037/1082-989X.6.4.430.

Guadagnoli, E., & Velicer, W. F. (1988). Relation of sample size to the stability of component patterns. *Psychological Bulletin*, *103*(2), 265–275. https://doi.org/10.1037/0033-2909.103.2.265.

Hägglund, G. (2001). Milestones in the history of factor analysis. In R. Cukeck, S. du Toit, & D. Sörbom (Eds.), *Structural equation modeling: Present and future* (pp. 11–38). Scientific Software International.

Haig, B. D. (2018). *Method matters in psychology: Essays in applied philosophy of science*. Springer.

Hair, J. F., Black, W. C., Babin, B. J., & Anderson, R. E. (2019). *Multivariate data analysis* (8th ed.). Cengage Learning.

Hancock, G. R., & Liu, M. (2012). Bootstrapping standard errors and data-model fit statistics in structural equation modeling. In R. H. Hoyle (Ed.), *Handbook of structural equation modeling* (pp. 296–306). Guilford.

Hancock, G. R., & Schoonen, R. (2015). Structural equation modeling: Possibilities for language learning researchers. *Language Learning*, *65*(S1), 160–184. https://doi.org/10.1111/lang.12116.

Harman, H. H. (1976). *Modern factor analysis* (3rd ed.). University of Chicago Press.

Hattori, M., Zhang, G., & Preacher, K. J. (2017). Multiple local solutions and geomin rotation. *Multivariate Behavioral Research*, *52*(6), 720–731. https://doi.org/10.1080/00273171.2017.1361312.

Hayashi, K., Bentler, P. M., & Yuan, K.-H. (2007). On the likelihood ratio test for the number of factors in exploratory factor analysis. *Structural Equation Modeling*, *14*(3), 505–526. https://doi.org/10.1080/10705510701301891.

Hayduk, L. A. (2014). Shame for disrespecting evidence: The personal consequences of insufficient respect for structural equation model testing. *BMC Medical Research Methodology*, *14*(124), 1–24. https://doi.org/10.1186/1471-2288-14-124.

Hayton, J. C., Allen, D. G., & Scarpello, V. (2004). Factor retention decisions in exploratory factor analysis: A tutorial on parallel analysis. *Organizational Research Methods*, 7(2), 191–205. https://doi.org/10.1177/1094428104263675.

Heene, M., Hilbert, S., Draxler, C., Ziegler, M., & Bühner, M. (2011). Masking misfit in confirmatory factor analysis by increasing variances: A cautionary note on the usefulness of cutoff values of fit indices. *Psychological Methods*, 16(3), 319–336. https://doi.org/10.1037/a0024917.

Hendrickson, A. E., & White, P. O. (1964). Promax: A quick method for rotation to oblique simple structure. *British Journal of Mathematical Psychology*, 17(1), 65–70. https://doi.org/10.1111/j.2044-8317.1964.tb00244.x.

Henson, R. K., Hull, D. M., & Williams, C. S. (2010). Methodology in our education research culture: Toward a stronger collective quantitative proficiency. *Educational Researcher*, 39(3), 229–240. https://doi.org/10.3102/0013189×10365102.

Henson, R. K., & Roberts, J. K. (2006). Use of exploratory factor analysis in published research: Common errors and some comment on improved practice. *Educational and Psychological Measurement*, 66(3), 393–416. https://doi.org/10.1177/0013164405282485.

Hetzel, R. D. (1996). A primer on factor analysis with comments on patterns of practice and reporting. In B. Thompson (Ed.), *Advances in social science methodology* (Vol. 4, pp. 175–206). JAI Press.

Hoelzle, J. B., & Meyer, G. J. (2013). Exploratory factor analysis: Basics and beyond. In I. B. Weiner, J. A. Schinka, & W. F. Velicer (Eds.), *Handbook of psychology: Research methods in psychology* (Vol. 2, 2nd ed., pp. 164–188). Wiley.

Hogarty, K. Y., Hines, C. V., Kromrey, J. D., Ferron, J. M., & Mumford, K. R. (2005). The quality of factor solutions in exploratory factor analysis: The influence of sample size, communality, and overdetermination. *Educational and Psychological Measurement*, 65(2), 202–226. https://doi.org/10.1177/0013164404267287.

Holgado-Tello, F. P., Chacón-Moscoso, S., Barbero-García, I., & Vila-Abad, E. (2010). Polychoric versus Pearson correlations in exploratory and confirmatory factor analysis of ordinal variables. *Quality & Quantity*, 44(1), 153–166. https://doi.org/10.1007/s11135-008-9190-y.

Holzinger, K. J., & Harman, H. H. (1941). *Factor analysis; a synthesis of factorial methods*. University of Chicago Press.

Holzinger, K. J., & Swineford, F. (1937). The bi-factor method. *Psychometrika*, 2(1), 41–54. https://doi.org/10.1007/BF02287965.

Hopwood, C. J., & Donnellan, M. B. (2010). How should the internal structure of personality inventories be evaluated? *Personality and Social Psychology Review*, 14(3), 332–346. https://doi.org/10.1177/1088868310361240.

Horn, J. L. (1965). A rationale and test for the number of factors in factor analysis. *Psychometrika*, 30(2), 179–185. https://doi.org/10.1007/BF02289447.

Horton, N. J., & Kleinman, K. (2015). *Using R and RStudio for data management, statistical analysis, and graphics* (2nd ed.). CRC Press.

Howard, M. C. (2016). A review of exploratory factor analysis decisions and overview of current practices: What we are doing and how can we improve? *International Journal of Human-Computer Interaction*, 32(1), 51–62. https://doi.org/10.1080/10447318.2015.1087664.

Hoyle, R. H. (2000). Confirmatory factor analysis. In H. E. A. Tinsley & S. D. Brown (Eds.), *Handbook of multivariate statistics and mathematical modeling* (pp. 465–497). Academic Press.

Hoyle, R. H., & Duvall, J. L. (2004). Determining the number of factors in exploratory and confirmatory factor analysis. In D. Kaplan (Ed.), *The Sage handbook of quantitative methodology for the social sciences* (pp. 301–315). Sage.

Hu, L., & Bentler, P. M. (1999). Cutoff criteria for fit indexes in covariance structure analysis: Conventional criteria versus new alternatives. *Structural Equation Modeling*, 6(1), 1–55. https://doi.org/10.1080/10705519909540118.

Humphreys, L. G. (1982). The hierarchical factor model and general intelligence. In N. Hirschberg & L. G. Humphreys (Eds.), *Multivariate applications in the social sciences* (pp. 223–239). Erlbaum.

Hunsley, J., & Mash, E. J. (2007). Evidence-based assessment. *Annual Review of Clinical Psychology*, 3(1), 29–51. https://doi.org/10.1146/annurev.clinpsy.3.022806.091419.

Hurley, A. E., Scandura, T. A., Schriesheim, C. A., Brannick, M. T., Seers, A., Vandenberg, R. J., & Williams, L. J. (1997). Exploratory and confirmatory factor analysis: Guidelines, issues, and alternatives. *Journal of Organizational Behavior*, 18(6), 667–683. http://doi.org/cg5sf7.

Hussey, I., & Hughes, S. (2020). Hidden invalidity among 15 commonly used measures in social and personality psychology. *Advances in Methods and Practices in Psychological Science*, 3(2), 166–184. https://doi.org/10.1177/2515245919882903.

Izquierdo, I., Olea, J., & Abad, F. J. (2014). Exploratory factor analysis in validation studies: Uses and recommendations. *Psicothema*, 26(3), 395–400. https://doi.org/10.7334/psicothema2013.349.

Jebb, A. T., Parrigon, S., & Woo, S. E. (2017). Exploratory data analysis as a foundation of inductive research. *Human Resource Management Review*, 27(2), 265–276. https://doi.org/10.1016/j.hrmr.2016.08.003.

Jennrich, R. I., & Bentler, P. M. (2011). Exploratory bi-factor analysis. *Psychometrika*, 76(4), 537–549. https://doi.org/10.1007/s11336-011-9218-4.

Jennrich, R. I., & Sampson, P. F. (1966). Rotation for simple loading. *Psychometrika*, 31(3), 313–323. https://doi.org/10.1007/BF02289465.

Johnson, R. L., & Morgan, G. B. (2016). *Survey scales: A guide to development, analysis, and reporting*. Guilford.

Kahn, J. H. (2006). Factor analysis in counseling psychology research, training, and practice: Principles, advances, and applications. *Counseling Psychologist*, 34(5), 684–718. https://doi.org/10.1177/0011000006286347.

Kaiser, H. F. (1958). The varimax criterion for analytic rotation in factor analysis. *Psychometrika*, 23(3), 187–200. https://doi.org/10.1007/BF02289233.

Kaiser, H. F. (1974). An index of factorial simplicity. *Psychometrika*, 39(1), 31–36. https://doi.org/10.1007/BF02291575.

Kanyongo, G. Y. (2005). Determining the correct number of components to extract from a principal components analysis: A Monte Carlo study of the accuracy of the scree plot. *Journal of Modern Applied Statistical Methods*, 4(1), 120–133. https://doi.org/10.22237/jmasm/1114906380.

Kelley, K., & Pornprasertmanit, S. (2016). Confidence intervals for population reliability coefficients: Evaluation of methods, recommendations, and software for composite measures. *Psychological Methods*, 21(1), 69–92. https://doi.org/10.1037/a0040086.

Kline, P. (1991). *Intelligence: The psychometric view*. Routledge.

Kline, P. (1994). *An easy guide to factor analysis*. Routledge.

Kline, P. (2000). *A psychometrics primer*. Free Association Books.

Kline, R. B. (2012). Assumptions in structural equation modeling. In R. Hoyle (Ed.), *Handbook of structural equation modeling* (pp. 111–125). Guilford.

Kline, R. B. (2013). Exploratory and confirmatory factor analysis. In Y. Petscher, C. Schatschneider, & D. L. Compton (Eds.), *Applied quantitative analysis in education and the social sciences* (pp. 171–207). Routledge.

Koul, A., Becchio, C., & Cavallo, A. (2018). Cross-validation approaches for replicability in psychology. *Frontiers in Psychology, 9*(1117), 1–4. https://doi.org/10.3389/fpsyg.2018.01117.

Lai, K., & Green, S. B. (2016). The problem with having two watches: Assessment of fit when RMSEA and CFI disagree. *Multivariate Behavioral Research, 51*(2-3), 220–239. https://doi.org/10.1080/00273171.2015.1134306.

Larsen, K. R., & Bong, C. H. (2016). A tool for addressing construct identity in literature reviews and meta-analyses. *MIS Quarterly, 40*(3), 529–551. https://doi.org/10.25300/MISQ/2016/40.3.01.

Lawley, D. N., & Maxwell, A. E. (1963). *Factor analysis as a statistical method*. Butterworth.

Lawrence, F. R., & Hancock, G. R. (1999). Conditions affecting integrity of a factor solution under varying degrees of overextraction. *Educational and Psychological Measurement, 59*(4), 549–579. https://doi.org/10.1177/00131649921970026.

Le, H., Schmidt, F. L., Harter, J. K., & Lauver, K. J. (2010). The problem of empirical redundancy of constructs in organizational research: An empirical investigation. *Organizational Behavior and Human Decision Processes, 112*(2), 112–125. https://doi.org/10.1016/j.obhdp.2010.02.003.

Lee, C.-T., Zhang, G., & Edwards, M. C. (2012). Ordinary least squares estimation of parameters in exploratory factor analysis with ordinal data. *Multivariate Behavioral Research, 47*(2), 314–339. https://doi.org/10.1080/00273171.2012.658340.

Lee, K., & Ashton, M. C. (2007). Factor analysis in personality research. In R. W. Robins, R. C. Fraley, & R. F. Krueger (Eds.), *Handbook of research methods in personality psychology* (pp. 424–443). Guilford.

Lee, S., Sriutaisuk, S., & Kim, H. (2020). Using the Tidyverse package in R for simulation studies in SEM. *Structural Equation Modeling, 27*(3), 468–482. https://doi.org/10.1080/10705511.2019.1644515.

Leech, N. L., & Goodwin, L. D. (2008). Building a methodological foundation: Doctoral-level methods courses in colleges of education. *Research in the Schools, 15*(1), 1–8.

Lei, P.-W., & Wu, Q. (2012). Estimation in structural equation modeling. In R. H. Hoyle (Ed.), *Handbook of structural equation modeling* (pp. 164–180). Guilford.

Lester, P. E., & Bishop, L. K. (2000). Factor analysis. In P. E. Lester & L. K. Bishop (Eds.), *Handbook of tests and measurement in education and the social sciences* (2nd ed., pp. 27–45). Scarecrow Press.

Leys, C., Klein, O., Dominicy, Y., & Ley, C. (2018). Detecting multivariate outliers: Use a robust variant of the Mahalanobis distance. *Journal of Experimental Social Psychology, 74*, 150–156. https://doi.org/10.1016/j.jesp.2017.09.011.

Likert, R. (1932). A technique for the measurement of attitudes. *Archives of Psychology, 22*(140), 1–55.

Lim, S., & Jahng, S. (2019). Determining the number of factors using parallel analysis and its recent variants. *Psychological Methods, 24*(4), 452–467. https://doi.org/10.1037/met0000230.

Little, T. D., Lindenberger, U., & Nesselroade, J. R. (1999). On selecting indicators for multivariate measurement and modeling with latent variables: When "good" indicators are bad and "bad" indicators are good. *Psychological Methods, 4*(2), 192–211. https://doi.org/10.1037/1082-989X.4.2.192.

Little, T. D., Wang, E. W., & Gorrall, B. K. (2017). VIII. The past, present, and future of developmental methodology. *Monographs of the Society for Research in Child Development*, *82*(2), 122–139. https://doi.org/10.1111/mono.12302.

Liu, Y., Zumbo, B. D., & Wu, A. D. (2012). A demonstration of the impact of outliers on the decisions about the number of factors in exploratory factor analysis. *Educational and Psychological Measurement*, *72*(2), 181–199. https://doi.org/10.1177/0013164411410878.

Lloret, S., Ferreres, A., Hernández, A., & Tomás, I. (2017). The exploratory factor analysis of items: Guided analysis based on empirical data and software. *Anales de Psicologia*, *33*(2), 417–432. https://doi.org/10.6018/analesps.33.2.270211.

Lorenzo-Seva, U., & Ferrando, P. J. (2019). A general approach for fitting pure ex ploratory bifactor models. *Multivariate Behavioral Research*, *54*(1), 15–30. https://doi.org/10.1080/00273171.2018.1484339.

Lorenzo-Seva, U., Timmerman, M. E., & Kiers, H. A. L. (2011). The hull method for selecting the number of common factors. *Multivariate Behavioral Research*, *46*(2), 340–364. https://doi.org/10.1080/00273171.2011.564527.

Lozano, L. M., Garcia-Cueto, E., & Muniz, J. (2008). Effect of the number of response categories on the reliability and validity of rating scales. *Methodology*, *4*(2), 73–79. https://doi.org/10.1027/1614-2241.4.2.73.

Lubinski, D., & Dawis, R. V. (1992). Aptitudes, skills, and proficiencies. In M. D. Dunnette & L. M. Hough (Eds.), *Handbook of industrial and organizational psychology* (Vol. 3, 2nd ed., pp. 1–59). Consulting Psychology Press.

MacCallum, R. C. (2003). Working with imperfect models. *Multivariate Behavioral Research*, *38*(1), 113–139. https://doi.org/10.1207/S15327906MBR3801_5.

MacCallum, R. C., & Austin, J. T. (2000). Applications of structural equation modeling in psychological research. *Annual Review of Psychology*, *51*(1), 201–226. https://doi.org/10.1146/annurev.psych.51.1.201.

MacCallum, R. C., Browne, M. W., & Cai, L. (2007). Factor analysis models as approximations. In R. Cudeck & R. C. MacCallum (Eds.), *Factor analysis at 100: Historical developments and future directions* (pp. 153–175). Erlbaum.

MacCallum, R. C., Roznowski, M., & Necowitz, L. B. (1992). Model modifications in covariance structure analysis: The problem of capitalization on chance. *Psychological Bulletin*, *111*(3), 490–504. https://doi.org/10.1037/0033-2909.111.3.490.

MacCallum, R. C., Widaman, K. F., Preacher, K. J., & Hong, S. (2001). Sample size in factor analysis: The role of model error. *Multivariate Behavioral Research*, *36*(4), 611–637. https://doi.org/10.1207/S15327906MBR3604_06.

MacCallum, R. C., Widaman, K. F., Zhang, S., & Hong, S. (1999). Sample size in factor analysis. *Psychological Methods*, *4*(1), 84–99. https://doi.org/10.1037/1082-989X.4.1.84.

Malone, P. S., & Lubansky, J. B. (2012). Preparing data for structural equation modeling: Doing your homework. In R. H. Hoyle (Ed.), *Handbook of structural equation modeling* (pp. 263–276). Guilford.

Mansolf, M., & Reise, S. P. (2015). Local minima in exploratory bifactor analysis. *Multivariate Behavioral Research*, *50*(6), 738. https://doi.org/10.1080/00273171.2015.1121127.

Mansolf, M., & Reise, S. P. (2016). Exploratory bifactor analysis: The Schmid-Leiman orthogonalization and Jennrich-Bentler analytic rotations. *Multivariate Behavioral Research*, *51*(5), 698–717. https://doi.org/10.1080/00273171.2016.1215898.

Mardia, K. V. (1970). Measures of multivariate skewness and kurtosis with applications. *Biometrika*, *57*(3), 519–530. https://doi.org/10.1093/biomet/57.3.519.

Marsh, H. W. (1990). *Self-Description Questionnaire–II manual.* University of Western Sydney, Macarthur.

Marsh, H. W., Muthen, B., Asparouhov, T., Ludtke, O., Robitzsch, A., Morin, A. J. S., & Trautwein, U. (2009). Exploratory structural equation modeling, integrating CFA and EFA: Application to students' evaluations of university teaching. *Structural Equation Modeling, 16*(3), 439–476. https://doi.org/10.1080/10705510903008220.

Matsunaga, M. (2010). How to factor-analyze your data right: Do's, don'ts, and how-to's. *International Journal of Psychological Research, 3*(1), 97–110. https://doi.org/10.21500/20112084.854.

Maydeu-Olivares, A. (2017). Assessing the size of model misfit in structural equation models. *Psychometrika, 82*(3), 533–558. https://doi.org/10.1007/s11336-016-9552-7.

McArdle, J. J. (2011). Some ethical issues in factor analysis. In A. T. Panter & S. K. Sterba (Eds.), *Handbook of ethics in quantitative methodology* (pp. 313–339). Routledge.

McClain, A. L. (1996). Hierarchical analytic methods that yield different perspectives on dynamics: Aids to interpretation. In B. Thompson (Ed.), *Advances in social science methodology* (Vol. 4, pp. 229–240). JAI Press.

McCoach, D. B., Gable, R. K., & Madura, J. P. (2013). *Instrument development in the affective domain: School and corporate applications.* Springer.

McCroskey, J. C., & Young, T. J. (1979). The use and abuse of factor analysis in communication research. *Human Communication Research, 5*(4), 375–382. https://doi.org/10.1111/j.1468-2958.1979.tb00651.x.

McDonald, R. P. (1985). *Factor analysis and related methods.* Erlbaum.

McDonald, R. P. (1999). *Test theory: A unified approach.* Erlbaum.

McDonald, R. P. (2010). Structural models and the art of approximation. *Perspectives on Psychological Science, 5*(6), 675–686. https://doi.org/10.1177/1745691610388766.

Meehl, P. E. (1990). Why summaries of research on psychological theories are often uninterpretable. *Psychological Reports, 66*(1), 195–244. https://doi.org/10.2466/pr0.1990.66.1.195.

Meehl, P. E. (2006). The power of quantitative thinking. In N. G. Waller, L. J. Yonce, W. M. Grove, D. Faust, & M. F. Lenzenweger (Eds.), *A Paul Meehl reader: Essays on the practice of scientific psychology* (pp. 433–444). Erlbaum.

Mertler, C. A., & Vannatta, R. A. (2001). *Advanced and multivariate statistical methods: Practical application and interpretation.* Pyrczak Publishing.

Messick, S. (1995). Validity of psychological assessment. *American Psychologist, 50*(9), 741–749. https://doi.org/10.1037/0003-066X.50.9.741.

Morin, A. J. S., Arens, A. K., Tran, A., & Caci, H. (2016). Exploring sources of construct-relevant multidimensionality in psychiatric measurement: A tutorial and illustration using the composite scale of morningness. *International Journal of Methods in Psychiatric Research, 25*(4), 277–288. https://doi.org/10.1002/mpr.1485.

Morin, A. J. S., Myers, N. D., & Lee, S. (2020). Modern factor analytic techniques. In G. Tenenbaum & R. C. Eklund (Eds.), *Handbook of sport psychology* (4th ed., pp. 1044–1073). Wiley.

Morrison, J. T. (2009). Evaluating factor analysis decisions for scale design in communication research. *Communication Methods and Measures, 3*(4), 195–215. https://doi.org/10.1080/19312450903378917.

Mucherah, W., & Finch, H. (2010). The construct validity of the Self Description Questionnaire on high school students in Kenya. *International Journal of Testing, 10*(2), 166–184. https://doi.org/10.1080/15305051003739904.

Mueller, R. O., & Hancock, G. R. (2019). Structural equation modeling. In G. R. Hancock, L. M. Stapleton, & R. O. Mueller (Eds.), *The reviewer's guide to quantitative methods in the social sciences* (2nd ed., pp. 445–456). Routledge.

Mulaik, S. A. (1987). A brief history of the philosophical foundations of exploratory factor analysis. *Multivariate Behavioral Research, 22*(3), 267–305. https://doi.org/10.1207/s15327906mbr2203_3.

Mulaik, S. A. (2010). *Foundations of factor analysis* (2nd ed.). Chapman & Hall/CRC.

Mulaik, S. A. (2018). Fundamentals of common factor analysis. In R. Irwing, T. Booth, & D. J. Hughes (Eds.), *The Wiley handbook of psychometric testing: A multidisciplinary reference on survey, scale and test development* (pp. 211–251). Wiley.

Mundfrom, D. J., Shaw, D. G., & Ke, T. L. (2005). Minimum sample size recommendations for conducting factor analyses. *International Journal of Testing, 5*(2), 159–168. https://doi.org/10.1207/s15327574ijt0502_4.

Murphy, K. R., & Aguinis, H. (2019). HARKing: How badly can cherry-picking and question trolling produce bias in published results? *Journal of Business and Psychology, 34*(1), 1–17. https://doi.org/10.1007/s10869-017-9524-7.

Mvududu, N. H., & Sink, C. A. (2013). Factor analysis in counseling research and practice. *Counseling Outcome Research and Evaluation, 4*(2), 75–98. https://doi.org/10.1177/2150137813494766.

Nasser, F., Benson, J., & Wisenbaker, J. (2002). The performance of regression-based variations of the visual scree for determining the number of common factors. *Educational and Psychological Measurement, 62*(3), 397–419. https://doi.org/10.1177/00164402062003001.

Nesselroade, J. R. (1994). Exploratory factor analysis with latent variables and the study of processes of development and change. In A. von Eye & C. C. Clogg (Eds.), *Latent variables analysis: Applications for developmental research* (pp. 131–154). Sage.

Newman, D. A. (2014). Missing data: Five practical guidelines. *Organizational Research Methods, 17*(4), 372–411. https://doi.org/10.1177/1094428114548590.

Nichols, J. Q. V. A., Shoulberg, E. K., Garner, A. A., Hoza, B., Burt, K. B., Murray-Close, D., & Arnold, L. E. (2017). Exploration of the factor structure of ADHD in adolescence through self, parent, and teacher reports of symptomatology. *Journal of Abnormal Child Psychology, 45*(3), 625–641. https://doi.org/10.1007/s10802-016-0183-3.

Norman, G. R., & Streiner, D. L. (2014). *Biostatistics: The bare essentials* (4th ed.). People's Medical Publishing.

Norris, M., & Lecavalier, L. (2010). Evaluating the use of exploratory factor analysis in developmental disability psychological research. *Journal of Autism and Developmental Disorders, 40*(1), 8–20. https://doi.org/10.1007/s10803-009-0816-2.

Nunnally, J. C., & Bernstein, I. H. (1994). *Psychometric theory* (3rd ed.). McGraw-Hill.

Onwuegbuzie, A. J., & Daniel, L. G. (2002). Uses and misuses of the correlation coefficient. *Research in the Schools, 9*(1), 73–90.

Open Science Collaboration. (2015). Estimating the reproducibility of psychological science. *Science, 349*(6251), 1–8. https://doi.org/10.1126/science.aac4716.

Orcan, F. (2018). Exploratory and confirmatory factor analysis: Which one to use first? *Journal of Measurement and Evaluation in Education and Psychology, 9*(4), 414–421. https://doi.org/10.21031/epod.394323.

Osborne, J. W. (2014). *Best practices in exploratory factor analysis*. CreateSpace Independent Publishing.

Osborne, J. W., & Banjanovic, E. S. (2016). *Exploratory factor analysis with SAS*. SAS Institute.

Osborne, J. W., Costello, A. B., & Kellow, J. T. (2007). Best practices in exploratory factor analysis. In J. W. Osborne (Ed.), *Best practices in quantitative methods* (pp. 86–99). Sage.

Osborne, J. W., & Fitzpatrick, D. C. (2012). Replication analysis in exploratory factor analysis: What it is and why it makes your analysis better. *Practical Assessment, Research & Evaluation, 17*(15), 1–8. https://doi.org/10.7275/h0bd-4d11.

Panter, A. T., Swygert, K. A., Dahlstrom, W. G., & Tanaka, J. S. (1997). Factor analytic approaches to personality item-level data. *Journal of Personality Assessment, 68*(3), 561–589. https://doi.org/10.1207/s15327752jpa6803_6.

Park, H. S., Dailey, R., & Lemus, D. (2002). The use of exploratory factor analysis and principal components analysis in communication research. *Human Communication Research, 28*(4), 562–577. https://doi.org/10.1111/j.1468-2958.2002.tb00824.x.

Pearson, R. H., & Mundfrom, D. J. (2010). Recommended sample size for conducting exploratory factor analysis on dichotomous data. *Journal of Modern Applied Statistical Methods, 9*(2), 359–368. https://doi.org/10.22237/jmasm/1288584240.

Peres-Neto, P., Jackson, D., & Somers, K. (2005). How many principal components? Stopping rules for determining the number of non-trivial axes revisited. *Computational Statistics Data Analysis, 49*(4), 974–997. https://doi.org/10.1016/j.csda.2004.06.015.

Peterson, C. (2017). Exploratory factor analysis and theory generation in psychology. *Review of Philosophy and Psychology, 8*(3), 519–540. https://doi.org/10.1007/s13164-016-0325-0.

Peterson, R. A. (2000). A meta-analysis of variance accounted for and factor loadings in exploratory factor analysis. *Marketing Letters, 11*(3), 261–275. https://doi.org/10.1023/A:1008191211004.

Pett, M. A., Lackey, N. R., & Sullivan, J. J. (2003). *Making sense of factor analysis*. Sage.

Pituch, K. A., & Stevens, J. P. (2016). *Applied multivariate statistics for the social sciences* (6th ed.). Routledge.

Platt, J. R. (1964). Strong inference. *Science, 146*(3642), 347–353. https://doi.org/10.1126/science.146.3642.347.

Plonsky, L., & Gonulal, T. (2015). Methodological synthesis in quantitative L2 research: A review of reviews and a case study of exploratory factor analysis. *Language Learning, 65*(S1), 9–36. https://doi.org/10.1111/lang.12111.

Podsakoff, P. M., MacKenzie, S. B., & Podsakoff, N. P. (2012). Sources of method bias in social science research and recommendations on how to control it. *Annual Review of Psychology, 63*(1), 539–569. https://doi.org/10.1146/annurev-psych-120710-100452.

Popper, K. (2002). *Conjectures and refutations: The growth of scientific knowledge*. Routledge.

Preacher, K. J., & MacCallum, R. C. (2003). Repairing Tom Swift's electric factor analysis machine. *Understanding Statistics, 2*(1), 13–43. https://doi.org/10.1207/S15328031US0201_02.

Preacher, K. J., & Merkle, E. C. (2012). The problem of model selection uncertainty in structural equation modeling. *Psychological Methods, 17*(1), 1–14. https://doi.org/10.1037/a0026804.

Preacher, K. J., Zhang, G., Kim, C., & Mels, G. (2013). Choosing the optimal number of factors in exploratory factor analysis: A model selection perspective. *Multivariate Behavioral Research, 48*(1), 28–56. https://doi.org/10.1080/00273171.2012.710386.

Puth, M.-T., Neuhäuser, M., & Ruxton, G. D. (2015). Effective use of Spearman's and Kendall's correlation coefficients for association between two measured traits. *Animal Behaviour, 102*, 77–84. https://doi.org/10.1016/j.anbehav.2015.01.010.

Raîche, G., Walls, T. A., Magis, D., Riopel, M., & Blais, J.-G. (2013). Non-graphical solutions for Cattell's scree test. *Methodology*, *9*(1), 23–29. https://doi.org/10.1027/1614-2241/a000051.

Ramlall, I. (2017). *Applied structural equation modelling for researchers and practitioners*. Emerald Group Publishing.

R Core Team. (2020). *R: A language and environment for statistical computing*. R Foundation for Statistical Computing.

Reio, T. G., & Shuck, B. (2015). Exploratory factor analysis: Implications for theory, research, and practice. *Advances in Developing Human Resources*, *17*(1), 12–25. https://doi.org/10.1177/1523422314559804.

Reise, S. P. (2012). The rediscovery of bifactor measurement models. *Multivariate Behavioral Research*, *47*(5), 667–696. https://doi.org/10.1080/00273171.2012.715555.

Reise, S. P., Bonifay, W., & Haviland, M. G. (2018). Bifactor modelling and the evaluation of scale scores. In P. Irwing, T. Booth, & D. J. Hughes (Eds.), *The Wiley handbook of psychometric testing: A multidisciplinary reference on survey, scale and test development* (pp. 677–707). Wiley.

Reise, S. P., Moore, T. M., & Haviland, M. G. (2010). Bifactor models and rotations: Exploring the extent to which multidimensional data yield univocal scale scores. *Journal of Personality Assessment*, *92*(6), 544–559. https://doi.org/10.1080/00223891.2010.496477.

Reise, S. P., Waller, N. G., & Comrey, A. L. (2000). Factor analysis and scale revision. *Psychological Assessment*, *12*(3), 287–297. https://doi.org/10.1037/1040-3590.12.3.287.

Rencher, A. C., & Christensen, W. F. (2012). *Methods of multivariate analysis* (3rd ed.). Wiley.

Revelle, W. (2016). An introduction to psychometric theory with applications in R. Retrieved from http://personality-project.org/r/book/.

Revelle, W. (2019). *An introduction to the psych package*. Northwestern University.

Revelle, W., and Rocklin, T. (1979). Very simple structure – alternative procedure for estimating the optimal number of interpretable factors. *Multivariate Behavioral Research*, *14*(4), 403–414. https://doi.org/10.1207/s15327906mbr1404_2.

Rhemtulla, M., Brosseau-Liard, P. E., & Savalei, V. (2012). When can categorical variables be treated as continuous? A comparison of continuous and categorical SEM estimation methods under suboptimal conditions. *Psychological Methods*, *17*(3), 354–373. https://doi.org/10.1037/a0029315.

Rhemtulla, M., van Bork, R., & Borsboom, D. (2020). Worse than measurement error: Consequences of inappropriate latent variable measurement models. *Psychological Methods*, *25*(1), 30–45. https://doi.org/10.1037/met0000220.

Rigdon, E. E., Becker, J.-M., & Sarstedt, M. (2019). Factor indeterminacy as metrological uncertainty: Implications for advancing psychological measurement. *Multivariate Behavioral Research*, *54*(3), 429–443. https://doi.org/10.1080/00273171.2018.1535420.

Roberson, R. B., Elliott, T. R., Chang, J. E., & Hill, J. N. (2014). Exploratory factor analysis in rehabilitation psychology: A content analysis. *Rehabilitation Psychology*, *59*(4), 429–438. https://doi.org/10.1037/a0037899.

Roberts, S., & Pashler, H. (2000). How persuasive is a good fit? A comment on theory testing. *Psychological Review*, *107*(2), 358–367. https://doi.org/10.1037/0033-295X.107.2.358.

Rodriguez, A., Reise, S. P., & Haviland, M. G. (2016). Applying bifactor statistical indices in the evaluation of psychological measures. *Journal of Personality Assessment*, *98*(3), 223–237. https://doi.org/10.1080/00223891.2015.1089249.

Ropovik, I. (2015). A cautionary note on testing latent variable models. *Frontiers in Psychology, 6*(1715), 1–8. https://doi.org/10.3389/fpsyg.2015.01715.

Roth, P. L. (1994). Missing data: A conceptual review for applied psychologists. *Personnel Psychology, 47*(3), 537–560. https://doi.org/10.1111/j.1744-6570.1994.tb01736.x.

Rouquette, A., & Falissard, B. (2011). Sample size requirements for the validation of psychiatric scales. *International Journal of Methods in Psychiatric Research, 20*(4), 235–249. https://doi.org/10.1002/mpr.352.

Rubin, D. B. (1976). Inference and missing data. *Biometrika, 63*(3), 581–592. https://doi.org/10.1093/biomet/63.3.581.

Rubin, M. (2017). When does HARKing hurt? Identifying when different types of undisclosed post hoc hypothesizing harm scientific progress. *Review of General Psychology, 21*(4), 308–320. https://doi.org/10.1037/gpr0000128.

Rummel, R. J. (1967). Understanding factor analysis. *Journal of Conflict Resolution, 11*(4), 444–480. https://doi.org/10.1177/002200276701100405.

Rummel, R. J. (1970). *Applied factor analysis.* Northwestern University Press.

Ruscio, J., & Roche, B. (2012). Determining the number of factors to retain in an exploratory factor analysis using comparison data of known factorial structure. *Psychological Assessment, 24*(2), 282–292. https://doi.org/10.1037/a0025697.

Russell, D. W. (2002). In search of underlying dimensions: The use (and abuse) of factor analysis in Personality and Social Psychology Bulletin. *Personality and Social Psychology Bulletin, 28*(12), 1629–1646. https://doi.org/10.1177/014616702237645.

Sakaluk, J. K., & Short, S. D. (2017). A methodological review of exploratory factor analysis in sexuality research: Used practices, best practices, and data analysis resources. *Journal of Sex Research, 54*(1), 1–9. https://doi.org/10.1080/00224499.2015.1137538.

Saris, W. E., Satorra, A., & van der Veld, W. M. (2009). Testing structural equation models or detection of misspecifications? *Structural Equation Modeling, 16*(4), 561–582. https://doi.org/10.1080/10705510903203433.

Sass, D. A. (2010). Factor loading estimation error and stability using exploratory factor analysis. *Educational and Psychological Measurement, 70*(4), 557–577. https://doi.org/10.1177/0013164409355695.

Sass, D. A., & Schmitt, T. A. (2010). A comparative investigation of rotation criteria within exploratory factor analysis. *Multivariate Behavioral Research, 45*(1), 73–103. https://doi.org/10.1080/00273170903504810.

Savalei, V. (2012). The relationship between root mean square error of approximation and model misspecification in confirmatory factor analysis models. *Educational and Psychological Measurement, 72*(6), 910–932. https://doi.org/10.1177/0013164412452564.

Schmid, J., & Leiman, J. M. (1957). The development of hierarchical factor solutions. *Psychometrika, 22*(1), 53–61. https://doi.org/10.1007/BF02289209.

Schmitt, T. A. (2011). Current methodological considerations in exploratory and confirmatory factor analysis. *Journal of Psychoeducational Assessment, 29*(4), 304–321. https://doi.org/10.1177/0734282911406653.

Schmitt, T. A., & Sass, D. A. (2011). Rotation criteria and hypothesis testing for exploratory factor analysis: Implications for factor pattern loadings and interfactor correlations. *Educational and Psychological Measurement, 71*(1), 95–113. https://doi.org/10.1177/0013164410387348.

Schmitt, T. A., Sass, D. A., Chappelle, W., & Thompson, W. (2018). Selecting the "best" factor structure and moving measurement validation forward: An illustration. *Journal of Personality Assessment, 100*(4), 345–362. https://doi.org/10.1080/00223891.2018.1449116.

Schönbrodt, F. D., & Perugini, M. (2013). At what sample size do correlations stabilize? *Journal of Research in Personality*, *47*(5), 609–612. https://doi.org/10.1016/j.jrp.2013.05.009.

Schumacker, R. E., & Lomax, R. G. (2004). *A beginner's guide to structural equation modeling* (2nd ed.). Erlbaum.

Schwarz, G. (1978). Estimating the dimension of a model. *Annals of Statistics*, *6*(2), 461–464. https://doi.org/10.1214/aos/1176344136.

Selbom, M., & Tellegen, A. (2019). Factor analysis in psychological assessment research: Common pitfalls and recommendations. *Psychological Assessment*, *31*(12), 1428–1441. https://doi.org/10.1037/pas0000623.

Shaffer, J. A., DeGeest, D., & Li, A. (2016). Tackling the problem of construct proliferation: A guide to assessing the discriminant validity of conceptually related constructs. *Organizational Research Methods*, *19*(1), 80–110. https://doi.org/10.1177/1094428115598239.

Shi, D., & Maydeu-Olivares, A. (2020). The effect of estimation methods on SEM fit indices. *Educational and Psychological Measurement*, *80*(3), 421–445. https://doi.org/10.1177/0013164419885164.

Simmons, J. P., Nelson, L. D., & Simonsohn, U. (2011). False-positive psychology: Undisclosed flexibility in data collection and analysis allows presenting anything as significant. *Psychological Science*, *22*(11), 1359–1366. https://doi.org/10.1177/0956797611417632.

Simms, L. J., & Watson, D. (2007). The construct validation approach to personality scale construction. In R. W. Roberts, R. C. Fraley, & R. F. Krueger (Eds.), *Handbook of research methods in personality psychology* (pp. 240–258). Guilford.

Spearman, C. (1904). "General intelligence," objectively determined and measured. *American Journal of Psychology*, *15*(2), 201–293. https://doi.org/10.1037/11491-006.

Spector, P. E., Van Katwyk, P. T., Brannick, M. T., & Chen, P. Y. (1997). When two factors don't reflect two constructs: How item characteristics can produce artifactual factors. *Journal of Management*, *23*(5), 659–677. https://doi.org/10.1177/014920639702300503.

Spurgeon, S. L. (2017). Evaluating the unintended consequences of assessment practices: Construct irrelevance and construct underrepresentation. *Measurement and Evaluation in Counseling and Development*, *50*(4), 275–281. https://doi.org/10.1080/07481756.2017.1339563.

Steiger, J. H. (1990). Structural model evaluation and modification: An interval estimation approach. *Multivariate Behavioral Research*, *25*(2), 173–180. https://doi.org/10.1207/s15327906mbr2502_4.

Steiger, J. H. (2001). Driving fast in reverse: The relationship between software development, theory, and education in structural equation modeling. *Journal of the American Statistical Association*, *96*(453), 331–338. https://doi.org/10.1198/016214501750332893.

Stevens, S. S. (1946). On the theory of scales of measurement. *Science*, *103*(2684), 677–680. https://doi.org/10.1126/science.103.2684.677.

Stewart, D. W. (1981). The application and misapplication of factor analysis in marketing research. *Journal of Marketing Research*, *18*(1), 51–62. https://doi.org/10.1177/002224378101800105.

Stewart, D. W. (2001). Factor analysis. *Journal of Consumer Psychology*, *10*(1–2), 75–82. https://onlinelibrary.wiley.com/doi/10.1207/S15327663JCP1001%262_07.

Streiner, D. L. (1994). Figuring out factors: The use and misuse of factor analysis. *Canadian Journal of Psychiatry, 39*(3), 135–140. https://doi.org/10.1177/070674379403900303.

Streiner, D. L. (1998). Factors affecting reliability of interpretations of scree plots. *Psychological Reports, 83*(2), 687–694. https://doi.org/10.2466/pr0.1998.83.2.687.

Streiner, D. L. (2018). Commentary no. 26: Dealing with outliers. *Journal of Clinical Psychopharmacology, 38*(3), 170–171. https://doi.org/10.1097/jcp.0000000000000865.

Tabachnick, B. G., & Fidell, L. S. (2019). *Using multivariate statistics* (7th ed.). Pearson.

Tarka, P. (2018). An overview of structural equation modeling: Its beginnings, historical development, usefulness and controversies in the social sciences. *Quality & Quantity, 52*(1), 313–354. https://doi.org/10.1007/s11135-017-0469-8.

Tataryn, D. J., Wood, J. M., & Gorsuch, R. L. (1999). Setting the value of k in promax: A Monte Carlo study. *Educational and Psychological Measurement, 59*(3), 384–391. https://doi.org/10.1177/00131649921969938.

Themessl-Huber, M. (2014). Evaluation of the X^2-statistic and different fit-indices under misspecified number of factors in confirmatory factor analysis. *Psychological Test and Assessment Modeling, 56*(3), 219–236.

Thompson, B. (2004). *Exploratory and confirmatory factor analysis: Understanding concepts and applications.* American Psychological Association.

Thomson, G. (1950). *The factorial analysis of human ability* (4th ed.). University of London Press.

Thurstone, L. L. (1931). Multiple factor analysis. *Psychological Review, 38*(5), 406–427. https://doi.org/10.1037/h0069792.

Thurstone, L. L. (1935). *The vectors of mind: Multiple-factor analysis for the isolation of primary traits.* University of Chicago Press.

Thurstone, L. L. (1937). Current misuse of the factorial methods. *Psychometrika, 2*(2), 73–76. https://doi.org/10.1007/BF02288060.

Thurstone, L. L. (1940). Current issues in factor analysis. *Psychological Bulletin, 37*(4), 189–236. https://doi.org/10.1037/h0059402.

Thurstone, L. L. (1947). *Multiple factor analysis.* University of Chicago Press.

Tinsley, H. E. A., & Tinsley, D. J. (1987). Uses of factor analysis in counseling psychology research. *Journal of Counseling Psychology, 34*(4), 414–424. https://doi.org/10.1037/0022-0167.34.4.414.

Tomarken, A. J., & Waller, N. G. (2003). Potential problems with "well fitting" models. *Journal of Abnormal Psychology, 112*(4), 578–598. https://doi.org/10.1037/0021-843X.112.4.578.

Tomarken, A. J., & Waller, N. G. (2005). Structural equation modeling: Strengths, limitations, and misconceptions. *Annual Review of Clinical Psychology, 1*(1), 31–65. https://doi.org/10.1146/annurev.clinpsy.1.102803.144239.

Tukey, J. W. (1980). We need both exploratory and confirmatory. *American Statistician, 34*(1), 23–25. https://doi.org/10.1080/00031305.1980.10482706.

van der Eijk, C., & Rose, J. (2015). Risky business: Factor analysis of survey data – Assessing the probability of incorrect dimensionalisation. *PLoS One, 10*(3), e0118900. https://doi.org/10.1371/journal.pone.0118900.

Velicer, W. F. (1976). Determining the number of components from the matrix of partial correlations. *Psychometrika, 41*(3), 321–327. https://doi.org/10.1007/BF02293557.

Velicer, W. F., Eaton, C. A., & Fava, J. L. (2000). Construct explication through factor or component analysis: A review and evaluation of alternative procedures for determining the number of factors or components. In R. D. Goffin & E. Helmes (Eds.), *Problems and solutions in human assessment: Honoring Douglas N. Jackson at seventy* (pp. 41–71). Kluwer Academic Publishers.

Velicer, W. F., & Fava, J. L. (1998). Effects of variable and subject sampling on factor pattern recovery. *Psychological Methods, 3*(2), 231–251. https://doi.org/10.1037/1082-989X.3.2.231.

Velicer, W. F., & Jackson, D. N. (1990). Component analysis versus common factor analysis: Some issues in selecting an appropriate procedure. *Multivariate Behavioral Research, 25*(1), 1–28. https://doi.org/10.1207/s15327906mbr2501_1.

Vernon, P. E. (1961). *The structure of human abilities* (2nd ed.). Methuen.

Wainer, H. (1976). Estimating coefficients in linear models: It don't make no nevermind. *Psychological Bulletin, 83*(2), 213–217. https://doi.org/10.1037/0033-2909.83.2.213.

Walkey, F., & Welch, G. (2010). *Demystifying factor analysis: How it works and how to use it.* Xlibris.

Walsh, B. D. (1996). A note on factors that attenuate the correlation coefficient and its analogs. In B. Thompson (Ed.), *Advances in social science methodology* (Vol. 4, pp. 21–31). JAI Press.

Wang, L. L., Watts, A. S., Anderson, R. A., & Little, T. D. (2013). Common fallacies in quantitative research methodology. In T. D. Little (Ed.), *Oxford handbook of quantitative methods: Statistical analysis* (Vol. 2, pp. 718–758). Oxford University Press.

Warne, R. T., & Burningham, C. (2019). Spearman's *g* found in 31 non-Western nations: Strong evidence that *g* is a universal phenomenon. *Psychological Bulletin, 145*(3), 237–272. http://dx.doi.org/10.1037/bul0000184.

Warner, R. M. (2007). *Applied statistics: From bivariate through multivariate techniques.* Sage.

Wasserstein, R. L., & Lazar, N. A. (2016). The ASA's statement on *p*-values: Context, process, and purpose. *The American Statistician, 70*(2), 129–133. https://doi.org/10.1080/00031305.2016.1154108.

Watkins, M. W. (2006). Orthogonal higher-order structure of the Wechsler Intelligence Scale for Children–Fourth Edition. *Psychological Assessment, 18*(1), 123–125. https://doi.org/10.1037/1040-3590.18.1.123.

Watkins, M. W. (2009). Errors in diagnostic decision making and clinical judgment. In T. B. Gutkin & C. R. Reynolds (Eds.), *Handbook of school psychology* (4th ed., pp. 210–229). Wiley.

Watkins, M. W. (2017). The reliability of multidimensional neuropsychological measures: From alpha to omega. *The Clinical Neuropsychologist, 31*(6–7), 1113–1126. https://doi.org/10.1080/13854046.2017.1317364.

Watkins, M. W. (2018). Exploratory factor analysis: A guide to best practice. *Journal of Black Psychology, 44*(3), 219–246. https://doi.org/10.1177/0095798418771807.

Watkins, M. W., & Browning, L. J. (2015). The Baylor revision of the Motivation to Read Survey (B-MRS). *Research and Practice in the Schools, 3*(1), 37–50.

Watkins, M. W., Greenawalt, C. G., & Marcell, C. M. (2002). Factor structure of the Wechsler Intelligence Scale for Children–Third Edition among gifted students. *Educational and Psychological Measurement, 62*(1), 164–172. https://doi.org/10.1177/0013164402062001011.

Watson, J. C. (2017). Establishing evidence for internal structure using exploratory factor analysis. *Measurement and Evaluation in Counseling and Development, 50*(4), 232–238. https://doi.org/10.1080/07481756.2017.1336931.

Wegener, D. T., & Fabrigar, L. R. (2000). Analysis and design for nonexperimental data. In H. T. Reis & C. M. Judd (Eds.), *Handbook of research methods in social and personality psychology* (pp. 412–450). Cambridge University Press.

Widaman, K. F. (1993). Common factor analysis versus principal component analysis: Differential bias in representing model parameters? *Multivariate Behavioral Research, 28*(3), 263–311. https://doi.org/10.1207/s15327906mbr2803_1.

Widaman, K. F. (2012). Exploratory factor analysis and confirmatory factor analysis. In H. Cooper (Ed.), *APA handbook of research methods in psychology: Data analysis and research publication* (Vol. 3, pp. 361–389). American Psychological Association.

Widaman, K. F. (2018). On common factor and principal component representations of data: Implications for theory and for confirmatory replications. *Structural Equation Modeling, 25*(6), 829–847. https://doi.org/10.1080/10705511.2018.1478730.

Williams, B., Onsman, A., & Brown, T. (2010). Exploratory factor analysis: A five-step guide for novices. *Journal of Emergency Primary Health Care, 8*(3), 1–13. https://doi.org/10.33151/ajp.8.3.93.

Wolf, E. J., Harrington, K. M., Clark, S. L., & Miller, M. W. (2013). Sample size requirements for structural equation models: An evaluation of power, bias, and solution propriety. *Educational and Psychological Measurement, 73*(6), 913–934. https://doi.org/10.1177/0013164413495237.

Wolff, H.-G., & Preising, K. (2005). Exploring item and higher order factor structure with the Schmid-Leiman solution: Syntax codes for SPSS and SAS. *Behavior Research Methods, 37*(1), 48–58. https://doi.org/10.3758/BF03206397.

Wood, J. M., Tataryn, D. J., & Gorsuch, R. L. (1996). Effects of under- and over-extraction on principal axis factor analysis with varimax rotation. *Psychological Methods, 1*(4), 254–265. https://doi.org/10.1037/1082-989X.1.4.354.

Woods, C. M. (2006). Careless responding to reverse-worded items: Implications for confirmatory factor analysis. *Journal of Psychopathology and Behavioral Assessment, 28*(3), 189–194. https://doi.org/10.1007/s10862-005-9004-7.

Worthington, R. L., & Whittaker, T. A. (2006). Scale development research: A content analysis and recommendations for best practices. *Counseling Psychologist, 34*(6), 806–838. https://doi.org/10.1177/0011000006288127.

Wothke, W. (1993). Nonpositive definite matrices in structural modeling. In K. A. Bollen & J. S. Long (Eds.), *Testing structural equation models* (pp. 256–293). Sage.

Xia, Y., & Yang, Y. (2019). RMSEA, CFI, and TLI in structural equation modeling with ordered categorical data: The story they tell depends on the estimation methods. *Behavior Research Methods, 51*(1), 409–428. https://doi.org/10.3758/s13428-018-1055-2.

Xiao, C., Bruner, D. W., Dai, T., Guo, Y., & Hanlon, A. (2019). A comparison of missing-data imputation techniques in exploratory factor analysis. *Journal of Nursing Measurement, 27*(2), 313–334. https://doi.org/10.1891/1061-3749.27.2.313.

Ximénez, C. (2009). Recovery of weak factor loadings in confirmatory factor analysis under conditions of model misspecification, *Behavior Research Methods, 41*(4), 1038–1052. https://doi.org/10.3758/BRM.41.4.1038.

Yakovitz, S., & Szidarovszky, F. (1986). *An introduction to numerical computation.* Macmillan.

Yuan, K.-H. (2005). Fit indices versus test statistics. *Multivariate Behavioral Research, 40*(1), 115–148. https://doi.org/10.1207/s15327906mbr4001_5.

Zhang, G. (2014). Estimating standard errors in exploratory factor analysis. *Multivariate Behavioral Research, 49*(4), 339–353. https://doi.org/10.1080/00273171.2014.908271.

Zhang, G., & Browne, M. W. (2006). Bootstrap fit testing, confidence intervals, and standard error estimation in the factor analysis of polychoric correlation matrices. *Behaviormetrika, 33*(1), 61–74. https://doi.org/10.2333/bhmk.33.61.

Zhang, G., & Preacher, K. J. (2015). Factor rotation and standard errors in exploratory factor analysis. *Journal of Educational and Behavioral Statistics, 40*(6), 579–603. https://doi.org/10.3102/1076998615606098.

Zinbarg, R. E., Revelle, W., Yovel, I., & Li, W. (2005). Cronbach's α, Revelle's β, and Mcdonald's ωh: Their relations with each other and two alternative conceptualizations of reliability. *Psychometrika*, *70*(1), 123–133. https://doi.org/10.1007/s11336-003-0974-7.

Zoski, K. W., & Jurs, S. (1996). An objective counterpart to the visual scree test for factor analysis: The standard error scree. *Educational and Psychological Measurement*, *56*(3), 443–451. https://doi.org/10.1177/0013164496056003006.

Zwick, W. R., & Velicer, W. F. (1986). A comparison of five rules for determining the number of components to retain. *Psychological Bulletin*, *99*(3), 432–442. https://doi.org/10.1037/0033-2909.99.3.432.

Zygmont, C., & Smith, M. R. (2014). Robust factor analysis in the presence of normality violations, missing data, and outliers: Empirical questions and possible solutions. *Tutorial in Quantitative Methods for Psychology*, *10*(1), 40–55. https://doi.org/10.20982/tqmp.10.1.p040.

INDEX